VEDIC MICROBIOLOGY

(A SCIENTIFIC APPROACH)

R.C. DUBEY

M.Sc., Ph.D., F.B.S., F.P.S.I., Dip. (Yoga), *Madhyamā* (Bhagavad Gītā)

MOTILAL BANARSIDASS
INTERNATIONAL
DELHI

First Edition, Delhi, 2021

ISBN : 978-93-90696-33-8 (Paper)
ISBN : 978-93-90696-25-3 (Cloth)

Also available at
MOTILAL BANARSIDASS INTERNATIONAL
41 U.A. Bungalow Road, (Back Lane)Jawahar Nagar, Delhi - 110 007
203 Royapettah High Road, Mylapore, Chennai 600 004
Samar Auddy 56/2, Ahiritola Street, Kolkata- 700 005

Printed & Bound by
MOTILAL BANARSIDASS INTERNATIONAL

AUM

Mātṛ Devo Bhav.
Pitṛ Devo Bhav.
Ācārya devo Bhav.
(Tattirīya Upaniṣad 1.11.2)
(See God in Mother Father and Teachers)

॥ ओ३म् ॥

गुरुकुल काङ्गड़ी (समविश्वविद्यालय)

(नैक से "A" ग्रेड प्राप्त एवं यू० जी० सी० एक्ट 1956 के सेक्शन 3 के अन्तर्गत समविश्वविद्यालय)

Gurukula Kangri (Deemed to be University)

(NAAC 'A' Grade Accredited Deemed to be University u/s 3 of UGC act 1956)

डॉ० रूप किशोर शास्त्री
कुलपति
(पूर्व सचिव-म.सा.रा.वे.वि.प्र., उज्जैन
मानव संसाधन विकास मन्त्रालय, भारत सरकार)

Dr. Roop Kishor Shastri
Vice-Chancellor
(Ex. Secretary-MSRVVP Ujjain
Ministry of HRD, Govt. of India)

क्रमांक/Ref. No. 12/VCO/EC/...

दिनांक/Dated 13.07.2021....

ŚUBHĀŚANSANĪYAM

I have the pleasure in writing the Śubhāśansaniyam (Foreword with appreciataion) of the book **Vedic Microbiology- A Scientific Approach** by Prof. R.C. Dubey of our University. Undoubtedly, the Vedas are the Revealed Truth, perceived by our ancient Riśis and Sages millennium-years ago, and which came into existence in the form of first script of the world during 7,500 BCE. This subtle knowledge spread in the whole world for the benefit of humanity. However, learning the Vedic knowledge and leading the whole life following the Vedic principles had become the motto of every individual. For example, Śri Rām and Śri Kṛsna went to the Āśrama of their respective Guru (teacher), stayed for years, studied the Vedas and followed the principles whole life. Peoples from different parts of the world used to come to Āryāvart (undivided ancient India) to learn the Vedic Knowledge. Unfortunately, this ancient knowledge was attempted to destroy by the foreign invaders and looters.

In this book, Prof. Dubey has scientifically explained the hymns related to the microbial diseases, factors causing the diseases and therapies, in addition to the origin of the Universe. He has also elaborated the effect the Vedic technology i.e. Yajña on plants, microbes, environment and human. He has interpreted some of the Vedic hymns referring to microorganisms, their association with plants and animals as well as certain ailments. This is the first book in english language on Vedic Microbiology explaining the hymns with a profound scientific background.

Ṛgveda (10.129.3) describes *'Tama āsīttamasā gūḍhahamagre, apraketaṁ salilaṁ sarvamā idaṁ'*. (तमं आसीत्तमंसा गूळ्हमग्रेऽप्रकेतं सलिलं सर्वमा इदम् ।) that is before the creation everything ignorant was in an 'aqueous form' (salilaṁ) covered by dense darkness. The coacervate theory of origin of life explains that the life originated in water as an aqueous phase consisting of macromolecules, polymers and proteins. These proteinoid microspheres were described as the 'Primeval Cell'. Further, Ṛgveda (1.191.5) describes 'Adṛṣtā viśvadṛṣtā pratibuddhā abhūtan', i.e. microorganisms see everyone but remain invisible themselves.

With the profound scientific background Prof. Dubey has explained the Vedic hymns that can be studied by the students, teachers and common man who have interest in the Vedic principles. Interestingly, he has been teaching Vedic Microbiology to the Post-Graduate students. This is the only University, where Vedic microbiology has also been introduced both at Post-Graduate and Under-Graduate levels. The Vedas should not be limited only to certain departments but it must be studied by the students and teachers of other departments in our country, so that our ancient heritage can be disseminated and preserved through teaching. Prof. Dubey has done a marvellous work with full devotion and disseminating the Vedic knowledge through teaching and deliberations in national and international seminars and webinars. I extend my heartfelt congratulations to him for bringing out the book by interpreting some of the Vedic hymns.

(Roop Kishor Shastri)
Vice Chancellor

Contents 2.

Prologue

It is universally accepted that the oldest books of the world i.e. Vedas are of non-human in origin and the Revealed Truth (Apauruṣeya) to the sages. After deep meditation in the Himalayan caves by our sages and Riṣi, the Divine Truth was perceived in the form of the hymns and verses (Ricā). Then this subtle Divine knowledge spread to the whole world for the benefit of humanity. The Vedic knowledge is not merely contributed by a single sage or Riṣi but it is a huge collection of the Devine knowledge of the sages down the ages, which have been compiled in the form of many thousands of verses, in due course of time after the development of Devanāgari script in Sanskrit language. Those verses have immense wealth of diverse knowledge such as astrology, mathematics, physics, chemistry, Āyurveda (the knowledge of health), medicine, science, agronomy, microbiology, geography, astronomy, etc.

The oldest library of our Takṣaśilā and Nālandā Universities became extinct due to the cruelty of foreign invaders and looters hundreds of times. Due to the forced entry of foreign robbers, the Western culture and the change of mind through the temptation of money, the modern materialistic society moved away from millennia-old our ancient culture, knowledge and traditions for thousands of years. Gradually, many of us of new generation became alienated from Indian traditions, abandoned reading of the Veda and accepted only Karmakānd during the rituals. But any nation can survive as long as its culture survives, because the culture of any nation is its 'Live Soul'. After independence from the struggle of hundreds of years, this country was stuck in other controversies including linguistic, racial and religious disputes. We kept fighting amongst ourselves and the indigenous and foreign enemies kept plotting to divide our country. This sequence is still going on. Since the independence, the Indian education system became based on Macaulay's education system and not on Indian culture. As a result, the youth classes have become unknown and untouched by Indian culture and traditions. In contrast, foreigners are now coming to India to learn Indian religion, philosophy, culture, yoga, Sanskṛt grammar, etc.

The contribution of many great personalities like Swami Dayānand Saraswati, Swāmi Śraddhānand, Swami Vivekānanda, Mahrṣi Arvido and many more can never be forgotten. I was also overwhelmed during my stay at this sacred place of Swami Śraddhānand, Gurukula Kangri Deemed University that based on the foundation of ancient Indian culture and tradition. I made up my mind for coming out of the periphery of microbiological science. I thought, if I put some splash of sacred water of Vedicism on me, it would probably be worthwhile to come to this holy place. But the biggest obstacle with me is that I have neither been a student of Sanskrit nor Veda, but I have a deep attachment and eternal love to my thousands year-old culture. It may be my audacity to embark on this inaccessible journey. My courage increased when I thought that 'if

God is pleased and if 'Mūkaṁ karoti vācālaṁ paṅgu laṅghayate girīṁ' is true, then why my dream can't be true? Thinking this, I started the journey for making true the dream of 'Vedic Microbiology– A Scientific Approach'.

In the book, Vedic Microbiology– A Scientific Approach, the main topics of discussion that have been covered are– a brief introduction of Vedas, Vedic period and Āryans, cosmogony (the origin of the universe), the distribution and classification of microorganisms, human health and disease-causing Kṛmis (germs, microorganisms), prophylaxis (precautionary measures), the destruction of diseases produced by the Kṛmis, and the science of Agnihotra. Some selected Vedic verses have been scientifically explained scientifically and some through the pictures and line diagrams so that the readers can grasp the subjects matter easily. Just as students put questions to their teachers, and teachers satisfy the students with their answers, similarly in this book, scientific explanations of Vedic hymns (Mantras) have been done through questions and answers as well as major headings and sub-headings. Among Indian education institutions/ universities, the Department of Botany and Microbiology of Gurukula Kangri (Deemed to be University), Haridwar, is the only department where Vedic microbiology has been incorporated into the curriculum as a unit/paper at the undergraduate/postgraduate level. I hope that this small effort of mine will create an interest in the readers and they will be able to acquire the Vedic knowledge given by sages on Vedic microbiology. The views of other researchers have also been mentioned and cited in the reference. There has been continuous support from my colleagues of the university during the course of writing of the book. I am thankful to my colleagues Dr. Ved Prakāśa Śāstri, Dr. D.K. Māheshwari, Dr. Navneet and senior technician Mr. Chandra Prakāśa Ārya for multifarious support during the course of writing of this book. I thank Dr. Manudev Bandhu and Dr. Dinesh Chandra Śāstri (Department of Veda) who have corrected many errors in the original manuscript. I am especially grateful to Professor Roop Kishor Śāstri, Vice Chancellor, Gurukula Kāngri (Deemed to be University), who has extended his continuous encouragement and supports during writing the book.

I am especially grateful to Late Pūjyā Mā Bhārti, all my teachers and my elder brothers, namely Mr. L.C. Dubey and Dr. H.C. Dubey, who have always had their helping-hands on me with constant blessings and encouragement. I am heartily grateful to Upendra Kumar Tripathi (Director, Ved Vjñān Centre, Banaras Hindu University), Dr. D.S. Tripāthi (Banaras Hindu University) for their special support for making the book informative. I extend my thanks to my wife Mrs. Mālti Dubey and my lonely son Sujān Dubey for their endurance during the writing of the book. In the last but not the least, I thank Mr. J.P. Jain, Messer Motilal Banarasidas International (Delhi), who has published this book in a fascinating and attractive form.

R.C. Dubey

Email: profrcdubey@gmail.com

Ram Navami

April 21, 2021

Introduction to Vedas 1.

The Vedas are the largest text of human civilization in the world. The word 'Veda' has its origin in the Sanskṛt script of 'Vid' Dhatu, which means 'knowledge' or 'knowing'. The sacred hymns of the Vedas are considered as the divine manifestations; because none has written the Vedas, it is not of human origin. Vedas are the 'Revealed Truth" or Divine Knowledge which has its two forms— 'Śabdarūpa Vedas' (verbal form) and 'Artharūpa Vedas' (object form). When there were no scripts, the Vedas were in verbal form and being narrated by the Sages and their disciples. Vedas in verbal form, i.e. in the form of words, contain hymns (Mantras). But the Vedas in the form of objects, i.e. Artharūpa, represent the whole universe. It means that the word 'Vedas' represent the entire universe. Vedas are the first Indian text of the world, which have a vast repository of knowledge of cosmology, science, astrology, medicine, mathematics, astronomy and nature. It also teaches us the art of living a healthy life. Knowledge is the light from which darkness of human ignorance is removed. Therefore, Vedas are the backbone of Indian culture. Its creator is the Supreme Father, who in the beginning of creation imparted the knowledge in the form of Vedas to the four sages who were under penance. However, Vedas came in written form only after the development of the 'Devanāgari script' approximately 6500-7500 BCE.

THE ORIGIN OF VEDAS

According to the Śatapatha Brāhman, the four Ṛṣis namely Agni, Vāyu, Āditya and Angirā, performed intense austerities and acquired the Vedas viz., Ṛgveda, Yajurveda, Sāmaveda and Atharvaveda, respectively in the form of knowledge, from the Supreme Father. There are thousands of hymns in the Vedas that deal with various aspects of life, Nature and divinity. There are 10,5890 hymns in the Ṛgveda, which describe the geographical location of the earth and the call of the Gods as well as duties of cow guarding, king's duty, relationships between fạther and son, husband and wife, nations and different subjects, etc. The Yajurveda having 1975 hymns describes the astrological knowledge and Yajñā. There are two branches of this Yajurveda- Kṛśṇa Yajurveda and Śukla Yajurveda. Kṛshna Yajurveda is related to Maharṣi Vaiśampāyana and Śukla Yajurveda is related to Ṛṣi Yājñavalkya. There are 1,875 hymns in the Sāmaveda, which describe music and worship of the Nature. It has a musical form of the Ṛgveda verses. All the hymns of the Sāmaveda, except 1,875, are of the Ṛgveda. The Atharvaveda has 5,987 hymns that focus mainly on betterment of human health by using medicinal plants.

1. Parts of the Vedas

The four Vedas are divided into four parts- Brāhmaṇ, Āraṇyaka, Upanishad and Up-Vedas. Each Veda has its own Brāhmṇ, Āraṇyakas, Upaniṣad and sub-Veda, but they all have different

Brāhmṇ, Āraṇyakas, Upaniṣad and sub-Veda. In the Vedas, the Gods have been prayed well and their position is described in planetary world (Deva loka). Yajña-therapy, water-therapy and medicinal treatments are described in these texts (Figure 1.1).

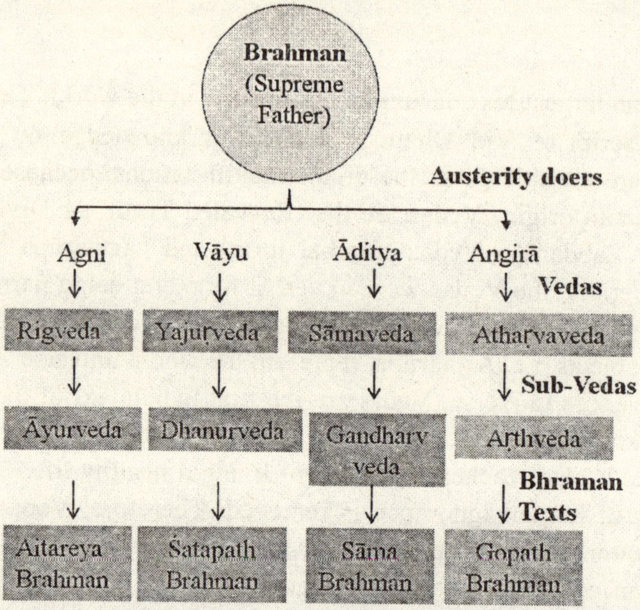

Figure 1.1. The origin of Vedas.

2. Sub-Vedas of the Vedas

The four Vedas have different sub-Vedas, such as the sub-Veda of the Ṛgveda, Yajurveda, Sāmaveda and Atharvaveda are the Āyurveda, the Dhanurveda, the Gaṅdharvaveda and the Arthaveda, respectively.

3. Mahāvākya (the Great Sayings) of Vedas

There are thousands of Mantras in the Vedas, but each Veda has one basic Mantra, which is the essence of all the hymns (Ṛcas). This is called Mahāvākya or the Great Sayings. These Mahāvākyas are stated in the four different subdivisions of the four Vedas, which express the essence of the four Vedas in a very concise form (Figure 1.2). According to Advaita philosophy, the four Mahāvākya express the ultimate unity of the soul and Brahma that whatever is in the universe is the Supreme Father, the Supreme Being, nothing else (*Eko Brahma dvitīyo nāsti*).

- **Prajñānaṁ Brahma:** This hymn is mentioned in the Aitareya Upaniṣad (3.3) of the Ṛgveda, which means 'the special knowledge'. That is, Prajñā (special knowledge) is Brahma. Knowledge is said to be all true, not false. So Brahma is the 'truth and special eternal knowledge' (Satyaṁ Jñānamantanaṁ Brahm).

- **Aham Brahmāsmi**: In the Brihadāraṇyaka Upaniṣad (1.4.10) of the Yajurveda, this hymn is mentioned, which means 'I am Brahma'. In this hymn there is no distinction between self and Brahma.
- **Tattvamasi:** This hymn is mentioned in the Chāndogya Upaniṣad (6.8.7) of the Sāmaveda, which means 'you are the same' (Tat tvaṁ asi) who is Brahma. That is, there is no difference between you and Brahma.
- **Ayamātmā Brahma**: This hymn is given in Māṇḍukya Upaniṣad (1.2) of Atharvaveda which means 'this soul is Brahma'. It means that there is no difference between the soul and the divine. This soul (present in all born) is representing the Supreme God.

Table 1.1. The great sayings (Mahāvākya) of the Vedas.

Vedas		The Great Sayings	Upaniṣad
Ṛgveda	→	Prajñānaṁ Brahm	Aitareya (3.3)
Yajurveda	→	Ahaṁ Brahmāsmi	Bṛhadāraṇyaka (1.4.10
Sāmveda	→	Tatvamasi	Chāndojña (6.8.7)
Atharvaveda	→	Ayamātmā Brahm	Māṇḍukya (1.2)

The Other Great Sayings

- **Ekaṁ Eva Dvitiyo Brahma:** This is the hymn of Chāndogya Upaniṣad which means there is 'only Brahma, nothing another'. All born are transitory; they have to die because they are born, only unborn is eternal.
- **Sohaṁ (*So Aso Ahaṁ*)**: This is the hymn of Iśāvasyopaniṣad (16), which means 'I am the same as Brahma'. The God gave originated everything in the universe, it is obvious that He exists in everything. Nothing is possible in His absence and everything is possible in His presence.
- **Sarvāṁ Khalvidaṁ Brahm:** This is the hymn of Chāṅdogya Upaniṣad (3.14.1), which means 'all that is Brahman alone', i.e. all this universe is Brahman. Nothing is beyond the Brahman because the Brahman is everlasting and eternal, the other born are transitory. It is the Brahman that holds the universe and pervades in every born.

Vedas are a tremendous repository of knowledge. The knowledge of everything that makes human life meaningful is given in the Vedas (Figure 1.2).

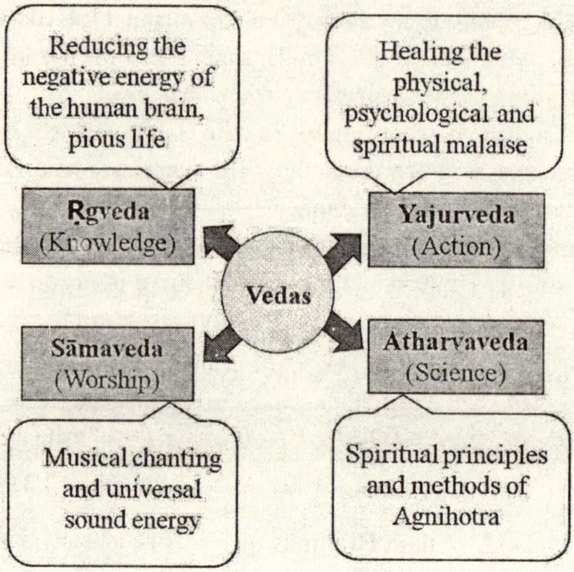

Figure 1.2: The extracts of Vedas.

ĀRYANS AND VEDIC PERIOD

Often people ask that 'when Vedas were written' and 'who wrote the Vedas'? It is imperative to understand that the Vedas are the 'Revealed Truth' (Apauruṣeya). Nobody had written it in the form of text, because during those days none of the scripts were known. There was neither pen nor paper during the period when Vedas were originated from the Supreme Father. Therefore, Vedas are the reservoirs of special hymns directly transmitted by the Supreme Father to the intense austerity performing Sages. The Vedas are the Divine knowledge acquired by the Ṛṣis from the Supreme father called Brahma. The names of ascetic Ṛṣis are given in Figure 1.1. Million years ago in Āryāvarta, the Divine knowledge was perceived by the indigenous Indian ascetics and sages in the forms of Ṛcas emerged as Veda.

1. Explaining the Vedas from History and Mythology

Vedas are the subtle Devine knowledge achieved by the ancient sages. The Vedic hymns are difficult to be explained properly and accurately. Vedas are scared of distorting the meaning of hymns by the persons having its little knowledge.

इतिहास पुराणाभ्यां वेदं समुपबृंहयेत्।
विभेत्यल्पश्रुताद्वेदो मामयं प्रतरिष्यति।।

(महाभारत–आदिपर्व 1.204)

Itihās purāṇābhyāṁ vedaṁ samupabṛṁhayet.
Vibhetyalpaśrutādvedo māmayaṁ pratariṣyati.

(Mahābhārat-Ādiparva 1.204)

[The meaning of Veda (*vedamṁ samupa bṛṅhayet*) must be explained from history and mythology (*itihās purāṇābhyāṁ*), because a man with a little knowledge (*vibhetya alpa śrutāt*), Veda (*vedo*) fears that they will spoil me (*māmayaṁ pratariṣyati*)]

Scientific Explanation: History is the all the past events, namely cultural, religious, intellectual, medical, socio-economical, etc. occurring in human society with time. I may be connected with somebody or the society. History helps to develop better understanding that has occurred in the past in the society of particular place. If any event has occurred, it leaves some evidences in certain forms. Archeological evidence recovered from ruins and written scripts serve the best evidences. The age of that period is also calculated on the basis of carbon dating. Similarly, Purānas tell about the Vedic philosophies that had occurred and been followed/ not followed during those periods. Therefore, the study of history and Purānas has been given due importance before explaining the meaning of Vedic hymns. In this chapter, evidences from historians and archeological excavation have also been mentioned.

2. What Does Ārya Means?

Many ancient texts including the Vedas and others like Valmīki Rāmāyaṇa (Bālakāṅḍa 19.19; Araṇyakāṅḍa 43.9), Vidur Nīti (1.30, 1.117-118) and the Mahabharata have defined the words 'Arya' and 'Anarya'. 'Anārya' word has also been used in Valmīki Rāmāyaṇa (Ayodhyakaṅḍa 13.5, 19.19) and Śrīmad Bhagavadgītā (2.2). The word 'Ārya' has its origin in the word 'Ṛta Gatau' which means 'to move' or the 'knowledge to go'. The Āryans are the 'Son of God', i.e. Īśvara Putra (*Ārya Īśvara Putraḥ*- Nirukta 6.26). It is said in the Ṛgveda that 'I provide the kingdom of this land for the Āryans' (*Ahaṁ bhūmimadadāmāyarya.* Ṛgveda 4.26.2) and the Divine Father has ordered that 'make the whole world Ārya' (*Indraṁ vardhanto apturaḥ Kṛṇvanto viśwamāryaṁ. Apaghranto arāvṇaḥ.* Ṛgveda 9.63.5). According to Amarakośa, a person who possesses the best nature, poise, civilization, gentleness and behaviour is called 'Ārya' (*Mahākulīn Arya sabhya sajjanasadhavaḥ.* Amarkośa 2.7.3). According to the ethics of Cāṇakya, the word 'Ārya' has been explained on the basis qualities of humans, and they can be identified well accordingly.

अभ्यासाद् धार्यते विद्या, कुलं शीलेन धार्यते।
गुणेन ज्ञायते त्वार्यः, कोपो नेत्रेण गम्यते।।

(चाणक्य नीति 5.8)

Abhyāsād dhāryate vidyā, kulaṁ shilen dhāryate.
Guṇen jñāyate tvāryaḥ, kopo netreṇ gamyate.

(Cāṇakya Nīi 5.8)

[Through continuous practice (*abhyāsād*) knowledge (*vidyā*) is attained (*dhāryate*), by perfect deeds and temperament (*śīlen*) the qualities of dynasty (*kulaṁ*) are attained (*dhāryate*), Ārya (*tva Āryaḥ*) i.e. the best person is known (*jñāyate*) by superior qualities (*guṇena*), anger (*kopaḥ*) is known (*gamyate*) by the eyes (*netreṇa*)].

It means that person's superior quality and its regular practice in behavior in the society make them 'Ārya'. The persons lacking these best qualities required by them in practice are called 'Anārya'. The practice of these best qualities in life in the society is more important than the presence of these qualities in them. Thus, Ārya means 'civilized' and Anārya (clumsy) means 'uncivilized' persons.

सर्वदाभिगतः सद्भिः समुद्र इव सिन्धुभिः।
आर्यः सर्वसमश्चैव सदैव प्रियदर्शनः।।
(वाल्मीकि रामायण– बालकाण्ड 1.16)

Sarvadābhigataḥ sadbhiḥ samudra iva sindhubhiḥ.
Āryaḥ sarvasamaścaiva sadaiva priya darśanaḥ.
(Vālmīki Rāmāyaṇa- Bālakāṇḍa 1.16)

[Śrī Rām is Ārya (*āryaḥ*), virtuous (*sarvadābhigataḥ*), pious Soul (*sadbhiḥ*), profound like ocean (*samudra iva sindhubhiḥ*), equitable (*sarvasamaścaiva*) and loving person (*priya darśanaḥ*)].

Those persons who lack the above qualities have been called clumsy (Anārya' or non-Ārya) because these good virtues are not found in them. Therefore, any kind of unsocial work can be done by such duty-less clumsy persons. For example, when Kaikeyī sought to send Śrī Rām to exile, the king Daśaratha used the word 'Anārya' for her (Vālmīki Rāmāyaṇa-Ayodhyākāṇḍa. 13.5). Similarly, in the Śrīmad Bhagavadgītā (2.2), Śrī Kṛṣṇa said to Arjuna's untimely infatuated and tenuous nature as un-followed by Āryans (Anāryajuṣṭha) (un-natured by superior person), un-heaven giving (asvargaṁ) and infamous (akīrtikara), when Arjuna was insisting not to fight and kill his relatives in the battle field.

3. Āryans were Indigenous not Invaders?

It is very important to understand that who were Āryans and where from they came to Āryāvart, the present name India? Were they indigenous or foreigner? If they were indigenous, are we their descendants? If they were foreigners, why did they come here? It is but natural for many such questions to spur into mind. However, due to subjugation of rulers for hundreds of years, the looters stole the Indian jewels, gold and texts, and took them to their country and also burnt those books kept in the world famous Nālandā University (Bihar). The foreign historians have distorted the cultural tradition of Indian, changed the names of pious cities, brutally killed millions of Indians and carried them to their country as slaves. They distorted and wrongly wrote the thousands years old culture of this country. According to them, the Āryans came to India from Central Asia, which is absolutely baseless and untrue. The Vedas originated in India itself (the name Āryāvarta is of Vedic period). Hence, the first ray of civilization originated in India. Then from here it spreads across the world. Ancient India was named Āryāvarta after the Āryan Ṛṣis living in this territory. That is why the desire to make the whole world itself Ārya has been expressed '*Kṛṇavanto viśvamāryaṁ*' (Ṛgveda 9.63.5).

One can ask the question, why did Vedas like texts was not written in any other country of the world? Even today all our rituals are performed according to Vedic customs, but in none of country, such rituals are performed according to Vedic tradition. Therefore, Āryans are the native of Āryāvarta that was later on known as Bhāratvarṣa and now as India. That is, the Āryans were our fore-fathers and were completely indigenous. They have not come from any other country as has been said by the foreigners as 'the migrants from the Central Asia'. According to Swami Dayānanda Saraswatī, the first Āryan was born in Tibet (now in China) who, after staying for some time, migrated to the south-west region of the Himalaya. In the Atharvaveda (19.39.1, 19.39.8) and other Vedas, the name Himalaya has been mentioned in many hymns and verses, no any name of other country has been mentioned in Vedas. The term Āryāvart was used for the entire region including Iran, Afghanistan, Pakistan, Tibet, Nepal, Bangladesh, Varmā (Myanmar) and Śrī Lankā, which today are the independent countries.

4. Scientific Proof of the Āryans for being Indigenous

From time to time, scientific evidence of Āryans for being completely indigent of Āryāvart has been available, but our governments did nothing to rectify the false history written by the non-Indians. The Aryans never invaded any country. Therefore, apart from Bhāratvarṣa of Āryans, there is no other country to occupy others as invader. Therefore, the ancestors of the people of entire South Asia were the same, who lived in Āryāvart. Further, the Indus Valley Civilization, i.e. Harappan Civilization, starting from 7000–6000 BCE in Iran and South-East Asia, got matured and occupied the north-western South Asia during 2600–1900 BCE. This fact is based on the start of farming system. It was the first and largest urban society residing during the ancient time. The Indus Valley Civilization had the well systematic and planned towns, granaries, drainage systems, and standardized weights and measures (Shinde *et al.*, 2019). In this area, the inhabitants were from different cultural groups who were residing in urban centres in a large area, for example Mohenjodaro (Sindh), Harappā (Punjab), Rākhīgaḍhī (Haryana), Dholāvīra (Kutch of Gujarat), and Ganweriwālā (Cholistan) (Mughal, 1990). Rākhīgaḍhī also had been a largest site during the Indus valley civilization. Archeological excavation in Rākhigaḍhī village in Hisār (Haryana) was carried out and oblation vessels (inverted pyramidal copper pot) and two human skeletons with different shapes and sizes in coal residues were recovered. After making the powder of human skeletons, DNA was extracted from it; DNA fingerprinting was done followed by DNA analysis. They generated ancient DNA data for a subset of the excavated burials at depths of 9–23m, which would have been during 2800–2300 BC. This study of archaeologists found evidence of Aryans and Dravidians having the same ancestor (Shinde *et al.*, 2019). These symbols found on the banks of Saraswatī provide evidence of worship by Āryans. All these years were found 5000 years ago on the banks of river Saraswatī during Harappan period.

Shinde *et al.* (2019) reported that a genome is the largest source for South Asians isolating from a population of the Indus Valley Civilization. But they did not find any detectable ancestry from the population of Steppe pastoralists or from that of farmers from Anatolian and Iranian.

This suggests that the farming in South Asia was done by the local foragers but not by the large-scale migrants from the West. They concluded that people living from Afghanistan to Andaman had the same type of chromosomes (genes), *i.e.* people from all over South Asia had the same chromosome for nearly 12,000 years, indicating that all people had the common ancestor. Therefore, this scientific evidence proves that the Aryans are the indigenous, and disapproves the theory that Āryan's invasion explaining that they came from outside as the invaders (Shinde *et al.*, 2019).

Genetic Mixture

Thousands of years ago, India was a prosperous nation having well developed culture, agriculture, spiritual science and multifarious knowledge. That is why it was called the 'golden bird'. People from other countries have been coming to India from time to time to learn knowledge and science. Therefore, due to the arrival of foreigners, there has been frequent adulteration time to time. Similarly, people from India have also gone to foreign countries and after coming back they settled in different parts of country. The people of Harappa continued to migrate westward to the east as evidenced by the evidence of Gonur of Turkmenistan and Śahr-e-Śokta of Iran. People from Harappa traded in all countries of Egypt, Iran, Bay of Pāras and South Asia (Shinde *et al.*, 2019).

The findings of Dr. Lālji Singh (the father of DNA fingerprinting in India) and his colleagues conclude that the chromosomes of Dravidians of, *i.e.* Ancestral South Indians resembled with that of populations living in nearby areas like Andaman, Nicobar and Lakshadweep, but not any castes or sub-castes of any other country. But the genetic data of Ancestral North Indians matched with that of populations of other countries like Europe, Central Asia, etc. If the chromosome of Ancestral North Indians is compatible with certain castes or sub-castes of countries like Afghanistan, Iran, Iraq etc., it proves the possibility of genealogical mixtures. However, in North Indian Ancestors there was 100% of the genetic mixture would have occurred during 1,900 – 4,200 BC (Moorjani *et al.*, 2013).

The logic of Max Muller's invasion of India from outside by Āryans during British Rule is completely base-less and untrue. Similarly, false and unscientific views have also been expressed by the greedy Indian Historians. If Āryans had come from outside, they would have killed many people; there would have been a massacre in India. They would have destroyed the Āryan's culture and imposed their culture in India, but things are not so. The ancient Vedic culture of Bhāratvarṣa has been completely intact and viable. In contrast, no injury or damage was found anywhere in the skeletons recovered from the burials. Hence, the logic of coming the Āryans from outside is completely wrong and misinterpreted (Shinde *et al.*, 2019).

CONCEPT OF VEDIC PERIOD

The Vedic period is divided into two parts– the pre-Vedic and the post-Vedic periods. As the Riṣis gained knowledge, the Vedas came into existence as narrations through discourses, then in the form of text after evolution of Devanāgari script in Sanskṛt. Hence, the four Vedas did not appear together but in four stages, which are in order– Ṛgveda, Yajurveda, Sāmaveda and

Atharvaveda. According to the teacher-taught tradition in Gurukulas, the teachers (Ṛṣis Gurus) used to preach the Vedas to the disciples (Śiṣyas) and the disciples memorised those verses and hymns and transmitted the Vedic knowledge to their disciples, in due course of time. During that period, the verses of the Vedas were not written but memorised and preserved in mind. For example, Śri Rām went to the ashram of Guru Vaśiṣṭha to learn Vedas. Śrī Kṛṣṇa also studied Vedas for 12 years in the Gurukula of Maharṣi Sandīpanī. Therefore, as many years as the seers have attained the Devine knowledge by penance and worship through meditation, and many sages have narrated about this subtle knowledge in other texts. That period can be called 'Vedic Period'. It means that from the origin of Vedas to some period of Ṣatyayuga (or Kṛtayuga), Tretāyuga, Dwāparyuga and Kaliyuga can be considered as 'Vedic Period' because during those period the texts like Vedas, Upaniṣds, Manusmṛti, Śruti, Saṁhitā, Purāṇa, etc. had emerged that deal with Vedic philosophy and subtle knowledge. One must remember that many forefathers of Śri Rām were born in Satyayuga (Kṛtayuga). All the kings studied Vedas, followed the path of truth and ruled properly for the wellbeing of the citizens. This means that the Vedas had already emerged before Satyayuga. This country was named Bhāratvarṣa after the name of King Bharata, who was an ideal king. According to Subhaṣa Candra Kāk (1993), who supported the idea of 'indigenous Indians', the intact Indian civilization started from the time of 'Indus-Saraswati tradition' from 7000 to 8000 BC. As Saraswati dried up, Āryans started settling on the banks of other rivers like Ganga and Yamuna.

According to Śrīmad Bhāgavat Purāṇa, Śrī Kṛṣṇa took incarnation in Dwāparyuga. After the Mahabharata war, it is considered the beginning of Kaliyuga after he reached his supreme abode. The Indic Study Foundation (2003) (California, USA) studied the gradual development of cultural heritage of India. The time was calculated by computer software to determine the day of the beginning of Mahabharata in Kurukṣetra (Haryaṇa), based on the astronomical position of that time and the position of twelve zodiac signs and constellations. On the basis of this study, it was concluded that the war of Mahabharata in Dwāparayuga took place about 3139 BCE (i.e. 5160 years ago from 2021). But foreign scholars have expressed their views on the basis of residuals, language usage and customs found after excavation of these timelines, which have more contradiction.

According to Hitebeitel (2005), 'Mahābhārata is a fictional tale'. According to Indian historian Singh (2009), 'Mahabharata war can neither be accepted nor rejected. Possibly a small-scale war would have taken place after a dispute between the two sides, Kauravas and Pāndavas. Witzel (2001) called the Vedic period as the 'Iron Age'. Thomas Trautmann (2005) in his book *'The Aryan Debate'* states that 'Vedas were written during the Indus Valley Civilization', which is totally base-less and wrong. Some historians of India may also agree with his views, but can the views of foreigners be given in favour of intact 'eternal Indian culture'? Till now we have been taught history written by foreign historians and we have accepted the truth as 'Aryans came from outside', but it is not so. Some flatterér Indian historians also continued to prove the truth on the basis of the arguments given by foreign historians without going in depth of thousands year's old Indian culture and tradition, and going away from the facts.

Table 1.2: Method of calculation of time of four Yuga.

Yug	Divine years		Human years
	1 Sun year	=	1 Human year
	1 Divine year	=	360 human years
Satya Yuga	4800 Divine years Yug - 4000 Sandhya- 400 Sandhyānsa- 400	=	17,28,000 (4800 × 3600) human years
Tretā Yuga	3600 Divine years Yug - 3000 Sandhya- 300 Sandhyanśa- 300	=	12,96,000 (3600 × 360) human years
Dwāpar Yuga	2400 Divine years Yug - 2000 Sandhya- 200 Sandhyānśa- 200	=	8,64,000 (2400 × 360) human years
Kali Yuga	1200 Divine years Yug - 1000 Sandhya- 100 Sandhyānśa- 100	=	4,32,000 (2400 × 360) human years
1 Caturyuga/ Mahāyuga	**= 12,000 Divine years**	**=**	**43,20,000 human years**
1 Manvantara	= 71 Mahāyuga	=	30,67,20,000 human years
	+ 14 Manavantar	=	4,29,40,80,000 human years
	+ 15 Sandhikāl+ Sandhyānśa	=	2,29,40,80,000 human years
1 Kalpa (Epoch)		**=**	**4,32,00,00,000 human years**
1 Kalpa	= 1000 Mahāyuga or Caturyuga		
1 Brahmā's night	= 2 Kalpa	=	8,64,00,00,000 human years
1 Brahmā's year	= 360 Brahmā's night	=	31,10,40,00,00,000 human years
Age of earth		=	4,60,00,00,000 human years
Time of Big Bang		=	13,79,90,00,000 human years

1. Calculation

According to Manusmṛti, the duration of four epochs (Yuga) viz., Satyayug, Tretāyug, Dwāparyug and Kaliyuga is 12,000 years, in the ratio of 4 : 3 : 2 : 1, respectively. According to Śrīmad Bhāgavat Purāṇa (3.11.19-20), these four epochs come at an interval of 1200 divine years simultaneously. It means, there are 4800 years of Satyayuga (4000 celestial years, 800 years of sandhikāl + sandhyānśa), 3600 celestial years of Tretā, 2400 celestial years of Dwāpar and 1200 celestial years of Kaliyuga. One human year is equal to 1 Divine day. Therefore, 1 Divine year is equal to 360 human years. Calculation based on Śrīmad Bhāgvat Purāṇa (3.11.19-20) is given in Table 1.2.

'Ṛṣi Kaṇva' must be regarded as the 'Father of Microbiology' for describing the germs as Kṛmis, Piśāca, Yātudhāna (all pathogenic microorganisms) and mentioning a variety of methods of treatment for the various types of Kṛmis in Vedas, and the diseases they cause. The knowledge of Kṛmis (visible and invisible) now as microbes, has been discussed by the great Sage Kaṇva in the Atharvaveda. Interestingly, Ṛṣi Kaṇva has mentioned the name of three other sages, for example Atrī, Yamadagni and Agastya (Atharvaveda 2.32.3), who were also skilled for such research work. This shows that 'Ṛṣi Kaṇva' performed research against microbial infection as a team work.

अत्त्रिवद्धः क्रिमयो हन्मि कण्ववज्जमदग्निवत्।
अगस्त्तस्य ब्रह्मणा सं पिनष्म्यहं क्रिमीन।।

(अथर्ववेद 2.32.3)

Atṛvaddhaḥ kṛmayo hanmi kaṇvavajjamadagnivat.
Agastasya brahmaṇā saṁ pinaṣmyahaṁ kṛmīn.

(Atharvaveda 2.32.3)

[O germs! (*kṛmayo*), I destroy you (*hanmi*) like Atri (*Atṛvat*), Kaṇva (*Kaṇvavat*) and Jamadagni (*Jamadagnivat*). I (*ahaṁ*) fully crush (*sam pinaṣmi*) the germs (*kṛmīn*) with the knowledge of (*brahmaṇā*) Agastya (*Agastasya*)]

Scientific Explanation: The four Ṛṣis namely Atri, Kaṇva, Jamadagni and Agastya who bore excellent qualities for destroying the germs have been mentioned in this hymn. These Ṛṣis have been exemplified because of bearing different quality. Atri ('A' means 'without', and 'tri' means 'three') meaning the Ṛṣi devoid of the three gates of hail, i.e. sexual desire or carnality (kāma), anger (krodha) and greed (lobha) is unaffected by the germs. Kaṇva means who, in spite of being intellectual, destroys the evil spirits and becomes uninfluenced by the germs. Jamadagni means whose digestive fire is very strong and he is not affected by the germs. Agastya means the persons who destroys crookedness is also unaffected by the pathogenic germs. These Ṛṣis were very strong in health and immunity; thence they have been exemplified to destroy and crush the germs like them, i.e. they were unaffected by any type of infectious diseases because of the very strong health, immunity, will power and knowledge of the medicinal herbs.

In brief, Kaṇva Ṛṣi has described the Kṛmis of different colours and structures with varying decaying capacity (Atharvaveda 5.23.4,5,9), their movement in the eyes, nose and in between the crevices of teeth (Atharvaveda 5.23.3), fast moving Kṛmis causing quick infection and pain (Atharvaveda 5.23.7), visible and invisible Kṛmi*s*, moving on the soil and killing them with 'Vaca' plant (Atharvaveda 2.31.2-4), Kṛmis found everywhere (Atharvaveda 2.31.5), killing them with their surviving structures (Atharvaveda 2.32.4,5), Kṛmis posing poisonous effects (Atharvaveda 2.32.6), and killing of Kṛmis by sun rays (Atharvaveda 5.23.6).

Antony Van Leeuwenhoek is regarded as the first observer of microorganisms. But, the discovery of Sage Kaṇva has been overlooked by the western philosophers and scientists because of lack of their known of Sanskṛt script. Therefore, the knowledge of Vedic microbiology remained locked within the Vedic texts (Padhi, 2016). Whose fault is this, Ṛṣi Kaṇva or the western and modern microbiologists? It is left to the readers to realise the facts of the discovery of invisible organisms (Kṛmis) by Ṛṣi Kaṇva during Vedic time, evaluate the facts based on Vedic texts, and regard him as the 'Father of Microbiology' for the first description of invisible organisms causing diseases in humans and their eradication methods.

MICROBIAL DISEASE DESCRIBED DURING VEDIC PERIOD

Most of the Vedic texts (Vedas, Purāṇas, Caraka Saṁhitā and Suśruta Samhitā, etc.) have mentioned the names of many diseases, such as Takmā (fever), Yakṣmā (tuberculosis), Kas (Kapha), Harimā (jaundice), Killāsā or Siddhamā (skin diseases), mania or Amāti (psychosis), Asu (impotence), Cleba (impotence), Amīva (primitive diseases and germs) and demons, Yātudhān, Arāti (contagious disease caused by invisible microbes that infect/ contaminate grain, beverages, food materials, and outside or inside of human body). In this context, an attempt has been made to highlight the origin of the universe, nomenclature of microorganisms/germs, their prevalence and presence, human health and germs, precautions (prophylaxis), destruction of germs and the science of Agnihotra (fire worship) with scientific explanation. Sun rays have the ability to get rid of many diseases. Not taking sun rays or taking in reduced amount there results in vitamin-D3 deficiency in the body. The Vedas have desired for the happy life of all, the disease-free life of all, the welfare of all and the sadness of none.

Sarve bhavaṅtu sukhinaḥ surve saṅtu nirāmayā.
Sarve bhadrāṇi paśyantu mā kascit dukhabhāgbhavet.

Cosmogony (the Origin of Universe) 2.

While looking at the sky, innumerable small and big stars are seen in the night. One can visualize the large one but most of the very small stars always remain twinkling, many are invisible. All of them are not at a fixed point but always are moving continuously from its position. Therefore, there arises curiosity in the mind that all these stars and planets viz., the sun, the moon, the jupiter, mercury, comets, the smoke, etc. have come from where? Why did they originate and what do they do? How long have they been in space and how long will they last? Are they immortal or indestructible? Are they self-originated, if yes, then why? Although our seers and Ṛṣis started thinking about them millions of years ago, but curiosity for science still exists. Science has also proposed many theories, but still the scientists have not reached at any concrete conclusion. Therefore, it is necessary to express the mixed views of Vedas and science related to the origin of the universe.

WHO IS THE CREATOR OF UNIVERSE?

It is but natural to put the question repeatedly who is the creator of the entire universe? According to Vedic philosophy, the creator of the universe is the Divine Supreme called Parampitā, Parabrahman or Param Mahān, no other. Everything visible to the world is due to that divinity and everything exists in the form of AUM (OM) (Omakāra) (*Ometi Brahman. Omitidaṁ sarvaṁ–* Taittiriyopanishad 9.1). Only God has been called Truth, Eternal knowledge and Brahman (*Satyaṁ jnānamanantaṁ Brahma-* Taittiriyopanishad 2.1). The utterance of the word AUM, the initial vibration, provides an idea that how all words or sounds are pronunciated by humans? All parts of the buccal cavity including vocal organ are used for pronunciation of all sounds including AUM. Hence, AUM is the matrix of all types of sounds. Hence, the creator of the universe is the only the Great Supreme, not others. Therefore, the whole world has originated from the Cosmic Egg (Hiraṇyagarbha).

हिरण्यगर्भः समवर्त्तताग्रे भूतस्य जातः पतिरेकऽआसीत।
स दाधार पृथिवीं द्यामुतेमां कस्मै देवाय हविषा विधेम।।
(यजुर्ववेद 13.4)

Hiraṇyagarbhaḥ samavartatāgre bhūtasyajātaḥ patirek,āsīt.
Sa dādhār pṛthivīṁ dyāmutemāṁ kasmai devāy haviṣā vidhem.
(Yajurveda 13.4)

[Sustenance of cosmic luminous objects like the sun (*Hiraṇyagarbhaḥ*) existed before the creation of the universe (*samavartātagre*), of the created world (*bhūtasyajātaḥ*). The One creator God (*patiḥ ek*) self-contained was (*āsīt*) He. He (*sa*) sustains (*dādhār*) the earth, sun, moon, etc.

(*pṛthivīṁ dyām*) and (*ut*) this (*emāṁ*) blissful (*kasmai*) God (*devāya*) with profound devotion (*haviṣā*) we should worship (*vidhem*)]. The God having all the bright constellation in His womb (Cosmic Egg) existed before all. He is the Supreme Father of everything born. He holds earth and other luminous planets as well as heaven. We adore our oblations to Him.

Exaplanation- The divine form was present before the origin of universe. It means that the complete basis and creator of the world and all the visible things like sun, moon, stars, earth, and all invisible entities like molecules, atoms, particles and microorganisms, etc. is none but the Supreme God. He was the only one before the creation, nothing else. Therefore, we should pay devotion to the Supreme Father (Patirek, i.e. patiḥ ek), who is the only cause of creation of the universe (*Eṣaḥ yoniḥ sarvasya* – Māndūkya Upaniṣad 3.6).

1. Meaning of Hiraṇyagarbha

The term 'Hiraṇyagarbha' is used in many ways, such as the rising sun in the east like a ball of fire, the Jyotirmaya Piṅda (from whose womb glows bright rays), the creator of the universe, the divine, etc. The term Hiraṇyagarbha is clearly mentioned in the first section of the Śrīmada Bhāgavat Purāṇa.

मृतेऽण्ड एष एतस्मिन यद्भूततो मार्तण्ड इति व्यपदेशः।
हिरण्यगर्भ इति यत् हिरण्याण्ड समुद्भवः।।
(श्रीमद् भागवत 5.20.44)

Mṛte,ṅḍaḥ eṣa etasmin yadbhūtatto mārtaṅḍa iti vyapadeśaḥ.
Hiraṇyagarbha iti yat hiraṇyāṅḍa samudbhavaḥ.
(Śṛīmad Bhāgavat 5.20.44)

[Thus (*iti*) it is named as the Sun (*mārtaṅda*) as it (*eṣa eta*) resides (*yat bhūttato*) in this dead egg (*asmin mṛtaḥ aṅḍaḥ*). Having been all these (*yata*) originated (*samudbhavaḥ*) from the Cosmic Egg (*hiraṇyāṅḍa*), is called luminous Cosmic Womb (*hiraṇyagarbha iti*)].

Scientific Analysis- There are innumerable stars and constellations in the universe from which electromagnetic waves continue flow as the intense energy. The star that produces the most intense electromagnetic rays is the Sun. The rays emanating from the outer photosphere of the sun have life-giving energy radiating in the form of continuous photons. If there were no bright rays in the center of the sun, it would remain a dead egg (mṛtaḥ aṅḍaḥ).

2. What was before Hiraṇyagarbha?

The entire universe i.e. cosmos (Brahmāṅḍa) originated from Hiraṇyagarbha, but before Hiraṇyagarbha there was nothing but God. It seems that there must have been a catastrophic situation before Hiraṇyagarbh. The origin of universe is described in the Nāsadīya Sūkta of Ṛgveda. Nāsadīya means 'not the non-existent' (na āsat). Nāsadīya Sūkta is also called the hymn of creation of the universe which is given in the 129th hymn of the 10th Maṅḍala of the Ṛgveda (10:129.1-7). This portion of the Ṛgveda has been most widely recited by the Indian scholars.

नासदासीन्नो सदासीत्तदानीं नासीद्रजो नो व्योमा परो यत् ।
किमावरीवः कुह कस्य शर्मन्नम्भः किमासीद्गहनं गभीरम् ।।
(ऋग्वेद 10.129.1)

Nāsdāsīnno sadāsīt tadānīm nāsīdrajo no vyomā paro yat.
kīmāvarīvaḥ kuha kasya śarmannambhaḥ kimāsidgahanaṁ gabhīraṁ.
(Ṛgveda 10.129.1)

[Then even untruth (*asad*) was not (*na āsīt*), nor existence (*na sad āsīt*), there was no (*na āsīt*) air then (sun air, water, sky moon, earth, planets, etc.) (*rajo*), nor the heavens (*na vyomḥ*) beyond it (*paroyat*). What (*kiṁ*) covered it (*avrīvaḥ*) ? Where was it (*kuḥ*) ?, in whose keeping (*kasy śarmana*)? Was there then (*āsīt*) cosmic water (*abhyaḥ*)?, in depths unfathomed (*gahanaṁ gabhīraṁ*) ?]

Scientific Explanation- It was a holocaust like situation before the origin of universe. In such a situation there was nothing even when everything was in place. But everything has originated from that 'nothing'. There was neither untruth nor truth, nor Raj (planetary world like sun, earth, moon, etc.). There was nothing beyond space; what were the elements that covered it? Where was it and in whose protection was it? But it is sure that something was existing. Therefore, it is very difficult to find out how the originator of everything had covered the very deep aqueous form root cause as a dense element in this space.

न मृत्युरासीदमृतं न तर्हि न रात्र्या अह्न आसीत्प्रकेतः ।
आनीदवातं स्वधया तदेकं तस्माद्धान्यन्न परः किं चनास ।।
(ऋग्वेद 10.129.2)

Na mṛtyúrāsidamṛtaṁ na tarhi rātryā ahna āsītpraketaḥ.
Ānīdavātaṁ svadhayā tadekaṁ tasmādhānyanna paraḥ kīṁ canāsa.
(Ṛgveda 10.129.2)

[Then (*tarhi*) there was neither death (*na mṛtyuḥ āsit*) nor immortality (*amritaṁ na*), nor was there then (*na āsīt*) the torch (*praketaḥ*) of night (*rātryāḥ*) and day (*anhaḥ*). There was (*āsīt*) only He (*tad ekaṁ*) breathed windless (*avātaṁ*) and self-sustaining (*svadhayā*). There was that One (*tad ekaṁ*) (that is timeless, space-less and the Sole Force) then there was no other (*anyat*) beyond it (*paraḥ*)].

Scientific Explanation: In that holocaust like situation there was neither death nor immortality. There were not even days and nights, but there was only one element consisting of Prāṇa linked with Māyā, called 'Brahma Tattva' (Supreme Power). There was nothing different and beyond than that. Moreover, according to 'string theory', the modern science believes that Big Bang occurred in the same fixed point, henceforth creation was started. Galaxies, nebula, stars, planets, comets, and every visible and non-visible, minute and the biggest entities of the world originated from Big Bang.

Scientifically, the universe has originated from small particles, which are called strings. The string theory is quite complex, it can be understood according to the rules of quantum dynamics. The string theory has everything and it has been redeveloped in a new form called M-theory. Therefore, M-theory has been created by combining quantum dynamics and string theory. According to the string theory, the fundamental particles located in an atom, such as electron, quark, etc., are not point particles. That is, these are the binary oscillators. So it is a link between rope, matter and energy. That is, it is a closed form of energy. Therefore, this is also the reason for Big Bag. It is different from photons because photon is a part of energy derived from liquid matter, while string-bond is based on the principle of energy. Hence, it matches more with boson. This is the first stage of the formation of a substance, which is considered as the cause of the creation of Big Bang. Well, this theory is not practical because before its understanding, it is necessary to understand the 11 dimensions of the universe. But science has only now understood the 4 dimensions of the universe. But this theory has proved more helpful in understanding the black hole.

3. Darkness Covered the Water

Ignorant darkness had covered the universe before the creation. No one knows about the cosmic elements of this darkness. In such darkness, no substance can be desired to be present. Where did the darkness come from, why did it come, nothing is known about all this? The prevailing darkness covered the dense mini water droplets-like darkness looking opaque, non-visible and something unclear. Nothing is known about this. That darkness was a form of determination of the Supreme.

तम आसीत्तमसा गूळ्हमग्रेऽप्रकेतं सलिलं सर्वमा इदम्।
तुच्छ्येनाभ्वपिहितं यदासीत्तपसस्तन्महिनाजायतैकम्।।
(ऋग्वेद 10.129.3)

Tama āsīttamasā gūḍhahamagre,apraketaṁ salilaṁ sarvamā idaṁ.
Tucchyenābhvapihitaṁ yad āsīt tapasastanmahinājāyataíkaṁ.
(Ṛgveda 10.129.3)

[Before the creation (*agre*), first there existed (*āsīt*) only the dense cosmic darkness (*tamasā*) wrapped in (*gūḍhahaṁ*) darkness (*tamasa*). All this (*idaṁ sarvamā*) was only un-illumined cosmic water (*saliláṁ*). From the glory of that One (*tat ekaṁ*) which came to be (*tamasa*) enclosed in frivolous nothing (*tucchyenābhu apihitaṁ āsīt*), born of the power of heat (*mahinā*) gross world from at the last (*ajāyata*)].

Scientific Explanation: It is well known that life has originated from water. This everything ignorant was in the form of water. If there would have been no water, then no life would have been possible. There is no life on other planets due to absence of water. Nevertheless, scientists are trying to find out whether there was less water or even water molecules on other planets. If there is life in some form or the other, it will surely happen. It is clear from the above hymn of the Ṛgveda that everything was in an 'aqueous form' (salilaṁ) before the creation.

4. Creation from Water

The root cause of creation of all live forms is water. If there was no water, this creation would never have happened because water has life-giving power. Yajurveda (36.17) describes water as one of the five elements of the organisms, '.... *pṛthivi śāntiḥ āpaḥ śāntiḥ*, where *āpaḥ* means water. It is said in the Śrīmad Bhagavadgītā (7.8) that *'Raso,hamapsu kaunteya prabhāsmi śaśisūryayóḥ. Praṇavaḥ sarvavedeṣu śabdaḥ khe pauruṣaṁ nṛṣu* (O! Arjuna I am the extract in water, illuminations in the moon and the sun, the Oṁkāra in Vedas, word in the sky, and the personality in the persons). Obviously, all the activities of life take place only in the presence of water. All food items dissolve in water and reach the various systems of beings and conduct life. The origin of life has been mentioned in the Śrīmad Bhāgavat also as below. This caused the origin of life from water.

सोऽनुविष्टो भगवता यः शेते सलिलाशये।
लोकसंस्थां यथापूर्वं निर्ममे संस्थया स्वया।।

(श्रीमद् भागवत 3.20.17)

So,nuviṣto bhagavatā yaḥ śete salilāśaye.
Loksaṅsthāṁ yathāpūrvaṁ nirmame saṅsthayā swayā.

(Śrīmad Bhāgvat 3.20.17)

[When that God (*So bhagavatā*) sleeping (*śete*), in the base of water (*salilāśaye*) like womb of cosmic egg entered (*anuviṣto*), He started creating the visible world (i.e. planetary system) (*loksaṅsthāṁ*) predestined as earlier (*yathāpūrvaṁ*) according to the name and forms (*nirmame saṅsthayā*) Himself (*svayā*)].

Scientific Explanation- There was nothing before creation, everything was in the form of dense darkness because light comes due to shining of the sun and that through planets and stars. But when there were no sun, stars, etc., there was a lack of light everywhere and everything was engulfed in darkness. The presence of this dense and opaque matter may be explained in the Big Bang theory. Everything was hidden in the ignorant aqueous form (cosmic egg) to which today's scientists call 'pregenote', i.e. before the genome. The genome refers to a total set of haploid number of chromosomes (RNA/DNA strands) that act as genetic material. But pregenote is the conditions that existed before the evolution of RNA, the genetic material that got evolved first. That condition would have been in the form of gases, atoms and molecules, but not macromolecules and very high temperature, uncongenial for any evolution of a life. Even the amount of oxygen would have been absent or in the process of evolution.

BIG BANG THEORY

Before the creation of the universe (13.8 billion years) there was only darkness. The same concept is also expressed in the Ṛgveda (10.129.3). Suddenly, a point beyond sub-atom was created which started moving and changes took place inside it. An explosion occurred inside this point, which is called Big Bang. Then the universe originated after merging the sound and point (light). The Big Bang theory is an 'effective cosmic paradigm' i.e. prevailing cosmological model of the evolution of the visual world. This model explains the expansion of the universe from the state of the fastest density and highest temperature. This theory also includes a multiplicity of light elements, the background of cosmic microwaves, the broad structure and 'Havel's theory'.

1. The Events of Big Bang

After the initial expansion of Big Bang, the universe began to cool, which resulted in the formation of subatomic particles and atoms. The oldest subatomic particles must have been mainly protons, neutrons and electrons. The atoms were formed by the joining of these particles. For a long duration, these atoms were electrically neutral; therefore, these atoms are also called 'primitive elements'. From these primitive elements, massive clouds developed. Primitive elements mainly contained some atoms of hydrogen along with helium lithium. Due to the gravitation, all the massive elemental clouds combined to form the initial stars and galaxies, whose remains are visible even today. The galaxies are covered with some densely charged substances (dark matter), which has a gravitational effect. Even today, it is not clear that how the dark matter was made? The hymns of the Ṛgveda (10.129.2–3) also describe the primitive matter was inert and the dense form of water was covered by the foggy darkness as if the galaxy was covered with dense foggy darkness. Thousands of years ago, our sages had expressed this cosmic phenomenon that 'Tamsā gūdhahaṁ tamah āsīt', that is, light darkness covered the dense darkness.

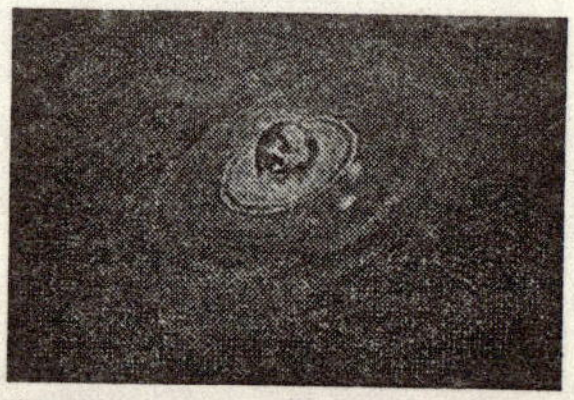

Figure 2.1: The Big Bang.

According to Big Bang theory of Stephens Hawking (1942–2018), physical elements and energy were confined to a single point about 13.8 billion years ago; the laws of physics and time stopped functioning. The whole universe shrunk to the size of a single atom. Then this point began to spread which caused Big Bang; consequently the particles spread everywhere in the universe running away from each other. In 1929, Edwin Hubble stated that 'the universe is expanding continuously'. It means that the universe must have been dense ever since, only then it is expanding continuously. Therefore, the scientists consider the phenomenon of Big Bang of the universe to be spontaneous. A hypothetical figure of Big Bang is given in Figure 2.1, which appears as a symbol of Śivaliṅgaṁ.

According to Stephens Hawking, the time before the Big Bang, did not exist. The time came after Big Bang. At the time of the creation of the universe, all the physical matter and energy in space were centered in one place. This theory has no mathematical relationship. Therefore, the Big Bang is also considered to be the cause of existence of matter, region and time. Hawking wrote in his book 'A Brief History of Time' that 'the creation is made of matter and energy'. Thousands years ago in Śvetāśvataropaniṣad (1.8), the creation of the universe from Kṣara (i.e. creation, which is destructible) and Akṣara (i.e. the Supreme Being, which is indestructible) has been mentioned. There is a lot of gravitation in the structure of a black hole. But Hawking could not provide its any proof. According to him, 'the time is constant and creation is in continuous motion'.

The God Particle (Sraṣṭā Kaṇa)

It became absolutely clear that the final form of an atom is a particle, which has been called the ultimate element in the Veda. From the first decade of the 21st century, scientists have started calling it 'Hinges Bosan', 'Sraṣṭā Kaṇa' or 'God Particle'. If creation has been made from invisible particles, then it is only fair to accept that the above sentence of our Vedic Ṛṣi, 'Aṇoraṇiyān Mahto Mahiyān' is true and final.

CONCEPT OF ATOMS AND MOLECULES IN VEDIC PERIOD

It appears that today's 'atomic theory' is the basis of the Vaiśeṣika philosophy of Ṛśis Kaṇād. Ṛśis Kaṇād has discussed first the duality (of two molecules) and the trinity (of three molecules) of the divine particle, which is the essence of his cosmic philosophy, the 'atomic theory of matter'. His Vaiśeṣika (cosmic) philosophy consists of six substances- matter, quality, action, general, special and equitable. From the very beginning, he called even the energy as mass, and the heat as element. However, Big Bang theory reminds us of the Vedic concept that everything originated from the Brahman that is 'subtler than the atoms and greater than the greatest' (Śvetaśvataropaniṣad 3.20).

अणोरणीयान् महतो महीयानात्मा गुहायां निहितोऽस्य जन्तो।

(श्वेताश्वतरोपनिषद् 3.20)

Aṇoraṇiyān mahato mahīyānātmā guhāyāṁ nihito,sya janto.

(Śvetāśvataropaniṣad 3.20)

[The Soul (*ātmā*) is hidden (*nihitaḥ*) in the small (*aṇoḥ*) to very smallest atoms (*aṇīyān*) i.e. particles as well as in big (*mahataḥ*) to the biggest objects (*mahīyān*) of the heart cave (*guhāyāṁ*) of this life (*asya janto*)].

Scientific Explanation- SOUL means the ***S***ubject ***O***f ***U***niversal ***L***ife, that is 'Ātmā' which is universally found in all life forms, i.e. bacteria to human beings. Without Ātmā, no life can be alive, i.e. capable of functiong in multifarious ways. Body exists in both dead and living forms, but what makes the body alive? All the elements are found in dead and liveforms, except the soul. What makes the soul, what does the soul do, what is the form of soul, and how does it works? All these questions need to be answered by the science. But science has the hypotheses, it does the expreriments, it requires matter and energy to solve the questions. Does soul need all these? Where is soul hidden in a body? Is it a cell, tissue, limb, organ, system or what is it? All these are the subtle questions to which there is no answer. These questions are unanswered.

Microbiologists say that DNA (deoryribonucleic acids) is found in all organisms, and DNA/ RNA (ribonucleic acid) is found in all viruses. But viruses have no life. Can you think that without the life Coronavirus (SAARS-CoVis 2 also called 'China Originated Virus Deasease 2019' or COVID-19) emerging from the Wuhan city of China spread globally and killed more than 4 lacs of people throughout the world. Coronavirus is (+) sense RNA- containing virus. Where the life lies in coronavirus? Where is its soul, in RNA of virus or cell of the hosts? It comes in active form at the moment when gets attached to the host. Without host it lies in inactive form and remains as the dead. It means its soul become activated and deactivated. What a miracle the God has done to make balance in the nature through destruction?

1. Atoms and Molecules

Probably, the Purāṇa came into existence in the form of text in Sanskrit script before 2,500 BC. In the Śṛimad Bhāgavat Purāṇa, the molecules and atoms have been described in different contexts at different places. The finest residual substances, i.e. atoms, cannot be further fragmented innumerable times by fissioning all the visible matter present in the universe. The ultimate residual remains of the atoms, i.e. particles shall be converted into energy. A similar description has been written in the Śrīmad Bhāgvát Purāna; one molecule, two molecules, three molecules, etc. are also mentioned in it.

चरमः सद्विशेषाणां अनेकोऽसंयुतः सदा।
परमाणुः स विज्ञेयो नृणामैक्यभ्रमो यतः।।

(श्रीमद्भागवत *3.11.1*)

Caramaḥ sadviśeṣāṇāṁ aneko,saṅyutaḥ sadā.
Paramāṇuḥ sa vijñeyo nṛṇāmaikyabhramo yataḥ.

(Śrīmad Bhāgavat 3.11.1)

[The smallest constituent of the matter (*caramaḥ*) that cannot be disintegrated further (*sat viśeṣāṇāṁ*) and always exists in uncombined form (*aneko,saṅyutaḥ sadā*) is called atom (*parmāṇu sa vijñeyaṁ*). Persons confusingly (*bhramo yataḥ*) assume (*nṛṇāmi*) the combinations of atoms as one component (*aikya*)]

Scientific Explanation- Modern scientist accepts that the smallest composition that remains after the fragmentation of substances is 'atomic'. The atom is the last unit of matter. They form molecules by mutual combination. Atoms are inseparable; however, much energy is required to break down the atoms into subatomic parts called particles. But the visible world appears that it is one, which is not true. Basically, it is a combination of many atoms and molecules that results in creation of visible world.

सत एव पदार्थस्य स्वरूपावस्थितस्य यत्।
कैवल्यं परममहान विशेषो निरन्तरः।।

(श्रीमद्भागवत 3.11.2)

Sat eva padārthasya svarūpāvsthitasya yata.

Kaivalyaṁ paramamahān viśeṣo nirantaraḥ.

(Śrīmad Bhāgvát 3.11.2)

[That (*yaṭ*) ultimate one (*saṭ eva*) of the materials (*padārthasya*) existing in the universe (*svarūpāvāsthitasya*) is called the Supreme Great (*Paraṁ Mahān*). The Supreme Great is uncountable times subtle and smaller than the atoms and has no difference, no space and leaves nothing (*viśeṣo nirantaraḥ*)].

Scientific Explanation- That ultimate One stays in his own form without forming different bodies. We know that the atom exists in complete manifested forms. But the Supreme Great is in more subtle form than the atom. For example, most of hydrogen atoms consist of only electrons and protons, but not neutrons. Atoms can be broken apart into particles; hence the particles remain in the form of energy. They have an electromagnetic effect; these particles also have the smallest part which is equally spread everywhere; it is called 'Param Mahān'. In that case, all electromagnetic effects cease; there is no such type of any effect. He lives in a state of action but does not remain beyond the action.

एवं कालोऽप्यनुमितः सौक्ष्म्ये स्थौल्ये च सत्तम।

संस्थानभुक्त्या भगवानव्यक्तो व्यक्त भुग्विभुः।।

(श्रीमद्भागवत 3.11.3)

Evaṁ kalo,pyanumitaḥ saukṣme sthaulye ca sattama.

Saṅsthān bhuktyā bhagavānavyakto vyakta bhugvibhuḥ.

(Śrīmad Bhāgvat 3.11.3)

[In this way (*evaṃ*) the subtle form (*saukṣmye*) and megaform (*sthaulye*) of materials are considered (*apyanumitaḥ*). In association of this (*sansthān*), the unmanifested form of Supreme Great (*bhagvāna avyakto*), capable of benefitting the creation (*bhuktyā*) and manifested form (*vyakta*), can be realised (*bhugvibhuḥ*)].

Scientific Explanation- All macro forms of creation have expanded only microscopically. The reason for the grossness is subtlety; the existence of the gross form is possible due to the mutual bond of subtlety. Therefore, by experiencing the subtle form, there is immense joy, which is a state of realization of ecstasy. That is why Ānaṅda is called Brahma or Brahmānaṅda (*Ānaṅdo Brahmiti vyajānāt-* Taittiriya Upaniṣad 6). The same happens when meditating and showing the subtlety or greatness of gross forms. But meditating on things in gross forms leads to worldly enjoyment. The senses and their rituals have emerged for worldly enjoyment. Only by meditating on the objects through the senses, attachment arises towards that subject, and by attachment the desire arises for its attainment. The meditation and attachment of the senses to the subjects is described very nicely in the Śrīmad Bhagavadgīta (*Dhyayate viṣayāna punsaḥ* *sangastesūpajāyate. Sangāta sanjāyate kāmaḥ, kamāt krodhobhi,jāyate.* Śrīmad Bhagavadgīta 2.62).

स कालः परमाणुर्वै यो भुङ्क्ते परमाणुताम्।
सतोऽविशेषभुग्यस्तु स कालः परमो महान्।।
(श्रीमद् भागवत 3.11.4)

Sa kālaḥ paramāṇurvai yo bhungkte paramāṇutām.
Sato,viśeṣabhugyastu sa kālaḥ paramo mahān.
(Śrīmad Bhāgvat 3.11.3)

[That unit of time (*sa kālaḥ*) that exists in the indivisible subtle state (*paramāṇurvai*), exists in the supreme micro level (*bhuṅkte paramāṇutāṁ*) and that (*yo*) (from creation to destruction) is the beneficiary of all states (*sato viśeṣa bhugyastu*), that time (*sa kālaḥ*) is the Supreme Great (*paramo mahān*). This unit of time corresponds to the time required by an atom (*paramāṇu*) for covering the space. That time is the Supreme Great].

Scientific Explanation- Here time has been compared to atoms because the ultimate component of creation is the atoms. But all the atoms have its existence. Therefore, they are called micro or final units. This subtlest entity is 'Param Mahān', which is beyond the sense organs to be realised similar to time, i.e. it cannot be known by our five sense organs.

2. Concept of Trident (Tri-atoms)

The atoms present in the universe bond together only when they have positive and negative charges over it. Uncharged (neutral) atoms cannot combine together. In Śrīmad Bhāgvat (3.11.5), three molecules are said to form a 'trident' or 'triatoms'.

अणुर्द्वौ परमाणू स्यात्त्रसरेणुस्त्रयः स्मृतः।
जालार्करश्म्यवगतः खमेवानुपतन्नगात्।।
(श्रीमद्भागवत 3.11.5)

Aṇurdhau paramāṇū syāttrasareṇustryayaḥ smṛtaḥ.
Jālārka raśmavagataḥ khamevānupatannagāt.
(Śrīmad Bhāgvat 3.11.3)

[It must be noted that two atoms (*dvau*) link together to form (*syāt*) one molecule (*aṇu*), and three atoms (*trayaḥ*) join together to form (*smritaḥ*)) one combination called tri-molecules or trident (*trasareṇuḥ*) that can be visualised (*ayavagataḥ*) in the sun light (*raśmiṁ*) coming through ventilator (*jālākṣa*)) from the sky (*khaṁ*)].

Scientific Explanation- A molecule is formed by joining two oppositely charged atoms, three atoms, four atoms, and so on. Modern science also agrees with this mode of action. For example, two molecules of negatively charged oxygen (O_2^-) and one molecule of positively charged carbon atom (C) form carbon dioxide (CO_2) (Figure 2.2). Similarly, the other atoms also form bonding with another oppositely charged atoms. The bonds formed between two atoms may be Van der Waals bond, hydrogen bond or covalent bond. An example of structural formula of carbon dioxide is given as below:

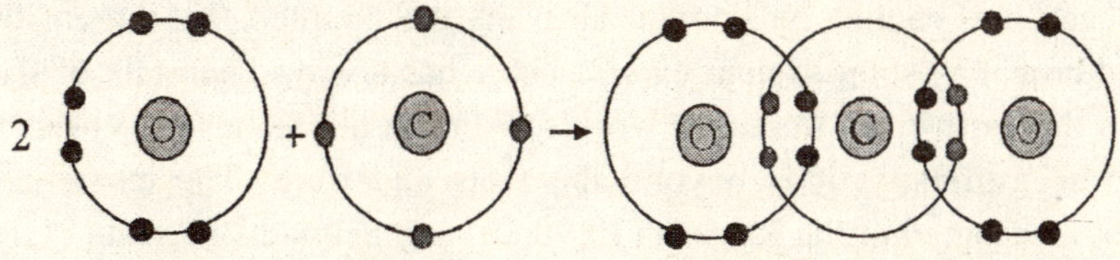

Figure 2.2. Oxygen and carbon atoms combine to form one molecule of carbon dioxide.

3. Concept of Millions of Universe

Numerous stars, big and small, are seen all around the space in the night, but when viewed with telescopes of high magnification, many planets, stars, comets, galaxies, etc. are visualized in the sky. Believably, there are many suns also. If all these are not the divine glory, why did the Supreme God created this visible and the invisible world, what would have been the purpose of creating it, what are the actions what could not happen if these are not there? All these questions come to mind again and again. Why did the God make beautiful mountains, rivers, waterfalls, seas, beautiful lakes, animals, birds and many microscopic animals on the earth? Besides the earth, on which planets human or other lives are possible, only the God knows all these. Scientists have still not found any evidence of life on any other planets. They are just seeking the prevailing conditions that make the life possible.

संख्यानं परमाणूनां कालेन क्रियते मया।
न तथा मे विभूतीनां सृजतोऽण्डानि कोटिशः।।

(श्रीमद्भागवत 11.16.39)

Saṅkhyānaṁ paramāṇūnaṁ kālen kriyate mayā.
Na tathā me vibhūtīnāṁ sṛjato,ṅḍāni kotiśaḥ.

(Śrīmad Bhāgvat 11.16.39)

[The number of atoms (*sankhyānaṃ parmānunāṃ*) can be counted any time by me (*kālen kriyate mayā*) but not my glorious forms, which I incarnate (*na tathā me vibhutināṃ*). When crores (several millions) of cosmic egg created by me (*kotiśaḥ srijataḥ aṅḍāni*) cannot be counted how my glorious forms can be?]

Scientific Explanation- The glory, the divine opulence (Vibhūti) of that Supreme Great (Param Mahān) is inaccessible and eternal; that is, it cannot be calculated nor has any end. Therefore, He is endless, He is everlasting and omnipresent that is why he is designated as OM, i.e. Om is omnipresent. Om is in gen**ome**, transcript**ome**, metabol**ome**, and metagen**om**ics. That is why even in the Vedas, He has been called 'Naiti Naiti' (no end no end). Modern science also believes that there are millions of planets, suns and galaxies. But we know about only one sun, not the others. In additions, is it possible to count the particles, atoms, molecules, macromolecules present in the cosmos? Suppose it is possible to count all these yet the significance of each one cannot be known. Has anyone counted the dimension of space, has anyone described how may solar system exist? There has always been talk of flying saucers and aliens landing on the earth from the other worlds. Film on aliens has also been made, but it has not been proved scientifically, it is beyond the facts and truth. The existence of millions of universe has been mentioned in the Ṛgveda (10.90.10) and Śrīmad Bhāgvat (11.16.39).

सहस्रशीर्षा पुरुषः सहस्राक्षः सहस्रपात्।
स भूमिंविश्वतो वृत्वात्यतिष्ठद्दशाङ्गुलम्।।
(ऋग्वेद 10.90.10)

Sahasraśīrṣā puruṣaḥ sahasrakṣaḥ sahasrapāta.
Sa bhumiṁviśwato vṛitvātytiṣṭhatdaśangulaṁ.
(Ṛgveda 10.90.10)

[The Supreme Man (*puruṣaḥ*) is with thousands of heads (*sahasra śīrṣā*), thousands of eyes (*sahasrākṣaḥ*), thousands of feet (*sahasrapāta*). He (Sa) covers (*vṛitvā*) this planet (*bhūmiṁ viśwato*) from all sides (*sarvataḥ*) and is staying (*atiṣṭhata*) by tapping in the tenth of the world (*daśāngulaṁ*). This universe is called 'Daśāngula' (one of ten finger width's dimension) because it is made up of five subtle and five gross elements].

Scientific Explanation- That Supreme Man bears enumerable heads, eyes and feet, and covering the whole cosmos, i.e. in spite of creation of all cosmic material, the universe is under His control. He is holding the creation. The five gross elements are possible only because of its link with five subtle elements. Hence, this Daśāngula (five subtle plus five gross = 10 elements) universe is one tenth of that. It means that He is beyond the cosmos; countless cosmos is within He.

A similar mention has been described in Śrīmad Bhagavadgitā (11.16). After seeing the Supreme form of Yogeśwara Śrī Kṛṣṇa amidst of the armies of Kauravas and Pāndavas adorned in Kurukṣetra at the time of Mahābhārata war, Arjuna said that-

अनेकबाहूदरवक्त्रनेत्रं पश्यामि त्वां सर्वतोऽनन्त रूपम्।
नान्तं न मध्यं न पुनस्तवादि पश्यामि विश्वेश्वर विश्वरूप।।
(श्रीमद् भगवद्गीता 11.16)

Anekbāhūdarvakranetraṁ paśyāmi tvāṁ sarvato,nant rūpam.
Nāntaṁ na madhyaṁ na punastavādi paśyāmi viśveśara viśvarūpam.
(Śrīmad Bhagavadgitā 11.16)

[O God! of universe (*viśveśvara*), I see the universal form (*viśvarūpaṁ*) in your body (*paśyāmi tvāṁ*), many arms (*anek bāhuḥ*), bellies (*udar*), mouths (*vaktra*) and eyes (*netraṁ*) expanded everywhere (*sarvato*), without limit (*ananta rūpaṁ*). I see (*paśyāmi*) in you no end (*nāntaṁ*), no middle (*na madhyaṁ*) and no beginning (*na punastavāadiṁ*)].

Scientific Explanation- The great saint Goswāmi Tulsīdās has also described in 'Rāmacarita Mānas' 'God is endless, his prayer is endless, and all the saints sing, listen and describe it'. It means that there are many forms of God, so the stories of his all forms are endless. All saints and the devotees sing and listen to the stories of these endless forms. Therefore, it may be possible to calculate the innumerable atoms and millions of cosmos created by the Supreme Father, but his divine glory cannot be calculated, it is uncountable and endless, i.e. naiti naiti. The scientists believe that entire particles, atoms, molecules, stars, planets, comments, galaxies, created by the Nature cannot be counted; all these are invisible and uncountable.

DESIRE OF CREATION OF THE UNIVERSE

Only Supreme Father existed before the origin of cosmos. It is only one form of the Almighty. The Almighty has two forms, subtle and visible. The subtle form is unknown but prays in different ways by the seers and sages. The visible form, i.e. creation has been done later on when the Supreme Mahan desired to do so. Therefore, the universe originated only due to the desire of the 'Para Brahman' to create the cosmos. The Supreme Father first desired to be many from One, 'Ekohaṁ Bahusyāma' (I am one, be many). This type of desire of the Almighty is also described in the Yajurveda (621).

ततो विराडजायत विराजो अधि पूरुषः।
स जातो अत्यरिच्यत पश्चाद्भूमिमथो पुरः।।
(यजुर्वेद 621)

Tato virādajāyata virājo adhi pūruṣaḥ.
Sa jāto atyaricyata paścādbhūmimatho puraḥ.
(Yajurved 621)

[A resplendent (*tataḥ*) luminous megabody (*virāṭ*) evolved (*ajāyata*) by the consciousness (*virājaḥ adhi pūruṣaḥ*). After that origin (*saḥ jātaḥ*), catharsis originated (*ati aricyata*); thereafter (*paścāt*) planets like earth originated (*bhūmiṃ*) followed by materials required for life (*puraḥ*)].

Scientific Explanation- The origin of creation from luminous primordial egg has been mentioned in Atharvaveda (4.2.7). Now it has become clear that the Supreme Father created a luminous body to which scientists call Big Bang, from which many types of compositions were made. All the seven planetary worlds (loka) including earth were created by him. Many kinds of substances, from particles and atoms to macromolecules and all life forms, have been created on earth to advance the order of life and to run life smoothly.

1. The Order of Origin of Universe

It has become clear that the Supreme Brahman created the first the primeval atom/the Cosmic Egg (Hiraṇyagarbha), which eventually led to the creation of the entire universe. The sequence of origin of creation is as follows.

स प्राणमसृजत प्राणात् श्रद्धां खं वायुर्ज्योतिरापः पृथिवीन्द्रियं।
मनोऽन्नमन्नाद्वीर्य तपो मन्त्राः कर्म लोका लोकेषु च नाम च।।

(प्रश्नोपनिषद्– 6.4)

Sa prāṇamsṛjat prāṇāt śraddhāṁ khaṁ vāyurjotirāpaḥ pṛthivīmṅdriyaṁ.

Mano,nnamannādvīrya tapo mantrāḥ karm lokā lokeṣu ca nām ca.

(Praśna Upaniṣad 6.4)

[He (*sa*) created the life (*prāṇa*), from life the faith (*śraddhā*), space (*khaṁ*), air (*vāyuḥ*), light (*jyotiḥ*) water (*āpaḥ*), earth (*pṛthivīṁ*), body organs (*indriyaṁ*), mind (*mana*), grains (*anna*), vigour (*vīrya*), penance (*tapa*), action (*karma*), planetary world (*loka*) and (*ca*) names (*nāma*) from planetary]

Scientific Explanation- All the activities in Nature went on smoothly and in well ordered ways; nothing happened in chaotic ways. Still the process of evolution is going on. If something happens in chaotic way, some subtle message the Nature desires to send us; there is some indications which need to understand. Those who understand these subtle indications, really they are the Ṛṣi and saints. The entire universe is the results of creation that evolved in well planned ways by the Nature. The particles, atoms and molecules evolved first and humans in the last. The humans did not evolve first; there is indication of the Nature, because humans depend on the resources of Nature for their existence. They utilize the elements as nutrients. Therefore, life (all active forms of Nature) was created first followed by faith, space, air, light, water, earth, body organs, mind, grains, and penance, and so on. Faith creates affinity and makes bond between two, may be particles, atoms or even organisms including humans. Faith links two entities or individuals whether smallest or biggest forms. Faith creates a relation between two or many, and unfaith makes antagonism. Antagonism is nothing but unfriendly relation; but all these friendly relations were established in the space that created affinity. In the space, the oxygen molecules stabled bonding to form oxygen and ozone molecules, which are necessary to bring about stability in the space. Unstable world has no faith. These lines of Praśnopaniṣad (6.4) very clearly mention the order of creation of Universe in a welled-planed and scientific way.

2. Progress in Creation of Molecules

Combination of molecules resulted in the formation of large-sized materials; the formation of these substances is possible only because of combination of Nature and consciousness. A similar quote is found in Śrīmad Bhāgavat.

अणुर्बृहत् कृशः स्थूलो यो यो भावः प्रसिद्धयति।
सर्वोऽप्युभय संयुक्तः प्रकृत्या पुरुषेण च।।
(श्रीमद्भागवत 11.24.16)

Aṇurbṛhata kṛśaḥ sthūlo yo yo bhāvaḥ prasidhyati.
Sarvo,pyubhay saṅyuktaḥ prakṛtyā puruṣeṇ ca.
(Śrīmad Bhāgvat 11.24.16)

[Atoms small or bigger (*aṇuḥ vṛhata*), thin or thicker (*kṛśaḥ sthulo*), whatever materials have been formed (*yo yo bhāvaḥ prasiḍhyati*), all (*sarvaḥ*) were possible by uniting (*api ubhaya saṅyuktaḥ*) the Nature (*prakṛtyā*) and consciousness (*puruṣeṇ ca*)]

Scientific Explanation- The world is created by the combination of Nature (Prakṛti) and or consciousness (Puruṣa). Scientifically, two conflicting powers (positive and negative) created atoms, molecules and substances larger than that. For example, the atoms of charged hydrogen (H^+) and chloride (Cl^-) combine to form a molecule of hydrochloric (HCl) acid ($H^+ + Cl^- \rightarrow HCl$) (Figure 2.3). Both ions are temporary due to their anti-charge. Hence, both of them are attracted towards each other and form a hydrogen bond using energy. They come closer due to affinity and for stable bonding. Broadly, the same attraction applies to all the small and large bodies and stars of the universe. For example, all the constellations revolve continuously around the Sun. The distance between sun and the other constellations are also always fixed with respect to time. For this reason, the duration of day and night, and that of weather change with time. The time of day and night does not remain the same in different countries, but varies. All these constellations and bodies rotate due to the attraction towards each other, which is called gravitation, as the earth revolves around the sun, and the moon around the earth.

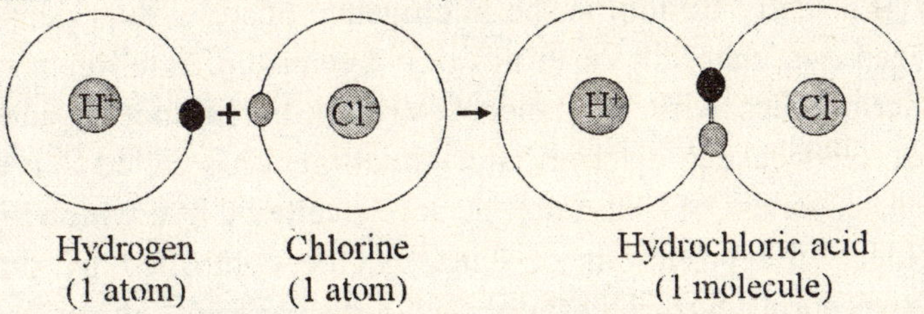

Figure 2.3. Hydrogen and chloride ions combine to form a molecule of hydrochloric acid.

3. Origin of Universe from Cosmic Egg

Altogether the substances of visible Nature (Prakṛti) formed the Cosmic Egg, and in the form of energy, that God created the universe by entering into that Cosmic Egg. Therefore, the creation of the universe was possible only with the combination of Nature and invisible Puruṣa. Such a view has been expressed in Śrīmad Bhāgvat.

तस्मिन्नहं समभवमण्डे सलिल संस्थितौ।
(श्रीमद्भागवत 11.24.10)

Tasminnahaṁ samabhavamaṇḍe salila saṅsthitau.

(Śrīmad Bhāgvat 11.24.10)

[When cosmic egg settled in water (*aṇḍaḥ salilaṁ saṅsthitaḥ*), I established in that egg (*tasmin ahaṁ sambhavaṁ*)]

Scientific Explanation- God himself seated in the primordial egg (Cosmic Egg) located in the water. It must be noted that why creation was started in water itself? What can be the reason for creation in water? What is the role of water in creation? All these are the subject of deep consideration. According to biologists, water is one of the most important matters for the emergence, growth and development of the organisms. All the activities of life take place in an aquatic medium. Water provides a medium for carrying out all metabolic and biochemical reactions. All organisms possess more that 80-85% water for smooth running of life. Probably, the primitive cell has originated from preginote (primeval egg) in aqueous medium. That is why the description of the origin of life from the egg-like structure in water is literally true.

4. Chronological Order of Creation

There are two forms of the Supreme Devine (Brahman), visible (Dṛśya) and non-visible (Druṣtā), the visible form is called Prakṛti (the factor form or nature) and the other non-visible form is called Puruṣ (subtle form, eternal truth, knowledge). There are three forms of Prakṛti- *Sat, Raj* and *Tam*. The Prakṛti gave rise to Sutra (action power-dominating form) and Mahat (the knowledge-dominating form, i.e. intelligence). The Sutra and Mahat are interlinked together. Mahat is all cosmic intelligence (Buddhi) that resides in the universe. When Puruṣa and Prakṛti (un-manifested) unite together, Mahat gets activated. Some philosophers say that Mahat is the synonym of Buddhi. But really Buddhi is the intelligence of individual person. A person is able to discriminate between two materials or things only because of intelligence. Intelligence thinks of a subject and discriminates with the help of Vivek (discriminatory intelligence), which is above the intelligence. Hence, such discriminatory intelligence is called 'Viveka'.

Besides, the consciousness of individual person is called Citta, which vibrates upon coming in the contact of object [the vibrations of Citta can be controlled by practice, called Yoga Sādhanā]. Since the creations possess atoms that bear particles, those atoms and molecules always remain in a condition of constant vibrations. Actually, vibration is the cause of creation. When things stop vibrating, the death becomes ascertained. The cosmos disintegrates into its original form, elemental of energy form. However, citta has a little similarity with Mānas or Mana (ego). Some philosophers assume the mind as Mānas; different schools of philosophers define Mānas in different ways.

Akaṅkār, a principle of cosmic egoism, manifests after activation of Mahat. Ahaṅkār was expressed due to a disorder in Mahat. Ahaṅkār is an ego at individual level. It is a sense of doership binding the consciousness of individual person with the action (Karma). It arises in the process of evolution. Ahaṅkār is of three types- Satva, Rajas and Tamas. The Cosmic Egoism is the cause of the senses, mind and Taṅmātrā (subject of those organs). Tamas gave rise to five cosmic elements (Pañca Mahābhuta) (earth, water, fire, air and ether) and five Taṅmātrā (words, touch, form, taste and smell). Rajas formed 10 organs (Iṅdriya) (5 Karmeṅdriya, namely mouth, hands, legs, anus and genital; 5 Jñāneṅdriya viz., ear, skin, eyes, tongue and nose) and 1 Manas (total 11). Saṭ gave rise to 11 Gods on earth [hymns of Atharvaveda (19.27.11-13) mention a total of 33 types of Gods [11 at Dyauloka (planetary world), 11 at Aṅtarikṣa (space) and 11 on Pṛthivī loka (earth)].

Every form of life has been created from 24 Tatva (cosmic creative principles) Maharṣi Suśruta has accepted 25 Tatva that form creation or Śṛṣti (Puruṣa). Among the 25 principles, 8 are the primordial elements (Prakṛti) and 16 are the derivatives (Vikṛti). The soul (atmā/puruṣa) i.e. life-element gets associated with these 24 elemental factors of the life-creator and thus there becomes a total of 25th Tatva (24+1).

- 8 Prakṛti are Vyakta, Mahat, Ahaṇkār and Pañca Taṅmātrā (the micro- or elemental form of the sense objects or Jñāneṅdriya). Lord Śrī Kṛṣṇa told to Arjun that every individual is created because of fundamental eight cosmic element of the Nature (Aṣtdhā Prakṛti), i.e. earth, water, fire, air, space or ether, mind, intelligence, ego principle (*Bhumirāponalo vāyu khaṁ mano buddhireva ca, ahaṅkār itīyaṁ me bhinnā prakṛtiraṣtdhā*) (Śrīmad Bhagavadgītā (7.4).
- 16 Vikṛti (derivatives) are 11 Iṅdriyas (organs), 5 Mahābhūt (5 elements of nature).

The five elements of Pañca Mahābhūta, i.e. five Jñāneṅdriya, five Karmeṅdriya and five Taṅmātra are given in Table 2.1.

Table 2.1: Five motor organs, sense organs, subject of that and controller of five elements.

Motor organs (Karmeṅdriya)	Sense organs (Jñāneṅdriya)	Subject of that organs (Taṅmātrā)	Controlling form of the five cosmic elements
Mouth	Ears	Sound	Ether
Hands	Skin	Touch	Air
Feet (legs)	Eyes	Form	Fire
Anus (Pāyu or Gudā)	Tongue	Taste (Rasa)	Water
Genitals (Upāstha)	Nose	Smell	Earth

The body organs (Iṅdriyas) were created from the Cosmic Egoism (Ahaṅkār) during the chronological order of creation of the universe. All these substances combining together revealed the former form of the universe, i.e. primordial egg. The three cosmic worlds (bhūḥ, bhuvaḥ, svaḥ) were born by Rajoguṇa under the inspiration of the Supreme God. He created heaven (Swarga Loka) for the abode of the God and Goddess, space (bhuvaḥ Loka) for the ghosts (Bhūta-Preta), and earth (Bhūḥ Loka) for humans and other beings. He created four another Loka (Mahaḥ Janaḥ, Tapaḥ and Satyaḥ) above these three planetary worlds (Loka) for the abode of the Siddha (who attains the supreme knowledge). These four Loka can be attained through Yoga, knowledge and renunciation (asceticism). But only the place of Brahman is attained through devotion. Thus, the order of creation progressed to form the universe (Śrīmad Bhāgvat 11.24.4–13) (Figure 2.4).

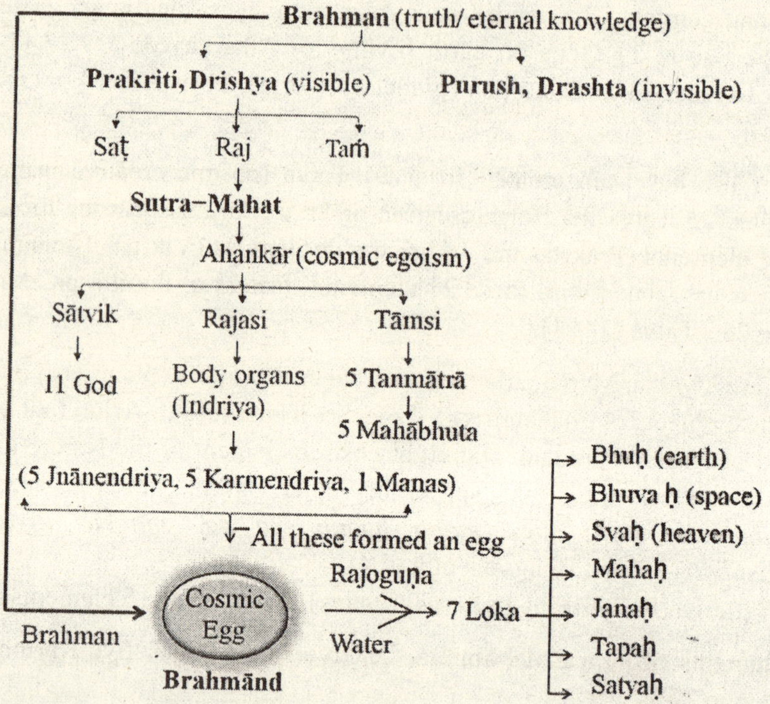

Figure 2.4: Chronological order of the origin of universe (based on Śrīmad Bhāgvat Purāna-11.24.4–13).

Thereafter, the Supreme Father meditated and expanded his Saṅkalpa, i.e. willingness (resolution, determination), created the cosmic egg (Brahmāṅda) and entered into it. How the creation took place when the absolute is Advait (only one, i.e. without a second)? Uddhav Gītā gives the answer '*Ekohaṁ bahuḥ Syām*', meaning 'I am one, let me be many'. The willingness of the Supreme Father projected him for being many from one. A similar narration has been mentioned in Taitttirīyopaniṣad (6.2)- *'So,kāmayat. Bahusyāṁ prajāyeyeti'*. That Supreme Being (saḥ) has contemplated (akāmayat) that I may appear (prajāyeya) and be many (bahuḥ) (syāt iti). Brahmānaṅda Purān, Śrīmad Bhāgvat Purāṇ and the other similar text also talk about the creation by determination and cosmic primordial egg. In spite of being many forms, there was/is no difference in being one, not two (Advait form).

The question arises that 'where from the solid materials came to create planets?' It obvious that Ākāśa originated from Saguṇa Brahman (Supreme Being with all quality). Hence, Ākāśa is best known as 'space' or 'ether' because all the worldly materials require space for their existence. Therefore, Ākāśa was created first in the order of creation followed by the other subtle elements that originated from Ākāśa. Then air (Vāyu) originated from space (Ākāśa) and fire (Agni) from air. Water (Āpa) originated from fire and earth (Pṛthivī) originated from water. These are subtle elements, not gross elements (Praśnopaniṣad 6.4). Therefore, space is regarded as the gender for creation of all worldly materials (*Ākāśasta liṅgāt*- Vedant Philosophy 1.1.22). The order of creation may be written as below:

Brahman (Supreme Being) → *Ākāśa* (space) → *Vāyu* (air) → *Agni* (fire) → *Āpa* (water) → *Pṛthivī* (earth)

SCIENTIFIC CONCEPT OF ATOMS AND PARTICLES

Scientific explanations of anything are done on the basis of many hypotheses and experiments. Some of these rules have been explained here according to Vedic thoughts and discourses. The universe has neither the beginning nor the end; it is a self-contained substance that is eternal. If all the substances of the universe are broken into pieces, they will be transformed into their subtlest state, i.e. atoms, particles and energy. All atoms have mass because of having its weight. But when the atoms are broken, they will be converted into different particles, such as electron, proton and neutron (Figure 2.5). Particles also have mass, so the entire mass of the particles is converted into energy when the particles are broken down. Energy is indestructible which cannot be destroyed. According to the law of thermodynamics, energy is beyond the creation and destruction but its forms are transformable.

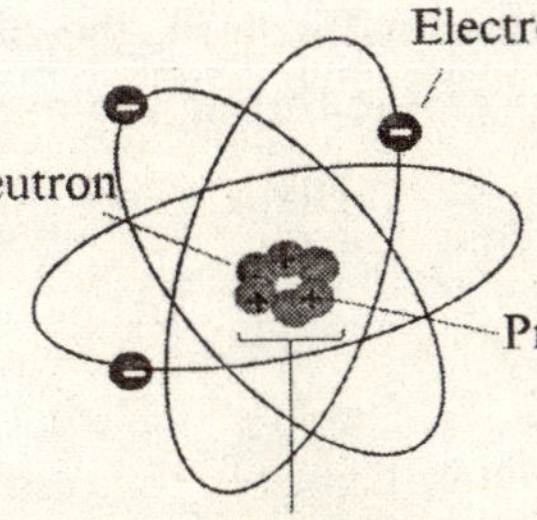

Figure 2.5. Structure of an atom.

1. The Soul (Energy) is Indestructible

According to Vedānta philosophy, the form of soul is also similar to that of God (So Ahaṁ). The Supreme Being is one who is beyond birth and death (*Janmādyasya yataḥ*- Vedānta Philosophy 1.1.2). Even in the Bhagavadgītā, Śrī Kṛṣṇa told Arjuna that this soul neither takes birth nor has its annihilation, because it is the one that is born. So how can someone who is not born die? Because it is beyond birth, is everlasting and is primeval. It does not die even after the body is destroyed after death.

न जायते म्रियते वा कदाचित् नायं भूत्वा भविता वा न भूयः।
अजो नित्यः शाश्वतोऽयं पुराणो न हन्यते हन्यमाने शरीरे ।।

(श्रीमद् भगवद्गीता 2.20)

Na jāyate mṛyate vā kadācit nāyaṁ bhūtvā bhavitā vā na bhūyaḥ.
Ajo nityaḥ śāśvato,yaṁ purāṇo na haṅyate haṅyamāne śarīre.

(Śrīmad Bhagvadgītā 2.20)

[The soul is never born (*na jāyate*) nor it ever dies (*mṛyate vā kadācit*), nor does it become (*nāyaṁ bhūtvā*) after being born (*bhavitā vā na bhūyaḥ*). For, it is unborn, eternal (*ajo nityaṁ*), everlasting and primeval (*śāśvatoyaṃ purāṇo*); even though the body is slain (*na haṅyate*), the soul is not (*haṅyamāne śarīre*).]

Scientific Explanation- This means that the energy like the soul is neither born nor dead. This is the law of thermodynamics "energy can neither be created nor destroyed, only it can be changed from one form to another". Just as the soul changes from the body and the conscious changes from the material, the state of the energy can be changed in the same way. That is, the soul is neither created nor destroyed (*Na jāyate mriyate vā kadācit*– Śrīmad Bhagvadgītā 2.20), it is eternal, indestructible and everlasting. But only the state of form changes as the humans leave his old cloth and bears a new one, similarly the soul also replaces the old body with a new one (*Vāsānsi jīrṇāni yathā vihāya*– Śrīmad Bhagvadgītā 2.22). From the above discussion it has became completely clear that the entire universe has two stages, latent (un-manifested) and expressed (manifested) ones. The latent form is expressed in relation to time and space, which is called creation. Albert Einstein, the great scientist of the 20th century, has said the same in his 'Theory of Relativity' ($E=mc^2$). According to Einstein, the change of mass (m) into energy (E) and the change of energy into mass are possible through to a factor (c^2) (Figure 2.5).

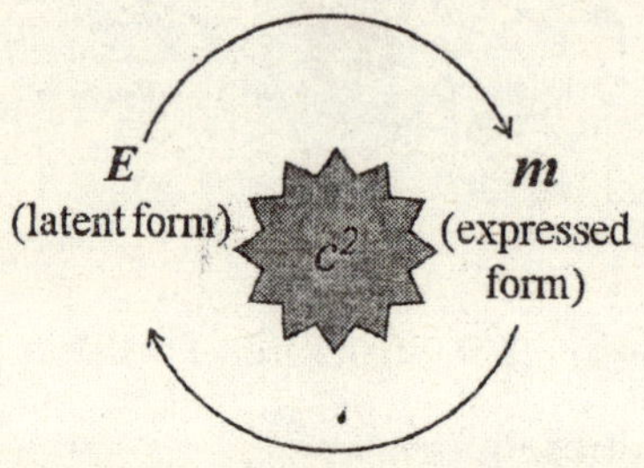

Figure 2.5. The latent (un-manifested) and expressed (manifested) forms of creation.

2. The World– True or False

Brahman is called eternal truth and the world is false; there is no difference between Brahman and life (Jīva), i.e. Brahman is not beyond the life but Brahman is with the life (*Brahma satyaṁ jagat mithyā jivo brahmai nā paraḥ*). That is, even after seeing all the creatures, animals, rivers, mountains, sun, moon, stars, etc. present in the world, it appears that they are true, because all of them exist in the universe. Actually, they are not true because they are born, hence they have to die. But they are not even untrue, because they are presently existing and visible. That is, there is no presence of untruth and even no absence of truth (*Nāsate vidyatebhāvo nā bhāvo vyate sataḥ*- Śrīmad Bhagavadgīta 2.16). This means that untruth can never be true because it does not exist, it's non-existing. But the truth can never be untrue because it always exists, it is everlasting and it is indestructible. Therefore, it is necessary to understand that Supreme Being (Brahman) is unborn and everlasting; therefore, he is beyond the birth and death (*Janmādasya yataḥ*- Vedanta Philosophy 1.1.2).

The entire universe is neither true nor untrue, so it is false. False means one that exists after birth and before death, i.e. one that appears to exist through senses, all sensory and action organs of body. This means that the entire universe exists with respect to time and space; hence, the universe is false because it is short-lived and it has to dies. Every born material has to dies; the Einstein's theory of relativity also says the same statement. The entire universe is born, so the world taking birth is untrue; it is true only for short period with respect to time and space. Hence, such world is called "false", i.e. it appears true only for short duration and "its presence only for short duration at a particular space and time" is called "life". Hence the life is to live for short period and it is transitory and false. Therefore, the annihilation of the world is fixed; it is also said in the Śrīmad Bhagvadgītā (2.27).

जातस्य हि ध्रुवो मृत्युर्ध्रुवं जन्म मृतस्य च।
तस्मादपरिहार्येऽर्थे न त्वं शोचितुमर्हसि।।

(श्रीमद् भगवद्गीता 2.27)

Jātasya hi dhruvo mṛtyurdhruvaṁ jaṅm mṛtasya ca.

Tasmāt parihārye,rthe na tvaṛ śocitumarhasi.

(Śrīmad Bhagvadgītā 2.27)

[In fact, death is certain (*dhruo mṛtyuḥ*) for born (*jātasya hi*); it is also a fact that (*dhruvaḥ*) birth of the dead (*jaṅma mṛtasya ca*) is inevitable. Therefore, for unavoidable (*parihārye*) matter (*arthe*) you (*tvaṁ*) should not grieve over the inevitable (*na śocituṁ arhasi*)]

Scientific Explanation- Everything born is to dies. Even the subtlest organisms and the largest constellation and body or the most powerful person is not immortal. The powerful person is also not invincible, because no one has conquered the death. Therefore, the death of all those born is certain and the birth of the dead is also fixed. The sun, moon, galaxies, every components of life have to dies because they are born. Hence, all born have life and they have to die. If anyone in this universe is beyond birth and death, he is only the Supreme Father, i.e. the supreme soul, and no one else.

3. The Forms of the World– Manifested (Expressed) and Un-manifested (Latent)

The cosmos widely pervades in two forms, visible and invisible which are commonly referred to as the expressed or manifested and the latent or un-manifested form, respectively. The expressed form is destructible (Kṣara) and the latent form is indestructible (Akṣara). Therefore, the entire creation is the result of a combination of these two forms. The Akṣara makes the Kṣara viable. Both these forms have been mentioned in Śvetaśvataropaniṣad (1.8).

संयुक्तमेतत् क्षरमक्षरं च व्यक्ताव्यक्तं भरते विश्वमीशः।

(श्वेताश्वतरोपनिषद् 1.8)

Sanyukatmetat kṣaramakṣaraṁ ca vyaktāvyaktaṁ bharte viśvamīśaḥ.

(Śhvetaśvataropaniṣad 1.8)

[The Supreme Father bears and nurtures (*bharte*) the manifested (*vyakta*) and un-manifested (*avyakta*) forms of this universe (*etaṭ viśvaṁ*), which is a combination of (*saṅyuktaṁ*) destructible (*kṣaraṁ*) and (*ca*) indestructible, i.e. everlasting (*akṣaraṁ*) forms.]

Scientific Explanation- Here, Kṣara means mass (material) i.e. creation, which is 'all the destructible substances'. The materials are made due to combinations of innumerable atoms, molecules and macromolecules. Hence, they degrade after some times; they have some life span, which are degraded upon its completion. Until they are not degraded, they appear in certain forms. Therefore, all of them have forms, none are formless; therefore, they are visible with naked eyes or with certain instrument. But the word Akṣara means 'all non-destructible substances' like energy (soul or Supreme Father). According to the thermodynamics law, there is no loss, but changes in the forms of energy. That is why Brahman is called Akṣara or indestructible (*Akṣaraṁ brahma paramaṁ svabhavo,dhyātmucyate*– Śrīmad Bhagavadgītā 8.3) because He is un-destructible.

Here, the terms manifested-nonmanifested are used for the entire creation. Similarly, the word expressed form has been used in the Śrīmad Bhagavadgītā for the middle stage between birth and death. These two forms of live (manifested and non-manifested) have been explained in detail in Śrīmad Bhagavadgītā (2.28).

अव्यक्तादीनि भूतानि व्यक्त मध्यानि भारत।

अव्यक्त निधनान्येव तत्र का परिवेदना।।

(श्रीमद् भगवद्गीता 2.28)

Avyakādīni bhūtāni vyakt madhyāni bhārat.

Avyak nidhanānyeva tatra kā parivedanā.

(Śrīmad Bhagvadgītā 2.8)

[All the creatures (*bhūtāni*) are non-manifested (*avyakta*) in their beginning (*adīni*), manifested (*vyakta*) in the middle (*madhyāni*) i.e. after birth and before death, and non-manifested ¼*avyakta*½ again after death; it is all like that (*iva*) when annihilated (*nidhanāni*). Therefore, what for (*tatra kā*) lamentation (*parivedanā*)]

With gradual growth in human life, there occur some spectacular changes. These changes of human life are– birth (jāyate), existence (asti), changing (vipariṇamate), increasing (vardhate), carrying erosion (apakṣīyate) and attaining death or annihilation (vinaśyati iti) (Figure 2.6). Rebirth can also be explained according to this life cycle. Śrīmad Bhagavadgītā (2.13) describes three major spectacular changes in human body, '*dehino,sminyathā dehe kaumāraṁ yauvanaṁ jarā*', i.e. virginity (kaumāraṁ), youth (yauvanaṁ) and old age (jarā). After death, the human body is cremated / buried by the followers of different religions. The building block of body called elements are released into the environment or soil.

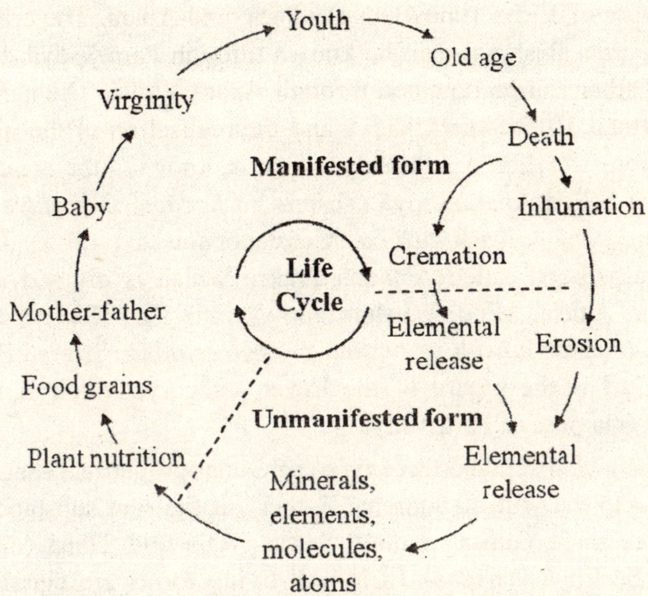

Figure 2.6. Human-life cycle (elemental cycle).

Scientific Explanation- These elements in due course of time are absorbed for growth and reproduction by the plants that are consumed by humans (male and female), who after being young give birth to a baby, and thus the elemental cycle gets completed. During this cycle, the elements make the body visible after birth and invisible after the death, but the elements and the particles that make them are never destroyed. It is the body that dies and disintegrated, not the energy binding the elements and holding them together.

Names and Classification of Germs (Kṛmis) 3.

There are two types of Vidyā (knowledge)– Parā and Aparā. The creator of this universe, the Supreme Father (Param Brahma), can be known through Parā Vidyā, but knowledge of the creation of Supreme Father can be obtained through Aparā Vidyā. The name of the four Vedas and the six Vedānga (total 10) is Aparā Vidyā and the realisation of the imperishable Supreme Being by these conditions is called Aparā Vidyā. That is, knowing the creator is Parā Vidyā and knowing the creation is called Aparā Vidyā (*Tasmai sa hovāca. Dve vidye veditavye iti sa sma yat brahmavido vadanti parā caivavaparā ca.* Mundakopaniṣad 1.1.4-5). The Aparā Prakriti of Param Brahman has also been called Aṣtadhā Prakṛti which is divided into eight types viz., Earth, Water, Fire, Air, Akāśa, Mind, Wisdom and Cosmic Ego (*Bhūmirāpo,nalo vāyuḥ khaṁ mano buddhireva ca. Ahankār etīyaṁ ye bhinnā prakṛtiraṣtadhā.* Śrīmad Bhagavadgītā 7.4). In fact, the Aṣtadhā Prakṛti is the nature of the lower category, which is imperishable and its existence is due to the greatness of Parā Vidyā.

Our ancient sages have discussed three types of Guṇa (properties) (Satoguṇa, Rajoguṇa and Tamoguṇa). According to the will of Supreme Father, all the root substances of nature exist in the same state in these three Guṇas, namely Sattva, Raja and Tama (*Sattva rajas tamasāṁ sāmāvasthā prakṛtiḥ.* Sāṅkhya Darśana- 1.61). All living forms are classified into these three Guṇas. According to Manusmṛti (12.42-44), some more visible creatures including Kṛmis have been classified as creatures with Tāmasī properties of life.

CLASSIFICATION OF ORGANISMS

Therefore, the organisms with Tāmasī Guṇa would have Tāmasī life and such organisms have been placed in the Tiryaka Yoni (species) among 84 lākh (840 millions) Yonis (origin). This means that our Ṛṣis have given proper place to microorganisms keeping in mind all the life forms. It has been described in the Vedas, Vedāṅg, Purānas, Manusmṛti, Upaniṣads, etc.

Manusmṛti describes the achievement of ultimate Yonis of all life forms according to their Gunas (Sātvika, Rājasi and Tāmsī).

देवत्वमं सात्त्विका यान्ति मनुष्यत्वं च राजसाः।
तिर्यक्त्वं तामसा नित्यं इत्येषां त्रिविधा गतिः।।

(मनुस्मृति 12.40)

Devatvaṁ sāttvikā yāṅti manuṣyatvaṁ ca rājasāḥ.
Tiryaktvaṁ tāmasā nityaṁ ityeṣāṁ trividhā gatiḥ.

(Manusmṛti 12.40)

[Among these (*iti yeshāṁ*) three types (*trividhā*) of destinies (*gatih*), persons always (*nityaṁ*) attain (*yānti*) Divinity (*devatvaṁ*) by Sāttvik qualities (*sāttvika*), humanity (*manuṣyatvaṁ*) by Rajoguna (*rājasā*), and (ca) Tiryaka Yoni (*tiryaktavaṁ*) by Tama virtues (*tāmasā*)]

Scientific Explanation- The Daiva Yoni i.e. the celestial bodies include the celestial beings, such as stars, planets, etc. that make balance of the universe. Secondly, humans bear virtuous characters called Rajas due to which they achieve Manuṣya Yoni. Organisms of Tiryak Yoni include all Menials, i.e. the being with low intelligence. Humans may attain Manuṣya or Daiva Yoni because of advanced intelligence and actions performed according to situations and opportunities.

Further, Manusmṛti describes different organisms of Tiryaka Yoni as below:

स्थावराः कृमि कीटाश्च मत्स्याः सर्पाः सकच्छपाः।
पशवश्च मृगाश्चैव जघन्या तामसी गतिः।।
(मनुस्मृति 12.42)

Sthāvarāḥ kṛmi kītāśca matsyāḥ sarpāḥ sakacchapāḥ.
Paśavaśca mṛgāścaiva jaghanyā tāmasīgatiḥ.
(Manusmṛti 12.42)

[All immovable beings (*sthāvarāḥ*), microorganisms (*kṛmi*) and insects (*kītāśca*) (both small and large sized), fishes (*matsyāḥ*), snakes (*sarpāḥ*), tortoises (*ca sakacchapāḥ*) and cattle (*paśavaśca eva*) and wild animals also (*mṛgāścaiva*), are the lowest conditions (*jaghanyā*) of organisms in which borne (*tāmasī gatiḥ*)]

Scientific Explanation- Tama quality of all life forms is the smallest of all three qualities. Individuals who have Tāmasic quality always remain lazy while sleeping. Such organisms always have laziness and pomp. However, Sattva component appears sometimes due to being calm, but it is not so. A person does not have knowledge inside because of having Tāmasic quality. Due to Tamas property, a person is not able to distinguish between truth and untruth because the conscience of such persons does not work properly. Hence, the curiosity of such persons also ends because of not taking proper decisions. Tamas quality of such person creates confusion. Whenever a person is under the influence of Tamas property, wrong things are done by him because such person does not have the knowledge of truth and untruth. Therefore, in such a state of confusion, the truth also appears to be untrue. For example, in the darkness of ignorance, the illusion of the serpent is formed in the illusory rope (i.e. *Yat satvāt mriśaivabhāti sakalaṁ rajjau yathā hay bhramaḥ.* Rāmcaritmānas 1).

सृट्वा पुराणि विविधन्यजयात्मशक्तया,
वृक्षान् सरीसृपपशून् खगदंशमत्स्यान्।
तैस्तैर अतुष्ट ह्रदयः पुरुषं विधाय,
ब्रह्मावलोकधिषणं मुदमाप देवः।।
(श्रीमद्भागवत् 11.9.28)

Sṛṣtvā purāni vividhanyajayātmaśaktayā,
Vṛkṣān sarīsṛpapaśūn khagadaṅśamatsyān.
Taistaira atuṣta hṛdayaḥ puruṣaṁ vidhāya,

Brahmāvalokadhiṣaṇaṁ mudamāp devaḥ.

(Śrīmad Bhāgavat 11.9.28)

[The Supreme Father by his power (*ātma śaktayā*) first (*purāni*) created many types (*vividhāni*) of liveforms like trees (*vṛkṣān*), reptiles (*sarīsṛpa*), animals (*paśūn*), birds, insects (*khagadaṅśa*), etc. Even after creating (*sṛṣtvā*) all these (*taistair*), the Father's heart was unsatisfied (*atuṣta hṛdayaḥ*), then He created humans (*puruṣaṁ vidhāya*), getting whom all the gods were pleased (*mudamāp devaḥ*) because only humans can realise the basic power of Brahman (*brahmāvalokadhiṣaṇaṁ*)].

Scientific Explanation- According to both Indian knowledge and modern science, life has originated gradually. The basic power of the universe is manifested in the form of creation. Trees, reptiles, animals, birds, insects, moths, fishes, etc. appeared sequentially, in which the human originated at the end. Apart from humans, no animal can realise the basic power of that Supreme. Science also explains the origin of organisms sequentially and gradually in a well ordered way.

Several thousand years ago, 84 Lākh Yonis (8.4 million species) have been mentioned in our Vedic text starting with minute size germs to humans. According to Padma Purāṇ, 84 lākh organisms are known.

जलजा नव लक्षाणि स्थावराः लक्ष विन्शति।
क्रिमयोः रुद्र संख्यकाः पक्षीणां दश लक्षणम्।।
त्रिंस लक्षाणि पशवः चतुर्लक्षाणि मानुषाः।।

(पद्म पुराण 78.5)

Jalajā nav lakṣāṇi sthāvarāḥ lakṣya vinśati.
Krimayoḥ rudra sankhyakāḥ pakṣīṇāṁ daśa lakṣaṇaṁ.
Triṅsa lakṣāṇi paśavaḥ caturlakṇāni mānuṣāḥ.

(Padma Purāṇ 78.5)

[There are nine lākh (*nav lakṣnāṇi*) water-born organisms (*jalajā*), twenty lākh (*lakṣa vinśati*) stagnant means plants (*sthāvarah*), eleven lākh (*rudra sankhyakāh*) microorganisms (*kṛmayoh*), ten lākh (*daś lakṣaṇam*) birds (*pakṣiṇām*), thirty lākh (*triṅsa lakṣāṇi*) animals (*paśavaḥ*), and four lākh (*caturlakṣāṇi*) humans (*mānuṣāh*)]

Scientific Explanation- There are a total of 84 lākh (8.4 million) species of organisms including 0.9 million (9 lakh) water-born organisms (germs, reptiles and amphibians), 2.0 million (20 lākh) immovable plants, 1.1 millions (11 lākh) worms and microorganisms (viruses, bacteria, protozoa, fungi,), 1.0 million (10 lākh) birds of all groups, 3.0 million (30 lākh) terrestrial quadruped animals, and 0.4 million (4 lākh) advanced mammals such as humans, apes, gorilla, Neanderthal, etc. Irrespective of these numbers, such counting of all groups of living organisms shows the researches done by our sages and seers during millenniums years ago and counted the number of all organisms existing in soil and water. This the first attempt of knowledge of diversity among living organisms which, in recent years, is called 'biodiversity'.

Table 3.1. Organisms in 84 Lakh Yonis (Padma Purāṇ 78.5).

Organisms	*Number (Lakh)*
Water-born	09
Stagnant (plants)	20
Kṛmis	11
Birds	10
Animals	30
Humans	04
Total	**84**

1. Knowledge of Invisible Organisms through Logic

It is very difficult to study the microorganisms in the absence of any microscope or the other means. But our sages have talked about reaching microorganisms through logic. In the modern century, a variety of methods based on a variety of means are used to study microorganisms. Although only about 3 percent of microorganisms have been studied, nothing is known about 97 percent of microorganisms. In the means times millions of organisms, including plants, animals and microbes, have become extinct possibly because of their failure to adapt the gradual changes in the environment. They could not cope with those changes brought about in the environment. In addition, thousands of plants and animals are also at the verge of extinction due to growing threat of 'global warming'. Moreover, the existence of microorganisms in the Śāṅtiparva of Mahābhārata, written over 3000 BCE, describes the knowledge experienced by ancient sages. According to the Śāṅtiparva, the information of microorganisms can be obtained by logistic method.

सूक्ष्मयोनीनि भूतानि तर्क गम्यानि कानि चित्।
पक्ष्मणोऽपि निपादेन येषां सयात सकन्धपर्ययः।।
(महाभारत– शान्तिपर्व 15.26)

Sukṣmayonīni bhutāni tarka gamyāni kāni cit.
Pakṣmaṇo,pi nipāden yeṣām sayāt sakandhaparyayaḥ.
(Mahābhārat- Śāṅtiparva 15.26)

[There are many types of so minute (*sukṣmayonīni*) creatures (*bhutāni*) that the existence of some (*kāṇicit*) can only be inferred by argument (*tarka gamyāni*). They are destroyed (*sakaṅdhparyayaḥ sayāt*) even only with the fall of (*nipāden*) the eyelids alone (*pakṣmaṇaḥ api*)]

Scientific Explanation - Logic is an important method to conclude any complex subject. Some facts of logic have to be given or discovered as evidence. Sukṣma Yoni is used for the kṛmis to describe the minute invisible organisms. For example, if 10-20 grams of curd is added into a litre of hot (37-40°C) milk, then whole milk becomes curd within 6 hours. It is a matter of logic that what can happen in 10 grams of curd that converts the whole milk into the curd? But there is something in the inoculum (small amount of curd used as the starter) of curd by adding which the milk turns into curd. Whatever is present in the curd is not visible through the naked eyes. But by logic it can be said that there is an invisible cause present in the curd that converts the whole milk into the curd within 5-6 hours at about 37°C. Similarly, other microorganisms not visible with the naked eyes but their existence in nature can also be experienced by the logic. The modern science believes that the tears from eyes and sweet glands secrete an enzyme (lysozyme) that destroys the microorganisms present on the surface of skin. Human body secretes the tears for its self-defence. Similarly, millions of bacteria live on outer surface of our body and trillions inside but we cannot see them because of their small size. However, they do their beneficial as well as harmful functions leading to maintenance of good health and serious diseases, respectively.

2. Observing the Microbes through the Divine Eyes

Microorganisms cannot be seen by naked eyes due to their very small size. Therefore, they can be visualized only by using the devices with magnifying lenses or the Divine Eyes (Divya Cakṣu). In the battle field of Kurukṣetra (Haryana), when Śrī Kṛṣṇa showed Arjuna his Divine Form but Arjuna could not see his form. He said that he is not able to see anything. Again Śrī Kṛṣṇa told to Arjuna that 'you cannot see my Divine Form through these naked eyes, which have seen all the worldly things; therefore, I give you the Divine Eyes for seeing the amazing and Supernatural Divine form of mine'. Saying this, Shri Krishna showed his Divine Form to Arjuna. This has been mentioned is in the Śrīmad Bhagavadgītā.

न तु मां शक्यसे द्रश्टुमनेनैव स्वचक्षुसा।
दिव्यं ददामि ते चक्षुः पश्य मे योगमैश्वरम्।।
(श्रीमद् भगवद्गीता 11.8)

Na tu māṁ śakyase draśtumanenaiva svacakṣusā.
Divyaṁ dadāmi te cakṣuḥ paśya me yogamaiśvaram.
(Śrīmad Bhagavadgītā 11.8)

[But (*tu*) certainly (*ev*) you are never (*na*) able (*śakyase*) to see (*druśtuṁ*) Me (*māṁ*) with your own physical eyes (*sva-cakṣusā*). Therefore, I give you (*dadāmi*) the Divine (*divyaṁ*) eyes (*cakṣuḥ*) to you (*te*). You behold (*paśya*) my (*me*) Devine power of yoga (*yogaṁ aiśvaraṁ*)]

Explanation- After revealing the Divine Power of Sri Kṛṣṇa, Arjuna began to see the entire universe. Millions of resplendent Suns, the entire planetary world, all galaxies, atoms and all beings became visible; but Arjuna was frightened on seeing this mega form. Therefore, Arjuna requested Śri Kṛṣṇa to stop such a scene and revert in the original normal form to which Śrī Kṛṣṇa did accordingly. Therefore, it can be said that Arjun was the first person to observe the minutest form of entire entities (including atoms and microbes) present in the cosmos and Śrī Kṛṣṇa was the first person to provide the Divine Eyes to Arjun for visualization of the all creations.

VARIOUS NAMES OF THE KṚMIS (GERMS)

The word 'Kṛmi' has varying meanings as used in Vedas. Kṛmi word has been used for both pathogenic as well as non-pathogenic organisms. Atharvaveda describes two different words for Kṛmis- the visible (insects like flies) and invisible (germs and worms) Kṛmis. Literary meaning of Kṛmi is as below:

क्रव्ये मेद्यति क्रमते वी स्यात सरण कर्मणः कामते वी।

(निरुक्त 6.12)

Kravye medyati kramate vī syata sarana karmaṇaḥ kāmte vī.

(Nirukta 6.12)

The term Kṛmi has been derived from the Kravya' Dhātu which means 'to derive nourishment from the unripe flesh/meat (Māṅsa). Similarly, Krama word is originated from 'Krama' Dhātu which means to move, i.e. moving from one part of body to another part; the term Kāṁ is originated from 'Kam' Dhātu which means to 'wish' or to 'desire'.

Dayānanda Nirukti-Vyutpatti Kośa also defines the word Kṛmis as:

क्राम्यति पादान् विक्षिप्तीति कृमिः क्षुद्रजन्तर्वा।
सम्प्रसारनानुवृत्तेः कृमिः इत्यपि।।

(उणादि कोश 4.122)

Krāmyati pādān vikṣipatīti kṛmiḥ kṣudrajantarvā.
Samprasāraṇānuvritteḥ kṛmiḥ ityapi.

(*Uṇādi Kośa* 4.122).

The minute (*kṣudra*) invisible uncontrolled (*vikṣipta*) microbes (*jantarvāh*) that crawl by feet (*krāmyati pādān*) on the surface are also called Kṛmis (*iti api Kṛmiḥ*).

1. Names of Kṛmis in Vedas

In addition, 111 names of Kṛmis have been mentioned in Vedas at different places according to their nature and function, for example Adraṣtā, Rākṣasa, Piśāca, Yātudhān, Kṣudrajantu, Jantorṇava, Kimidi, Gandharva, Apsarā, Amīvā, Durṇāmā, Sunāmā, etc. Some names of germs and their functions are given in Table 3.1.

Table 3.1. Names and functions of some Kṛmis (Germs).

Name of Kṛmis	*Function*
Akaṅkata	Air-born microorganisms
Amīvā	The foetus-infecting Kṛmis
Aśreṣa	Symbiotic Kṛmis
Asrukpava	Kṛmis that suck blood
Asura	Highly virulent Kṛmis that kill the persons
Bhūta	Quickly growing and rapidly multiplying Kṛmis
Durgandhī	Foul-smell imparting Kṛmis
Durṇāmā	The uterus-infecting Kṛmis

Kakuma	The vibrating Kṛmis
Kaṅka	Water-born Kṛmis
Kaṇva	Kṛmis that prey the foetus in the womb
Kaṣkaṣa	Invisible Kṛmis causing acute pain
Kravyāda	Kṛmis infecting and living upon blood
Lohita	Red-coloured Kṛmis
Manohana	Kṛmis that cause mental diseases
Piśāca	Kṛmis prey on raw blood and flesh for its nutrition
Pramilina	Kṛmis causing lethargy or drowsiness
Pramushāna	Highly contagious Kṛmis
Rajsya	Minute germs spread by infected droplets
Rakṣagrīva	Kṛmis infecting the throat with pain
Rākśasa	Kṛmis stealing away the vitality, catching the joints and killing patients
Reriha	Most aggressively infecting Kṛmis
Śrīmaha	Kṛmis that give rise to viruses (possibly bacteriophages)
Śroṇi pratodini	Kṛmis infecting the pelvis in females
Sunāmā	Kṛmis causing disease in females
Vatsapa	Kṛmis that infect foetus reducing fertility
Virūpa	Kṛmis that lack definite size and shape, such as amoeba
Yātudhāna	Kṛmis that result in pain (Yātanā) after infection

2. Names and Colours of Kṛmis as described by Caraka

Caraka has described different types of Kṛmis into two broad groups, Sahaja Kṛmis (normal microflora) and Vaikārika Kṛmis (pathogenic microflora). Sahaja Kṛmis are generally associated with human body without causing any harm. They derive nutrients from the hosts and multiply. They are beneficial to human health as they trigger the immunity that fight against pathogens. In contrast, the Vaikārik Kṛmis are the pathogenic microflora and harm different organs of human body. All the four types of Kṛmis are shown in Figure 3.1 and briefly described as below:

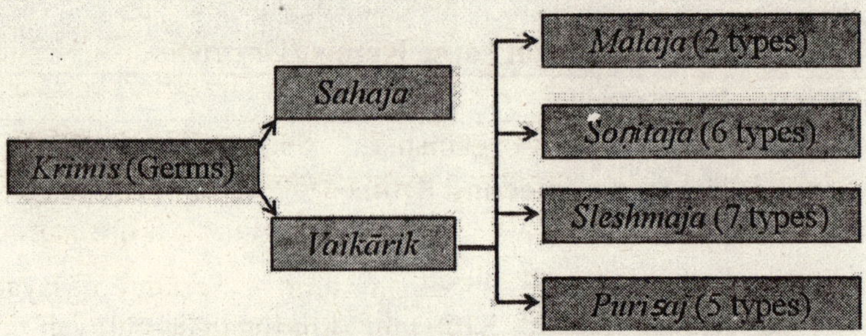

Figure 3.1. Classification of Kṛmis based on Caraka.

The Kṛmis of all the groups are further divided into 20 different types by Caraka.

इह खल्वग्निवेश! विंशतिविधाः कृमयः पूर्वमुद्दिष्टाः नानाविधेन प्रविभागेनान्यत्र सहजेभ्यः, ते पुनः प्रकृतिभिर्भिद्यमानाश्चतुर्विधा भवन्ति। तद्यथा–पुरीषजाः श्लेष्मजाः शोणितजा मलजाश्चेति।।

(चरक संहिता–विमान स्थान, 7.9)

Ih khalvagniveśaḥ! Viṅśatividhāḥ kṛmayaḥ pūrvamuddiṣṭāḥ nānāvidhen pravibhāgen anyatra sahajebhyaḥ, te punaḥ prakṛtibhirbhidyamānāścaturvidhā bhavanti. Tadyathā-purīṣajāḥ śleṣmajāḥ śoṇitajā malajāśceti.

(Caraka Saṁhitā- Vimāna Sthāna, 7.9)

[O Agniveś ! (*Ih khalvagniveśaḥ*), besides earlier description (*pūrvamuddiṣta*) (*sahaja Kṛmis* (*sahahajebhyah*), twenty types (*vinśatividhāḥ*) of many forms (*nānāvidhen*) of *Kṛmis* (*krimayaḥ*) have been mentioned from different sections (*pravibhāgen*). These (te) *Kṛmis* again (*punaḥ*), due to their different nature (*prakṛtibhirbhidyamānāḥ*), are of four types (*caturvidhā bhavanti*) viz., faecal material-born (*purīṣajāḥ*), phlegm-born (*śleṣmajāḥ*), blood-born (*śoṇitajā*) and waste material-born (*malajāḥ*)]

(a) **Purīshaja Kṛmis:** The Purīṣaja Kṛmis (faecal material-born microbes) reside in large intestine and rectum. They utilize the nutrients of undigested/partially digested food materials passed in large intestine. Depending on opportunities they also cause diseases in human, such as fistula, sepsis, cellulitis, urinary tract infection (UTI), etc. They have been called by five names by Caraka, for example, Kakeruka, Makeruka, Lelih, Saśulaka, and Sausurāda based on their different shapes and colours (for example, gray, blue, green and yellow).

पुरीषजास्तुल्य समुत्थानाः श्लेष्मजैस्तेषां स्थानं पक्वाशः . . . तेषां नामानि ककेरुका मकेरुका लेलिहाः सशूलकाः सौसुरादाश्चेति।

(चरकसंहिता– विमान स्थान 7.13)

Purīṣajāstulya samutthānāḥ śleṣmjaisteṣāṁ sthānaṁ pakvāśaḥ ...... teṣāṁ nāmāni kakerukā makerukā lelihāḥ saśūlakāḥ sausurādāśceti.

(Caraka Saṁhitā- Vimāna Sthāna 7.13)

(b) **Śleṣmaja Kṛmis:** The Śleṣmaja Kṛmis (phlegm-born microbes) are of 7 types, such as Antrāda, Udarāda, Hridayacara, Curu, Darbhapuśpa, Saugandhika and Mahāguda. The phlegm-born Kṛmis develop due to intake of sweet food (such as Guṇa), sesame oil, fish, imbalance diet, etc. They reside in stomach from where they migrate towards both upward and downward directions, i.e. esophagus and intestine, respectively.

श्लेष्मजाः क्षीर–गुडः–तिल–मत्स्यानूपमांसः. . . तेषाम् आमाशयः स्थानम् . . कृमिणां नामानि– अन्त्रादाः, उदरादाः, हृदयचराः, चुरवः, दर्भपुष्पाः, सौगन्धिकाः, महागुदाश्चेति।

(चरकसंहिता– विमान स्थान, 7.12)

Śleṣmajāḥ Kṣīra-guṇaḥ-tila-matyānūpamāṅsaḥ ...Teṣāṁ āmāśayaḥ sthānam . .. Kṛmiṇām nāmāni- antrādāḥ, udarādaḥ, hṛdayacarāḥ, curavaḥ' darbhapuṣpāḥ, saugaṅdhikāḥ, mahāgudāśceti.

(Caraka Saṁhitā- Vimāna Sthāna 7.12)

(c) **Śoṇitaja Kṛmis:** The Śoṇitaja/Raktaja Kṛmis (blood-born microbes) reside in arteries and veins of circulatory systems. They derive nutrition from blood as it is the rich source of carbohydrates, vitamins, proteins, amino acids, etc. They are so minute that they cannot be easily observed (for example, Plasmodium, *Trypanosoma, Rubella virus*). They are copper-coloured and are of 6 types, such as Keshād, Lomād, Lomdvīpa, Sauras and Udumbarā, and Jantumātar. They affect skin, nerves, veins, arteries, muscles and tender bones.

शोणितजानां . . . स्थानं रक्तवाहिन्यो धमन्यः। संस्थानं अणवो वृत्ताश्चापादाश्च सूक्ष्मत्वाश्चैके भवन्यदृश्याः। वर्णस्ताम्रः। नामानि केशादा लोमादा लोमद्वीपाः सौरसा औदुम्बरा जन्तुमातरश्चेति।

(चरकसंहिता– विमान स्थान, 7.11)

Śoṇitajānāṁ . . . sthānaṁ raktavāhinyo dhamanyaḥ. Saṅsthānaṁ aṇavo vṛttāścāpādāśca sūkṣmatvāścaike bhavanyadṛśyaḥ. Varṇstāmraḥ. Nāmāni keśādā lomādā lomadvīpāḥ saurasā audumbarā jantumātaraśceti.

(Caraka Saṁhitā- Vimāna Sthāna 7.11)

(d) **Malaja Kṛmis**: The Malaja Kṛmis (waste material-born microbes) are associated with the waste materials discharged by human body. These materials act as the source of nutrients for the microbes residing on body surface. The waste materials are of 2 types, the external waste and internal waste. The Kṛmis develop on body surface due secretion of external waste such as sweat that deposit on skin in dried form. Further, they spread to various places like skin, hairs, beard and eyelashes causing diseases. Malaja Kṛmis develop because of unhygienic condition of body and untimely bathing. Some of them are visible Kṛmis, such as lice and most of them invisible, for example causal agents of ringworm.

तत्र मलो बाह्यश्चाऽभ्यान्तरश्च। तत्र बाह्ये मले जातान्मलजान्संचक्षमहे।

(चरक संहिता–विमान स्थान, 7.10)

Tatra malo bāhyaścā,bhyāntaraśca. Tatra bāhye male jātānmalajāṅsancakṣamahe.

(Caraka Saṁhita- Vimāna Sthāna 7.10)

The Malaja Kṛmis reside on hairs on head, beard and mustaches (Śamaśru), body hairs (Loma), eyelashes (Pakṣa) and clothing (Vāsānsi). Out of the 20 types of Kṛmis, 5 types are Pūrīṣaja, 7 types Śleṣmaja, 6 types Śoṇitaja, 2 types Malaja (total 20 types).

MAJORS GROUPS OF KṚMIS IN VEDAS

A described earlier, names of 111 Kṛmis have been mentioned in Vedas. These terms have been used with different meaning and purpose, as well as the functions they perform in nature. However, they may be classified broadly in 4 major groups based on their characteristics.

- **Dṛṣta-** The Kṛmis visible to eyes are called Dṛṣta, i.e. they macroscopic e.g. Nīlgrīva, Gocara, Prithivīcara, Gadaha, Virūpa, Viśvarūpa, etc.

- **Adṛṣta**-The Kṛmis invisible to eyes are called Adṛṣta, i.e. they can be observed through a microscope or electron microscope. The examples of such Kṛmis are- Munikeś, Asur, Nabhacar, Yamadagni, etc.
- **Durṇāmā-** The disease-causing Kṛmis have bad name, i.e. they are pathogenic to human body. Some of the examples are Durnāmā are Bhūta, Piśāca, Yātudhān, Rākṣasa, etc.
- **Sunāmā-** They non-pathogenic Kṛmis have been called Sunāmā, e.g. Gandharva (like singer) that produce sounds.

In contrast, these two terms, Durnāmā and Sunāmā, have also been for the diseased and health persons, respectively in Atharvaveda (8.4.6).

दुर्णामा च सुनामा चोभा संवृतमीच्छतः।
अरायानपहन्मः सुनामा स्त्रैणमिच्छताम्।।
(अथर्ववेद 8.4.6)

Durnāmā ca sunāmā cobha samvṛtamīcchataḥ.
Arāyānapahaṅmaḥ sunāmā straiṇamicchatām.
(Atharvaveda 8.4.6)

[The diseased and ill-famed person (*durṇāmā*), and healthy and wealthy person (*sunāmā*) desire (*icchata*) for choosing, in ceremony, the bridegroom with certain conditions (*samvṛtam*); on this occasion, we smite off (*apahanmaḥ*) the evil person lacking health and wealth (*arāyān*). Let the healthy and wealthy person (*sunāmā*) desire (*icchatām*) for his bridegroom (*straiṇam*)]

1. Amīvā and Durṇāmā

Since the Vedic period, the Ṛṣis knew about different types of diseases and the causal agents resulting in a specific disease. The pathogens have been called by different names according to the specific locations. In the Rigveda (10.162.2), the two words, Amīvā and Durnāmā, have been used for the diseases occurring in the womb and uterus, respectively.

यस्ते गर्भममीवा दुर्णामा योनिमाशये।
अग्निष्टं ब्रह्मणा सह निष्क्रव्यादमनीनशत्।।
(ऋग्वेद 10.162.2)

Yaste garbhamamīvā durṇāmā yonimāśaye.
Agniṣtaṁ brahmaṇā saha niṣkravyādamanīnaśat.
(Rigveda 10.162.2)

[This (*yaḥ*) disease causing entity (*amīvā*) that resides (*āśaye*) in your foetus (*te garbhaṁ*) and that (*durṇāmā*) infects womb (*yoniṁ*). May that pathogen (*taṁ*) be destructed (*niḥ anīnśat*) skillfully by experts (*agniṁ*). May that be knowledgeable (*brahmanāsaḥ*) who destruct the meat-eaters (*nih kravyādaṁ*) to protect from such disease-causers]

Scientific Explanation- This hymn has been narrated about the Amīvā in the womb and abode of Durṇāmā in uterus, and destroying the both diseases. According to microbiology many types of diseases are caused in the womb by bacteria and viruses. For example, *Toxoplasma* *gondai, Treponima pallidum, Salmonella ifosa, Compylobacter fetus*, parvo virus, rubella virus, HIV, etc. cause diseases in the womb. Similarly, species of *Escherichia coli, Arcenobacterium pyogenes, Candida albicans* and *Lactobacillus* inhabit the vagina and cause disease. AIDS and cancer occurring in the vagina are very common and fatal diseases. Often patients die due to their side effects.

Foetus Destroying Pathogenic Germs- Atharvaveda describes many more diseases that occur in foetus/ womb and destroy it.

य आमं मांसमदन्ति पौरुषेयं च ये क्रविः।
गर्भान् खादन्ति केशवास्तानितो नाशयामसि।।

(अर्थववेद 8.6.23)

Ya āmaṁ māṅsamadanti pauruṣeyaṁ ca ye kraviḥ.
Garbhān khādanti keśavāstānito nāśayāmasi.

(Atharvaveda 8.6.23)

[That (*ya*) eats raw meat (*āmaṁ māṅsaṁ adanti*) and (*ca*) that (*ye*) eats meat of men (*pauruṣeyaṁ kraviḥ*), hairy krimis (*keśavāḥ*) that eat wombs (*garbhān khādanti*), destroy (*nāśayāmas*) all the pathogens (*tāni*) from here (*ita*)]

पिंग रक्ष जायमानं मा पुमांसं स्त्रियं कन्।
आण्डादो गर्भान्मा दमन बाधस्वेतः किमीदिनः।।

(अर्थववेद **8.6.25**)

Piṅgaṁ rakṣa jāyamānaṁ mā pumāṅsaṁ stṛyaṁ kan.
Āṅdādo garbhānmā daman badhasvetaḥ kimīdinaḥ.

(Atharvaveda 8.6.25)

[O Ping Oshadhi! (*Piṅg*), protect the baby born (*rakṣya jāyamānaṁ*), this germ should not compliment the man or the woman (*pumāṅsaṁ stṛyaṁ mā kan*). These egg-eating germs (*āṅdādaḥ*) should not harm the womb (*garbhān mā daman*); these pathogens (*kimīdinaḥ*) remove from near the womb (*iti badhasvaṁ*)]

Scientific Explanation- As mentioned above, there are many pathogenic microorganisms that infect womb and destroy the developing foetus.

उग्र इत्ते बनस्पत इन्द्र ओज्मानमा दधौ।
अमीवाः सर्वाश्चातयं जहि रक्षांस्योषधे।।

(अथर्ववेद 19.34.9)

Ugra itte banaspata Indra ojmānamā dadhau.

Amīvāh sarvāścātayaṁ jahi rakṣāṅsyoṣadhe.

(Atharvaved 19.34.9)

[You are potential (*it ugraḥ*) O! Herb (*banaspate*), that almighty God (*indraḥ*) has implanted potentiality in you (*te ojyamānaṁ ādadhau*). O! Drug plant (*oṣadhe*) let all diseases be eliminated (*rakṣānsi*) by destroying all these microbes (*sarvāḥ amīvāḥ cātayan*)]. It means the drug plants were capable of destroying diseases occurring in human during those days.

Scientific Explanation- The Supreme Father has given us a lot of plants having the ability to fight against diseases. Therefore, those plants are used as medicines. Here, the medicinal plants have been addressed for having the blessings of God. It has been addressed that O! Medicinal herbs you have special characteristic of eliminating all the guilt. Protect the sick people by destroying all the pathogenic microbes prevailing just like Amīvā. Later, using this kind of knowledge, our sages gave birth to Ayurveda, which describes the use of many types of medicinal plants in various remedies. Various types of biochemical compounds, having different functions, are found in these plants.

2. Piśāca and Yātudhān

In Vedas, Piśāca and Yātudhān have been groups in Adṛṣta (invisible) pathogenic microbes. Since ancient times in India, often Rākṣasa, Piśāca and many other words have been used terrible ghosts and demons. Both Piśāca and microbe are not visible with the naked eyes, but they move from one place to another through the air. That is why even today when people become ill due to an invisible reason then people say 'that person has received something through air'. There is also the presence of Piśāca in that air. Therefore, Guggul have been used to ward off some special air-born pathogenic microorganisms (Atharvaveda 19.38.1). In the Atharvaveda (5.29.5-11), the terms Piśāca and Yātudhāna have been used for invisible organisms and other factors including food-born pathogenic microbes.

आमे सुपक्वे शबले विपक्वे यो मा पिशाचो अशने ददम्भ।
तदात्मना प्रजया पिशाचा वि यातयन्तामगदोऽयमस्तु ।।
(अथर्ववेद 5.29.6)

Āme supakve śabale vipakve yo mā piśāco aśane dadambh.
Tadātmanā prajayā piśacā vi yātyantāmagado,yamastu.
(Atharvaveda 5.29.6)

[Whosoever (*yaḥ*), a blood-suckers or meat-eaters (*piśācaḥ*) injures me (*māṃ dadambha*) though entering (*aśane*) my unripe (*āme*), well-ripped (*supakve*), half-ripped (*śabale*) or over-ripped food (*vipakve*), let those blood-suckers (*taṭ*) themselves along with their progeny be removed (*ātmanā prajayā*). May all blood-dweller pathogens (*piśācā*) be killed (*viyatayantāṁ*) and the patients be cured (*ayaṁ agadaḥ astu*)]

Scientific Explanation- All types of food items (e.g. raw, semi-cooked, fully cooked, and over-cooked food) are contaminated by air-born microorganisms. Even the food materials may be blood and meat also. All the microbes cause diseases by infecting the other healthy people. The names of certain bacteria and viruses that infect food are- *Clostridium botulinum, Escherichia coli* 0157:H.7, *Salmonella typhi*, *Shigella, Toxoplasma gondai*, *Vibrio cholerae*, *Staphylococcus aureus, Listeria monocytogen,* etc. All these bacteria secrete specific different types of toxins. Some of these fatal diseases are- cholera, diarrhea, typhoid fever, etc. All these microorganisms cause food-poisoning; therefore, the affected persons fell ill.

The names of some meat-borne bacteria are- the species of *Shigella, Salmonella, Penicillium, Mucor, Cladosporium, Bacillus cereus,* etc. Sometimes, the injured wound does not heal quickly because at that place there is an infection of meat-eater Kṛmis, which continue to make persistent pus by putrefying the flesh of the wounds. Nature has given rise to some medicinal plants which have antibacterial and anti-fungal properties. It is well known that leaf and bark powders of Neem (*Azadirachta indica*) have been used to wash and heal wounds in India for centuries. In modern times, different types of medicines are being made using Neem leaves and oil. Now, Neem-based capsules and truth brushes are available in market. Food–borne diseases have also been described in many hymns in Chapter 5.

In Sāmaveda (80) and Atharvaveda (5.29.11), the term 'Yātudhān' has been used for pain-giving special types of microbes.

सनादग्ने मृणसि यातुधानान्न त्वा रक्षांसि पृतनासु जिग्युः।
सहमूराननु दह क्रव्यादो मा ते हेत्या मुक्षत दैव्यायाः।।

(अथर्ववेद 5.29.11)

Sanādagne mṛṇasi yātudhānānna tvā rakṣāṅsi pṛtanāsu jigyuḥ.
Sahmūrānanu dah kravyādo mā te hetyā mukṣata daivyāyāḥ.

(Atharvaveda 5.29.11)

[O biological fire! (*agne*); you have always been crushing (*sanāt mṛṇāsi*) the pain-causing non-visible special entities (*yātudhānān*). The germs (*rakṣānsi*) cannot conquer you in struggle (*pritanāsu na jigyuḥ*). May you burn (*anudaḥ*) the flesh-eaters (*kravyādaḥ*) down to their roots (*sahmūrān*). May they (*te*) not escape (*mā mukṣat*) your (*te*) Divine weapon (*hetyā*) willing to defeat diseases (*daivyaḥ*)]

Scientific Explanation: Some meat-born microbes and antibacterial and antifungal medicinal plants, produced by the Nature, have been described while explaining the hymns earlier.

Origin and Prevalence of Germs (Kṛmis)

The origin of microorganisms has not been given in the Vedas as per modern science, but different types of Kṛmis are described at many places in some different forms for the invisible and well as visible entities. It has already been mentioned in a hymn in Ṛgveda that the dense darkness covering the superfluous water was formed before the creation (*Taṁ āsittamsā gūdhahamagre,praketaṁ salilaṁ sarvamā idaṁ*. Ṛgveda 10.129.3). The creation started in that water itself.

The Origin of Life

According to scientific opinion, the origin of life began with the creation of 'pregenote' about 3.8 billion years ago. According to a biologist and Nobel Laureate J.D. Watson, ribonucleic acid (RNA) got developed the first. At the beginning of development, pregenote contained only RNA, which after few billion years of development acted as a very important enzyme called 'ribozyme'. Ribozyme possessed catalytic activity and helped some of the RNA molecules to be converted into the deoxyribonucleic acid (DNA) molecules. Therefore, many viruses like Coronavirus, HIV and poliovirus found in nature consist of RNA as genetic material. They are very dangerous in causing terrible disease in plants, animals and humans, such as COVID-19 (***C**hina **O**riginated **V**iral **D**isease* 2019), AIDS (***A**cquired **I**mmuno-**d**eficiency **S**yndrome*), polio, dengue, etc. Probably, the first prokaryotic cells would have been evolved from the DNA after evolution of protein.

During the Vedic period, the Ṛṣis divided all the beings into four major groups (Ubhij, Svedaj, Aṇḍaj and Jarayuj). Kṛmis have been placed in the Svedaj (sweat-born) group because they need enough water or moisture for their growth and development because of availability of nutrients dissolved in water. The surface of the human body gets moistened due excess sweetening. As a result, the chances of infection and growth of microorganisms on body surface becomes more because of the availability of moisture and nutrients for surface microflora. Nomenclature and classification of Kṛmis have already been described in Chapter 3.

Kṛmis are the microorganisms found everywhere; therefore, they are ubiquitous in nature. There is no such a place on earth where they are not found. They are able to grow in air, water, land, sky, soil, mountain, inside and outside of animals, and even under the harsh conditions. They adjust themselves to all types of unfavourable environments. They are found in various places at a temperature ranging from −20°C to 130°C.

MICROBIAL DIVERSITY

After birth, microorganisms adjusted themselves to the prevailing environment at that time. That is why even today microorganisms are commonly found under adverse conditions. The microbes are found everywhere, where is the possibility of live. There are found at −80°C (hyperpsychrophiles) as well as +121°C (hyperthermophiles) as well as at varying pH (2–11). Therefore, they are called 'ubiquitous' in nature. From the point of the microbiological diversity, found under different environmental conditions, they can be classified as follows (Figure 4.1).

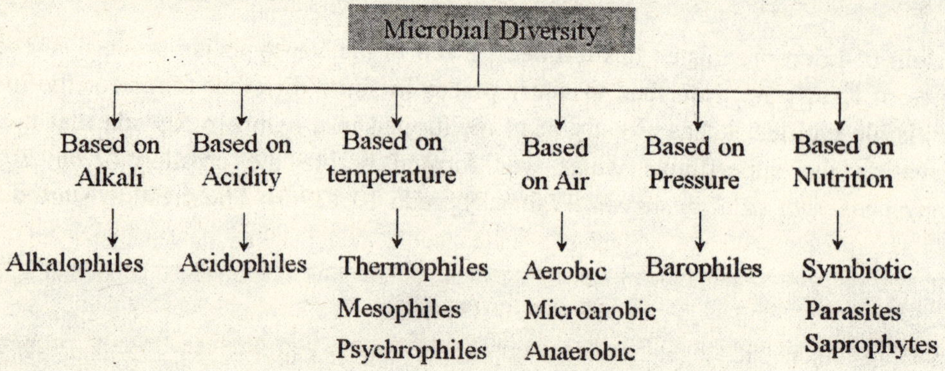

Figure 4.1. Microbial diversity.

- **Acidophiles-** Microorganisms that easily increase the minimum concentration of acid (pH 1.5–2.5) are called acidophilic microorganisms, such as *Lactobacillus acidophilus, Thiobacillus ferooxidans*, etc.
- **Alkalophiles -** Microorganisms that can grow at high concentrations of alkali (pH 8.5–11) are called alkalophiles, such as *Thiospira alkaliphila, Spirulina* species, etc.
- **Hyperthermophiles-** Microorganisms that grow easily at maximum temperature (above 80°C) are called hyperthermophiles, such as *Thermus aquaticus, Pyrococcus furiosus*, etc.
- **Thermophiles-** Microorganisms that grow at high temperatures (up to 50-70°C) are called thermophiles, such as *Methanopirus condlarae*, etc.
- **Mesophiles-** Microorganisms that grow easily at moderate temperatures (up to 20-45°C) are called mesophiles, such as *Escherichia coli, Staphylococcus aureus*, yeast, etc.
- **Psychrophiles -** Microorganisms that grow easily at moderate temperatures (-20 to -10°C) are called psychrophiles or low altitude microorganisms, such as *Pseudomonas syringae*, etc.
- **Barophiles-** Microorganisms that grow at a depth of more than 1000 meters of the sea are called barophiles, such as *Halomonas salinarua*.
- **Aerobic microorganisms -** Microorganisms that grow in the presence of air are called aerobic microorganisms, such as *Bacillus subtilis, Azotobacter chroococcum*, etc.
- **Anaerobic microorganisms-** Microorganisms that can grow in the absence of air are called anaerobic microorganisms, such as *Clostridium botulinum*, etc.
- **Microaerophiles-** Microorganisms that can grow even in the presence of small amounts of air are called microaerophiles, such as *Rhizobium* spores, yeast etc.

- **Symbiotic microorganisms-** Microorganisms that derive nutrients from the host cells and in return give them some food materials that host's cells cannot synthesize, those microorganisms are called symbiotic microbes. For example, *Frankia, Nostoc*, etc.
- **Parasites-** Microorganisms that depend on other living organisms for their nutrition are called parasitic microorganisms, such as *Pseudomonas solanacearum, Xanthomonas citri*, etc.
- **Saprophytes-** Microorganisms that derive nutrients from the other dead and decaying organic materials are called saprophytes, such as *Aspergillus niger, Penicillium citrinum*, etc.

1. Occurrence of Kṛmis in the Environment

The terms Kṛmi and Kṛmiroga have been mentioned in three Vedas, except Sāmaveda. However, Atharvaveda discusses Kṛmis in more detail. Kṛmis are found on the earth and mountains, in soil, in forest, in water, in plant roots, in rivers as well as inside and outside of all animals. They perform a variety of functions such as breaking of complex organic materials and releasing into elemental forms, fixing nitrogen, synthesizing phosphorus and beneficial antibiotics, and also spreading various types of diseases in humans. The presence of these Kṛmis at all places is described in the Atharvaveda.

ये क्रिमयः पर्वतेषु वनेष्वोषधीषु पशुष्वप्स्वन्तः।
ये अस्माकं तन्वमाविविशुः सर्वं तद्धन्मि जनिम क्रिमीणाम् ।।

(अथर्ववेद 2.31.5)

Ye kṛmayaḥ parvateṣu vaneṣvoṣadhīṣu paśuṣvapsvantaḥ.
Ye asmākaṁ tanvamāviviśuḥ sarvaṁ tadhanmi janim krimīṇām.

(Atharvaveda 2.31.5)

[The germs that (*ye krimayaḥ*) are found on mountains (*parvateṣu*), in the forests (*vaneṣu*), live in medicinal plants (*auṣadhīṣu*), in animals (*paśuḥ*), in the waters (*apsu*) and that enter in our body (*ye asmākaṁ tanvamāviviśuḥ*), I destroy whole generation (*sarvaṁ janiṁ inmi*) of that germs (*tat krimīṇām*)].

Scientific Explanation- These Kṛmis become fully established at various places in the environment like mountains, forests, medicine, animals, water and many organs of our body. Their spores disseminate by air from one place to another. Air and water-borne microbes are found in these places. There are many types of minerals in the mountains, using which all of them remain alive. They weather away the minerals locked up in the form of ores. Some special types of microbes are found in the forests on the leaves of trees and outside and inside fruits. For example, a pathogenic fungus (*Venturia inaequalis*) infects the upper-surface of the fruits and leaves of apple and pear, and turns into black-coloured blisters. Due to its infection, the quality of the fruits of apple and pear decreases. Similarly, a pathogenic fungus (*Taphrina deformans*) is also found on the leaves of peaches, which causes the peach leaf curl resulting in crooked leaves

(Figure 4.3.A-B). Further, the pathogenic fungi and bacteria are found on the body of animals. Scabies and itchy fungi viz., the species of *Trichophyton, Epidermophyton* and *Microsporum* are also found on our skins that have been found to cause various types of dermatitis.

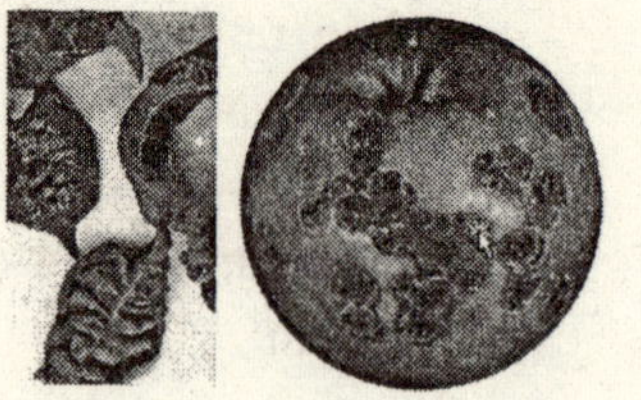

(A) (B)

Figure 4.3. Peach leaf-curl (**A**) and scab disease of apple (**B**).

In the first decade of the 21st century, hundreds of people died of the horrific diseases called 'bird flu' and 'swine flu'; the same virus (H1N1) by changing its genetic setup survived in nature and reached the humans through birds and pigs and causing thousands of death. Who can forget the COVID-19 that resulted in about 2.87 million deaths globally, including 0.166 million death in India by April 7, 2021. Moreover, some bacteria found in water are described below.

2. Prevalence of Kṛmis in Water

Water is considered as elixir of life, because life without water is not possible. All the biochemical mechanisms occur in water present in every cell of body. Whenever we eat or drink something, the nutrients of those food items first get dissolved in water. After reaching all parts of the body, those nutrients help in smooth functioning of body organs, because all the organs need nutritional requirement for proper functions. Therefore, life is impossible without water. There are many such water-born microorganisms that, living in water, become of the colour and form of water; because the microbes too derive nutrition only from that water. Therefore, the contaminated water should not be used for drinking. It is said in the Mahabharata.

सूक्ष्माणि जन्तूनि जलाश्रयाणि, जलस्य वर्णाकृति सन्धितानि।
तस्माज्जलं जीवदयानिमित्तं, निरग्रशूरा परिवर्जयन्ति।।

(महाभारत)

Sukṣmāni jantūni jalaśrayāṇi, jalasya varṇākṛti sandhitāni.
Tasmājjalaṁ jīvdayānimittaṁ, niragraśūrā parivarjayanti.

(Mahābhārat)

[Micro-organisms (*sukṣmāṇi jantūni*), being of the colour and form of water (*jalasya varṇākṛti*), reside therein (*sandhitāni*) depending on water (*jalaśrayāni*); henceforth wise persons (*niragraśurā*) do not accept (*parivarjayanti*) that water (*tasmājjalaṁ*) because of mercy for organisms (*jīvadayānimittaṁ*)]

Scientific Explanation- Innumerable microorganisms are continuously found in water entering through several ways. Therefore, all microorganisms living in water are called water-borne microorganisms. In the monsoon season, all the waste materials are mixed in the water. Sewage of some large cities and metros are also leaked and mixed up often with the drinking water sources. Due to the malfunctioning of the sewer system, untreated contaminated water flows into other water bodies. Untreated water from several industries and sewers are also being discharged into the famous rivers like Ganges and Yamuna, in spite of several time notice served to the concerned bodies. Bathing of millions of devotees in mass, in the global fairs like Kumbh and Kāvaṇa, causes manifold increase in the number of microorganisms in the Ganga River. As a result, water from such area is not suitable to be put in the mouth. Many species of microorganisms living in contaminated waters (such as *Entamoeba histolytica, Giardia, Escherichia coli, Salmonella typhi, Klebsiella pneumoniae* and species of *Bacillus, Staphylococcus* and *Streptococcus*) do not appear to be similar in colour to water (Figure 4.4). Therefore, knowledgeable people do not accept such contaminated water, because such water is not worthy of being accepted.

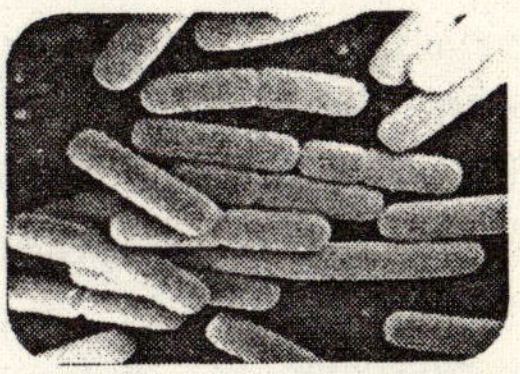

Figure 4.4. Cells of *Escherichia coli.*

3. Prevalence of Kṛmis in Milk, Whey and Food

Kṛmis (microbes) are found in foods like milk, curd, whey and food products. Microbiologists also accept this statement. In the Atharvaveda, the prevalence of Kṛmis is described in all types of food.

क्षीरे मा मन्थे यतमो ददम्भ कृश्टपऽच्ये अशने धान्येइयः।
तदात्मना प्रजया पिशाचा वि यातयन्तामगदोइऽयमस्तु।।
(अथर्ववेद 5.29.7)

Kṣīre mā manthe yatamo dadambh kṛśtapa,ccye aśane dhānye,yaḥ.
Tadātmanā prajayā piśācā vi yātyantām agado,yamastu.
(Atharvaveda 5.29.7)

[Whosoever injures me (*mā dadaṁbha*) through milk (*kṣīre*), butter-milk (*manthe*) and consumption of food grains (*aśane*) growing without cultivation (*kriṣtpacye dhānye*), let those organisms (*yaḥ*) be removed along with their progeny (*ātmanā prajayā*). May such persons be free from all diseases (*ayaṁ agadaḥ astu*)]

Scientific Explanation- Modern science says that all the Kṛmis live in the environment and infect food, due to which various types of diseases spread. It is known that the microorganisms are also found in milk. At the time of milking from the cow, the microorganisms infect the milk, due to which the milk gets spoiled (i.e. the milk clots appears) and is not suitable for consumption. Therefore, milk-tapping should be done carefully; the udders must be washed properly before taking out the milk.

Milk Bacteria: The lactic acid bacteria (such as the species of *Lactobacillus, Leuconostoc, Enterococcus* and *Streptococcus*), species of *Pseudomonas, Micrococcus* and *Staphylococcus* and yeasts are mostly found in milk. In addition, species of *Bacillus, Listeria, Flavobacterium, Acinitobacter, Arthrobacter, Bravibacterium* and *Propionibacterium* and *Corynibacterium* are also found in milk. *Lactobacillus lactis* and *Lactobacillus planitarum* are the main species present in milk.

Milk Bacteria from Mastitis: The milk from diseased animals is not suitable for drinking. Among the diseases occurring in the breast of animals, mastitis is a major disease. Mastitis is caused by several types of bacterial infections, among which the major bacteria are *Pseudomonas aeuriginosa, Staphylococcus aureus, Streptococcus aglacti, Streptococcus uberis, Brucella melitensis, Corynibacterium bovis, Mycoplasma bovis,* etc. Due to drinking milk of such sick animals infected with these bacteria, people also get infected by these pathogens. Therefore, consumption of milk infected with these bacteria is prohibited.

Bacteria found in Curd, whey and buttermilk: The method of making whey i.e. buttermilk from milk is the most important technique that was discovered by Indian sages thousands of years BCE. First of all, curd is made from milk and then buttermilk (Chāñcha) is made from curd. Curd is made from milk only when very small amount of stale curd (20-25 g curd per liter of milk) is mixed in warm milk (about 30-37°C) and incubated for 6-7 hours. It may be noted that stale curd contains certain bacterial species that convert milk into curd at the above temperature. Several species of *Lactobacillus* are found in those microorganisms, among which *Lactobacillus lactis, Lactobacillus planetarium and Lactobacillus bulgaricus* are the prominent ones (Figure 4.5).

Figure 4.5. Cells of *Lactobacillus lactis*.

At this temperature, *Lactobacillus* secretes a specific enzyme called beta-galactosidase to use lactose, the major milk sugar. This enzyme dissolves the milk lactose to form lactic acid. By this specific mechanism, the *Lactobacillus* species grows by using the milk. As a result, the number of *Lactobacillus* and other microorganisms in milk gets increased. Curd becomes sour due to the formation of lactic acid. This complex method of making Chāñcha, yogurt and buttermilk from milk was developed by our Āryan Ṛṣis thousands of years ago in the *Āryāvarta*. Even today, this traditional method is being adopted from villages to the cities (Figure 4.6). Likewise, the main species of bacteria found in yogurt are- *Enterococcus faecium, Enterococcus faecalis* and *Streptococcus thermophilus*. After churning, the cream, which comes on top of curd, it is taken out with butter, which is heated to get *ghee*. Thus the ghee extracted was used in the Agnihotra in the Vedic period. Mākhan Cori of ' Śrī Kṛṣṇa', in 'Dwāpar Yuga', is described in detail in the Śrīmad Bhāgvat Purāṇa. Since then the method of curd preparation and use of curd, Chāñcha and ghee have been adopted throughout India in all the States as well as in the world. All Indians use curd daily but in certain rituals, festivals and auspicious occasions like marriages use of curd is inevitable. In recent years, a National Dairy Research Institute (Karnal, Haryana, India) has been established for extensive research on mammals, milk and milk bacteria, probiotics, etc. Such research institutes have also been established in other countries also. This technology has given job to trillions of unemployed persons. Thanks to Aryans for giving this 'Vedic Technology' that has now taken the shape of institutes and industries throughout the world. In recent years capsules of probiotics bacteria are being prepared industrially.

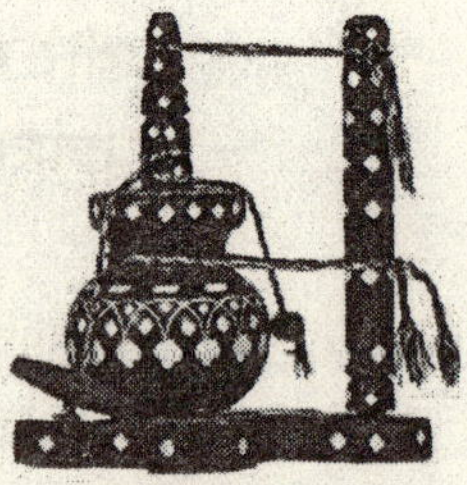

Figure 4.6. A traditional device for churning curd and making butter.

4. Prevalence of Kṛmis on/in the Body

In Caraka Saṁhitā (Vimāna Sthāna 7.9), the Kṛmis are divided into two categories- Bāhya Kṛmis (germs found on external surface of body) and Abhyāntara Kṛmis (germs found inside the body). The external Kṛmis are also called Malaja Kṛmis. All external Kṛmi arise because of living in dirty place and unhygienic environment. That is why such Kṛmis reside on hairs, skin and on the dirty clothes. Consequently, such Kṛmis also give rise to various skin diseases like pimples, eczema, ringworms, etc. (Carak Samhitā, Vimāna Sthāna 7.10). It has earlier been described in Chapter 3.

Kṛmis are found on the earth and mountains, in soil, in forest, in water, in plant roots, in rivers as well as inside and outside of all animals. The origin of blood Kṛmis is believed to be from blood because blood acts as the nutritional substance for the species of *Plasmodium* (causing malaria), *Trypanozoma* (sleeping disease), *Wuchereria* (causing filaria), etc. These Kṛmis remain in the blood vessels only and grow and multiply substantially. When their numbers are high, they adversely affect the skin, bone marrow, flesh and blood vessels. But the Śleṣamaj Kṛmis (microbe of phlegm) arise in large quantities due to ingestion of sweets, milk, taking contaminated food, and reluctance and affect health. Puriṣaja Kṛmis live inside our body and grow by using the available residual nutrients of food. Sometimes these Kṛmis adversely affect health (Carak Samhitā, Vimāna Sthāna 7.11-13) (see Chapter 3). There are certain pathogenic bacteria and fungi that grow inside our body organs such as mouth, teeth, lungs, heart, eyes, liver and meninges of brain. The Atharvaveda (5.23.3) describes the Kṛmis that cause disease in eye, nose and teeth.

यो अक्ष्यौ परिसर्पति यो नासे परिसर्पति।
दतां यो मध्यं गच्छति तं क्रिमिं जम्भयामसि।।
(अथर्ववेद 5.23.3)

Yo akṣau parisarpati yo nāse parisarpati.
Datāṁ yo madhyaṁ gacchati tam Kṛmiṁ jambhayāmasi.
(Atharvaveda 5.23.3)

[The one (*Kṛmi*), that (*yaḥ*) moves in his two eyes (*akṣau parisarpati*), that moves into his nose (*nāse parisarpati*) and that goes to the midst of his teeth (*datāṁ yo madhyaṁ gacchati*), to that microbe *(taṁ Kṛmi)*, I destroy completely (*jambhayāmasi*)]

Scientific Explanation- The pathogenic microorganisms infect the eyes and cause. Frequent infection of microorganisms also causes a cold. Dental caries is caused by microbial infection and the teeth also become black and loose and the patients also suffer more pain. All such microbes are not visible by the naked eye due to being very minute in sizes. The number of bacteria spreading the eye disease is not high because a specific enzyme in the saliva and sputum is found which is called lysozyme. Lysozyme protects the eyes by breaking the cell wall of microorganisms that infect the eyes from outside. However, some bacteria and viruses cause eye diseases such as eye flu, ophthalmia, conjunctivitis or pink eye and eye allergy. Eye flu causes swelling and exudation. Conjunctivitis is caused by several species of viruses (e.g. adenovirus) and bacteria (e.g. *Staphylococcus aureus, Pseudomonas aeruginosa, Haemophilus influenza,* etc.). Chlamydia causes an eye disease called trachoma.

Some bacteria secrete lactic acid on the upper surface of teeth when carbohydrate or other sources of sugar are present, for example sweets, chocolate, milk, jaggery etc. Due to the formation of acid, the tooth becomes sour and the upper surface of the tooth is gradually weakened. As a result, these bacteria make cavities inside the teeth. Therefore, such infected teeth begin rotting. This condition is known as or dental caries or teeth decay. The bacteria that cause dental caries are- *Compylobacter rectus, Actinobacillus actinomycetemcomitans, Porphyromonas gingivalis, Streptococcus mutans,* and *Eubacterium* sp. and *Lactobacillus* spp.

METHOD OF COUNTING THE NUMBER OF KṚMIS

These Kṛmis are found in large numbers in the universe, which is very difficult to calculate. According to modern method of enumeration, the numbers of microorganisms are written as 10^1, 10^2, 10^3, 10^4, 10^5, 10^6, 10^7, 10^8, etc. According to the American Society of Microbiology (2006), there can be about 5×10^{31} microorganisms on the Earth representing about 90 percent mass present on Earth. In Yajurveda (17.2), the method of sequentially increasing order of numbers has been described that can be used for the calculation of microorganisms.

इमा मेऽअग्नऽइष्टका धेनवः सन्त्वेका च दश च दश च शतं च शतं च सहस्रं च सहस्रं चायुतं चायुतं च नियुतं च नियुतं च प्रयुतं चार्बुदं च न्यर्बुदं च समुद्रश्च मध्यं चान्तश्च परार्द्धश्चैता मेऽ अग्नऽइश्टका धेनवः सन्त्वमुत्रामुष्मिल्लोके।।

(यजुर्ववेद 17.2)

Imā me,agn,iṣtakā dhenavaḥ santvekā ca daś ca daś ca śataṁ ca śataṁ ca sahasraṁ ca sahasraṁ cāyutaṁ cāyutaṁ ca niyutaṁ ca niyutaṁ ca prayutaṁ cārbudaṁ ca nyarbudaṁ ca samudraśca madhyaṁ cāṅtaśca parārdhaścaita me, agn,iśtakā dhenavaḥ santvamutrāmuṣmilloke.

(Yajurveda 17.2)

[O! Resplendent God (*agne*) as this my need-fulfilling (*me imāh iṣtakā*) oblation materials become like lactating cows (*dhenavaḥ santu*), similarly it may be for you too. This *yajña* be like one to ten (*saṇtvekā ca daśa ca*) ($10\times1=10^1$), ten to hundred (*daśa ca śataṁ*) ($10\times10=10^2$), hundred to thousand (*śataṁ ca sahasraṁ ca*) ($10\times100=10^3$), thousand to ten thousand (*sahasraṁ ca ayutaṁ*) ($10\times1000=10^4$), ten thousand to one lakh (*ayutaṁ ca niyutaṁ*) ($10\times10000=10^5$), one lakh to ten lakh (*niyutaṁ ca prayutaṁ*) ($10\times100000=10^6$) i.e. one million, and (*ca*) then one crore (*arbudaṁ ca*) ($10\times1000000=10^7$) i.e. ten million, then ten crore (*nyarbudaṁ ca*) ($10\times10000000=10^8$) i.e. one trillion, then ten crore or one *arab* (*samudraḥ ca*) ($10\times100000000=10^9$) i.e. ten trillion, and (*ca*) then ten *arab* (*madhyaṁ*) ($10\times1000000000=10^{10}$) i.e. one hundred trillion, then one *kharab* (*antaḥ ca*) ($10\times10000000000=10^{11}$) i.e. one thousand trillion, and (*ca*) then ten *kharab* (*parārdhaḥ*) ($10 \times 1000000000000 = 10^{12}$) i.e. ten thousand trillion. O! God (*agne*) may my *yajña* nurtures me (*dhenavaḥ santu*) in other world (*etā me iṣṭakā amutra*) or far away another world (*amuṣmin loke*)]

Scientific Explanation- Thousands of years ago, our sages wished for happiness and prosperity. Multiplying 1, 10, 100, 1000, 10000. . . . . numbers by 10, they have told the increasing number to 10 trillion (10^{12}), respectively,. This method is used everywhere. But due to the large number of microorganisms, they are also calculated by this method. If the number of bacteria in the soil is 10,00,00, it is expressed as 10^6 colony formation unit (cfu)/ gram soil. Similarly, if the number of cells of a bacterium in water is 10,000, then it is written as 10^4 cfu/mL water. It has been accepted that one colony formation unit is possible only because of one cell. Hence 10,000 colonies are formed due to similar number of cells.

SHAPE AND COLOR OF KṚMIS

Many types of microbes are found in the environment, which vary in form, color, shape and functions. There are many beneficial as well as harmful microorganisms, which produce many diseases or benefits the hosts. The Atharvaveda (5.23.4) describes the different shapes of the microorganisms and different colors like black, red and brown.

स्वरूपौ द्वौ विरूपौ द्वौ कृष्णौ द्वौ रोहितौ द्वौ।
बभ्रुश्च बभ्रुकर्णश्च गृधः कोकश्च ते हताः।।
(अथर्ववेद 5.23.4)

Svarūpau dvau virūpau dvau kṛṣnau dvau rohitau dvau.
Babhruśca babhrukarṇaśca gṛdhaḥ kokaśca te hatāḥ.
(Atharvaveda 5.23.4)

[Two of the same form (*swarūpau dvau*), two of different forms (*virūpau dvau*), two black (*kṛsnau dvau*), two red (*rohitau dvau*), the brown (*babhruḥ*) and (*ca*) brown-eared (*babhru karṇaśca*) greedy creatures (like vulture and wolf) (*gṛdhaḥ*) and eaters (*kokaśca*) have been killed (*hatā*)]. The vulture and wolf are the greedy animals.

Scientific Explanation- Here 'Dvau' means two, representing both male and female of the same or different forms of organisms. For knowledge the readers, some microorganisms of different shapes and sizes are given in Figure 4.7. All these microorganisms are visible only with the help of microscope, such as *Streptococcus, Staphylococcus, Vibrio, Escherichia coli,* Yeast, *Aspergillus, Penicillium, Amoeba,* etc. Amoeba is colorless, *E. coli, Staphylococcus* and *Streptococcus* are light yellowish; species of yeast are cream coloured and that of *Aspergillus* are black, white, brown, green, yellowish-green, etc. In addition, some microbes with unique shapes and characters are also found in nature. The species of *Serratia* is light red or dark pink, such as *Serratia marcensus*, which develops in bathrooms. It is an opportunistic bacterium that infects the urinary and respiratory tracts.

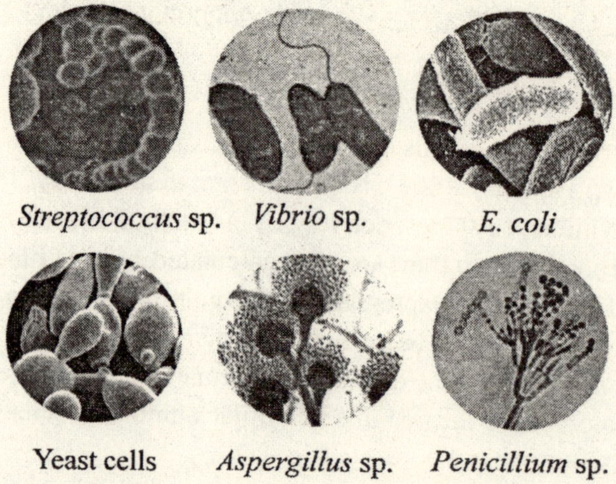

Figure 4.7. Some important microorganisms found in nature.

In the same way, *Pseudomonas aeruginosa* and other species of *Pseudomonas* produce green fluorescence; the red pigment in *Serratia marcensus* and the green fluorescent bio-chemicals compounds in *Pseudocamonas aeruginosa* are secreted. The green fluorescent pigment of *Pseudocamonas* is called siderophore which has the ability of combining with an iron ore, solubilize it enzymatically and utilize during cellular metabolism (Figure 4.8).

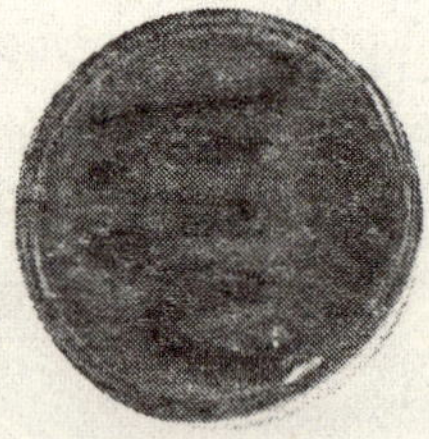

Figure 4.8. Production of siderophore.

Similarly, the colour of Nainā Lake of Nainitāl (Uttarakhand) changes in the month of October as compared to other moths. This change is due to the production of a special type of light red or pink pigment, along with the growth of a specific blue-green alga (*Microcystis aeruginosa*) found in Nainā Lake. Similarly, the other bacteria also appear with different colours.

Human Health and Pathogenic Germs (Kṛmis)

It is necessary to understand properly about the health. Health is a result of normal functions of all vital organs of body. What are the vital organs, and what are not? The heart, lungs, liver, kidneys and brain are the vital organs. Though these organs function independently but they work with mutual coordination. Dysfunction of an organ affects the others. Brain governs the function of all organs. One can live a long life with one hand and one leg, but not with abnormal functioning of vital organs or without any of these. Even brain must not be having any stress or anxiety. Suśrut has nicely mentioned about the symptoms of the healthy persons several thousand years ago.

समदोषः समाग्निश्च समधातुमलक्रियः।
प्रसन्नात्मेन्द्रिय यमनाः स्वस्थ इत्यमिधीयते।।

(सुश्रुत संहिता 15.41)

Samadoṣah samāgniśca samadhātumalakriyaḥ.
Prasannātmendriyah yamanāḥ svastha ityamidhīyate.

(Suśrut Saṁhita 15.41)

[Persons with equal *doṣa* (*samadoṣaḥ*) and equal digestive fire (*samāgniḥ ca*), all body tissues and its components i.e. equal Dhātu (*samadhātu*), equal excretory functions (*mal*), equal function of body organs (*kriyaḥ*), pleasantly excreted and contended mind-senses-spirit (*prasanna ātma indriyaḥ*) are said to be healthy (*svastha ityamidhīyate*)]

Scientific Explanation- According to World Health Organization, 'health is a state of completely physical, mental, and social well-being and not merely the absence of disease or infirmity'. But the health issues have always been a matter of discussion and attention since the Vedic period. Here, the word Sama means the 'proper, equal or natural'. Hence, the Sama Doṣa means equal or balanced Tridoṣa i.e. Vāta, Pitta and Kapha. Hence, the Vāta, Pitta and Kapha must be in a balanced way. None of these should be high or dominant otherwise unequal Vāta, Pitta and Kapha will cause a doṣa leading to an ailment. Similarly, Sama Agni means 'equal fire of body' or 'heat of body', which must be 'neither dilapidated, nor sharp nor odd, but equal'. Broadly, Agni (energy or biological fire) has been put into 3 major groups, *Jaṭharāgni, Dhātvāgni* and *Bhūtāgni*. According to Āyurveda, there are 13 types of all three groups of Agni as given below:

- ***Jaṭharāgni:*** It is only 1 type of energy required for digestion of food in stomach and duodenum called Jatharāgni.
- ***Dhātvāgni:*** It is of 7 types e.g. Raktāgni present in blood, Rasāgni present in plasma, Mānsāgni present in muscles, Medogni present in fat, Asthyāgni present in bones,

Majjāgni present in bone marrow and Śukrāgni present in tissues of reproductive organs. One Agni is present in each Dhātu. The seven element tissues of body consist of its own energy or Agni required for metabolism of nutrients and its transport in body.

- ***Bhūtāgni:*** It is 5 types, for example Pārthoṣmā (present earth), Āpyoṣmā (present in water), Āgneyoṣmā (present in Agni), Vāyoṣmā (present in Vāyu or air), and Nabhoṣmā (present in space or Ākāśa). Therefore, there are five Agni from five basic elements or Bhūtas.

The energy is always consumed for proper function of body organs like respiration, heart beating, impulses, reflex action, digestion, blood circulation and secretion. Hence, there should be an equal amount of natural energy of the body that is required to carry out all functions of all organs. Sapta Dhātu (seven Dhātus, i.e. seven types of materials) plays a major role in the body function. These Dhātus are rasa (plasma), Rakta (blood), Mānsa (muscles), Medā (fat), Asthi (bone), Majjā (marrow) and Śukra (semen in reproductive tissue). The seven Dhātus get aggravated by Vāt, Pitta and Kapha. There develops diseases according to weakness in any or all of Tridoṣa, i.e. Vāt, Pitta and/or Kapha. Malfunctioning of Vāt, Pitta and Kapha cause Sannipāta.

Whatever is eaten by humans, it is converted into its smallest functional forms called rasa which is transported in circulatory system where from they are transported to distant places of body forming Ṣaptadhātu. The Saptadhātus are as below:

रसाऽसं सृंगमांसमेदो अस्थि मज्जा शुक्राणु धातवः सप्त दूष्याः मला। (अ.द.सू. 1)

Rasā,sam sṛngamāṅsamesdo asthi majjā śukrāṇu dhatavaḥ sapta dūṣyāḥ malā (A.D.Su.1)

Imbalance in any of all seven Dhātus develops disease in human body. For examples imbalance in Rakta Dhātu causes blood pressure, blood cancer, leprosy, jaundice, arthritis, etc. Similarly, Medā (fat) Dhātu provides strength and ability for disease resistance. Beside, the meaning of the equal natural function (kṛyā) is the 'proper function of all the vital organs', such as intestine, heart, lungs, liver and brain, inside the body. Easy defecation also keeps people healthy and disease-free. A person, whose senses is healthy and mind is devoid of disorder, he lives a life free from anxiety and depression.

It is well known that by taking a balanced diet and living a moderate life, disease resistant ability increases in the body, and a person is always pleased healthy. A person always acquires vigour by conserving his Vīryamaṇi (virile) from restrained life. Many types of food nourish the body supplying varying types of nutrients. Many types of nutrients are found in food items, such as carbohydrates, proteins, fats, residues, minerals, vitamins, amino acids, etc. All these elements are necessary for living beings. After consuming the food, at the end of the digestive process, these nutrients are eventually produced and circulated in distant part of body. By absorbing these elements, our body re-synthesizes new types of biochemicals as per the requirement of the body, which leads to increased body growth and health. Not all types of chemicals are found in the same food item. Therefore, several different types of food materials should be consumed, such as vegetables, Dāl (pulses), milk, curd, cheese, fruits, nuts, etc. Availability the plant product varies according to seasons. Therefore, taking these fresh foods in adequate amounts keeps our body healthy and increases the immunity i.e. disease-resistant capacity.

The ability of body to fight against diseases in any person is called immunity. Immunity is natural in all organisms. However, it is triggered according to the surrounding environment and situation. This ability of body is of two types, the first is 'innate immunity' (pre-formed and immunity that develops in a baby with birth), and the second is 'acquired immunity' (immunity quickly triggered after the exposure of microorganisms / substances and external chemicals such as, flower pollinators). Therefore, disease-resistant capacity and body vigour increase by taking a nutrient-rich balanced diet and with a simple life. Such people remain healthy and happy for a lifetime. The origin of blood cells from pluripotent cells of the bone marrow is given in Figure 5.1.

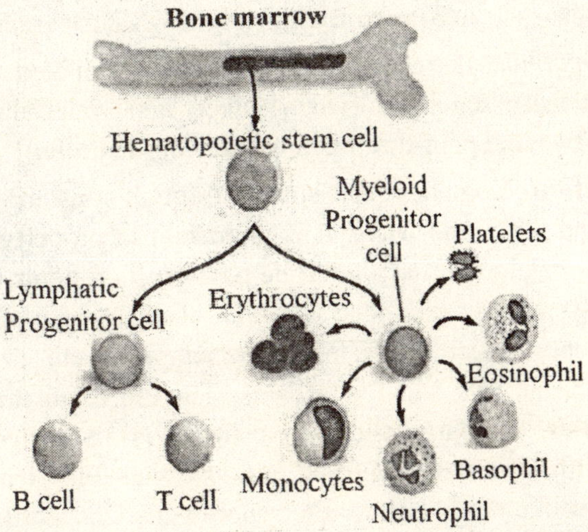

Figure 5.1. Origin of blood cells from pluripotent cells of bone marrow.

FOOD GRAINS– THE BASIS OF LIFE

Human life is possible only because of food grains. Food is the reason for the life of all living beings. Prāna is said to reside in food grains itself (*Kalau annagatā prāṇā lokā swalpāyukhastathā*). If the parents had not grown up after consuming food, their children would not have been born as well. Therefore, life of all living animals is possible only through food grains. Such views are expressed in the Bhagavad Gītā (3.14) *'Annāt bhavanti bhutāni parjanyāt anna sambhavaḥ'*. Taittiriyopaniṣad (2.2.1) also talks about the birth and development of all living beings only from food, *'Annāt bhootani jāyante. jātānyannen vardhante'* (all animals are born only because of food; they grow from food itself). A similar idea has been expressed in Taittiriyopanishad (3.2.1), *'Annaṁ brahmeti vyajānāt'. Annāt eva khalvimāni bhutāni jāyante. Annen jātāni jīvanti'* [it means, food grains are the Supreme Being (Brahman), knew by this; because all these beings are born from food grains, the born lives by food].

1. Regulated Diet, Recreation, Action and Desires

Life is governed by food (Āhār), people grow and maintain good health only by taking food. If people consuming suitable and regulated foods, they do not suffer from any type of disease and the person is always healthy provided daily physical exercise and recreations are done with calm and cool mind without any malice and delusion. Therefore, everyone should take the regulated diet and should also do Vihāra (walking peacefully) and actions accordingly.

युक्ताहारविहारस्य युक्तचेष्टस्य कर्मसु।
युक्त स्वप्नावबोधस्य योगो भवति दुःखहा।।
(श्रीमद् भगवद्गीता 6.17)

Yuktāhāra vihāraṣya yuktacestṣya karmasu.
Yukta svapnāvabodhasya yogo bhavati dukhahā.
(Śrimad Bhagavadgītā 6.17)

[Regulated diet (*yuktāhāra*)], recreation (*vihārasya*), regulated (*yukta*) desires (*ceṣtasya*) discharging duties (*karmasu*), regulated (*yukta*) sleep and wakefulness (*svapnāvabodhasya*), practice of yoga (*yogaḥ*) become pain-diminishing (*bhavati dukhahā*)]

Scientific Explanation- Yoga destructs sorrow through consumption of regulated food and recreation, meditation, and sleep and wake. It is important to properly understand the regulated diet and the recreation. Special attention should be paid on food items for the proper functioning of the body. Human body requires balanced amounts of all types of food. Many diseases arise due to excess or deficiency of proteins, minerals, vitamins, etc. which can be fulfilled by consuming vegetables, animal fats and food grains. Therefore, all these food items should be used in balanced quantities. Similarly, the liver efficacy is also affected due to excess / low amount of salt. Along with all these, dry fruits and seasonal juicy fruits like orange, lemon as well as papaya, carrot, milk, curd, honey, etc. should also be consumed time to time. The important things should be taken care of for a healthy life as given in Figure 5.2.

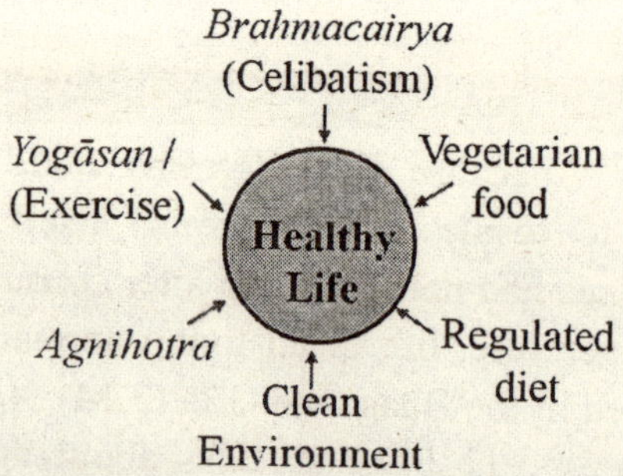

Figure 5.2. Important things to follow for a healthy life.

Proper digestion of all these food materials is necessary after its consumption. If someone's digestive function is impaired, then consuming these food materials is useless. Regular exercise and recreation is also essential for digestion; it also maintains good health. All the limbs are duly exercised and continue to function properly due to regular movement. The effectiveness of all of these makes the body organs very active. All types of hormones are secreted in a balanced way.

Without any disorder in the mind, there is no excitement in the mental instincts. Even if it happens, such things should be ignored; if there is attention, it should be controlled moderately. The attention may go on such things due to mind stuff on worldly objects, which are not good. One should neither sleep nor wake up according to the desire of mind. It is also important to control the mind in a moderate manner because the mind is very fickle. It is strong and churns the body like a Mathāni (a mechanical device used for churning the curd to get cream) (*Cañcalaṁ hi manaḥ Kṛṣṇa pramāthi balavaddṛḍhaṁ*- Śrīmad Bhagavadgītā, 6.34). Because of a fickle mind, a person deviates and slips off the path very quickly. Therefore, it is essential to control the powers of mind and will. In this way, a person becomes a Karmayogī (person perfect in action) by doing Sādhanā (penance).

2. Prohibition of Use of Contaminated Food and Water/Milk

Different types of food material are consumed by all animals including human being for nourishment and proper function of their bodies. However, microorganisms are ubiquitous; they are present everywhere in the environment and every place where ever the possibility of life is? They are also found on food grains, in milk and water and all edible materials if not properly handled or stored. Such contaminants spoil the food and secrete toxins, which after consumption caused diseases including death.

Spread of information about disease is more helpful in diagnosing diseases. Therefore, it is the duty of all the rulers to spread more information about what kind of food the people should consume, and which type of water and milk should they drink? The public should be made aware about consuming uncontaminated and balanced food, water and milk and living in a clean environment. In the Vedic period, the king was considered responsible for making the public aware of using pure food and clean vessels so that they would remain healthy. There is mention in Atharvaveda (19.39.5) of making the people aware of not consuming the contaminated food grains, and water and milk in such vessels.

येऽन्नेषु विविध्यन्ति पात्रेषु पिबतो जनान।
तेषां सहस्रयोजनेऽव धन्वानि तन्मसि।।
(अथर्ववेद 19.39.5)

Ye,nneṣu vividhyanti pātreṣu pibato janān.
Teṣāṁ sahasrayojane,va dhanvāni tanmasi.
(Atharvaveda 19.39.5)

[The king who (*yaḥ*) gives several directives (*vividhāni*) about food (*anneṣu*) to the people and governs (*vividhyanti*) the people (*janāṅa*) about drinking pots (*pātreṣu*), he spreads (*avatanmasi*) weapons (*dhanvāni*) of those disease-curing kings (*teṣāṁ*) up to thousands miles (*sahasra yojane*)].

It means that the disease curing information is just like weapons that spreads thousand miles and help in protection from various diseases. Furthermore, it is the duty of the rulers to make instructions about edible food, and not eating the contaminated food materials as well as the use of pots for drinking of water, milk, whey, etc.

Scientific Explanation- Undoubtedly, microorganisms and their secondary metabolites reach many parts of our body through contaminated food, food items, containers and vessels, because all these things are the carriers of microorganisms. Therefore, only healthy food and food items and clean vessels should be used. For example, if milkman takes out cow's milk at a polluted place or in a contaminated vessel, such milk also becomes contaminated and spoiled even when milk is purified. Consumers of such contaminated milk also become afflicted at the earliest. In the same way, those who consume contaminated food also get sick quickly because many types of microorganisms like fungi, bacteria, etc. are present in the infected grains; they reduce the quality of the grains by secreting various toxic secondary metabolites. Hence, those who consume contaminated grains quickly become ill. Groundnut seeds infected by *Aspergillus flavus* (A) and maize comb infected by *Fusarium moniliforme* (B) are given in Figure 5.3. These two fungi secrete mycotoxins that affect body organs.

(A) (B)

Figure 5.3. Infected groundnut (**A**) and maize comb (**B**).

In 1984, in several districts of Bihar district, after the rainy season, hundreds of persons who had been infected with corn maize suffered from vomiting and diarrhea. After intensive research, species of *Aspergillus flavus* and *Fusarium moniliforme* were found to be involved in maize comb and grains. *Aspergillus flavus* secretes a mycotoxin called aflatoxin and *Fusarium moniliforme* secretes fumonisin that affect our vital organs. Similarly, in 1976, after eating infected millet bread in South India, people became ill. After the research, it was found that millet grains (*Bājara*) were infected by a fungus called *Claviceps purpurea* due to secretion of a mycotoxin called 'ergotoxin'. This toxin also causes a disease in millet called ergot. Therefore, the persons consuming the ergotoxin-contaminated millet became ill. The diseases that occur in humans due to fungal or bacterial toxins are commonly called toxicoses. The names of some fungi and bacteria that secrete the toxins are given in Table 5.1.

Effect of Mycotoxins: All types of microbial toxins adversely affect the organs of all organisms. In 2004, 125 people died due to consuming corn in Kenya. In Germany, the chickens stopped laying eggs because of feeding contaminated fodder; aflatoxins were found in their eggs after research. For example, aflatoxins cause cancer in the liver, citrinin affects the kidney, and ergotoxin affects the nervous system. Often, grains and its processed foods are always contaminated by fungi due to lack of proper storage. Many fungal spices contribute mycotoxins in the spices, such as red pepper, black pepper and dry ginger (Jeswal and Kumar, 2015).

Table 5.1. Some fungi and bacteria secreting toxins.

Microorganisms	Toxins	Source

Fungi

Fusarium moniliformi	fumonisin	Wheat, corn, rice
Aspergillus flavus	aflatoxins	Corn, peanuts, all grains, peppers, spices
Aspergillus ochracius	ochratoxin	Corn, grains
Aspergillus carboris	aflatoxins	Vine
Claviceps purpuria	ergotoxin	Millets
Penicillium citrinum	citrinin	Orange, lemon and other juicy fruits
Penicillium expansum	patulin	Rotten apple, other fruits
Amanita phalloides	mycotoxin e.g. orelenine	*Amanita phalloides*

Bacteria

Escherichia coli	Enterotoxin	Contaminated water and food
Shiegella sp.	Shiga toxin	Contaminated water and food
Vibrio cholera	Cholera toxin	Contaminated water and food

3. Hymns of Healthy Life

Regulated and balanced foods are very important in leading the healthy human life (see Figure 5.2). To make our life blissful, four pure food materials are needed, such as milk, ghee, honey and water. Milk is an adequate food in itself; it contains all kinds of essential nutrients, fat, carbohydrates and proteins. Ghee and honey are energetic substances; its use gives strength and vigor in our body. All the digestive activities take place in water through metabolism; so pure water makes the body healthy by regulating temperature in all parts of body, carrying out physiological actions, transportation of nutrients, maintaining the excretory system, etc. Discharge of harmful substances from the body is possible only due to water.

पावमानीर्यो अध्येत्यृषिभिः संभृतं रसम्।
तस्मै सरस्वती दुहे क्षीरं सर्पिर्मधूदकम्।।

(सामवेद 10.8.2)

Pāvamānīryo adhyetṛṣibhiḥ saṁbhṛtaṁ rasam.
Tasmai Sarasvatī duhe kṣīraṁ sarpirmadhūdakaṁ.

(Sāmaveda 10.82)

[Who (*yaḥ*) studies (*adhyeti*) the pious hymns (*pāvamāni*) and through which Ṛṣis (*riṣibhiḥ*) had made their his enjoyable (*rasaṁ sabhṛtaṁ*), Saraswati (*saraswatī*) fulfils (*duhe*) his life extracting from milk (*kṣīraṁ*), ghee (*sarpi*), homey (*madhu*) and water (*udakaṁ*)]

Scientific Explanation- Our sages have mentioned pure milk, whey, honey and water as sacred to the body. Milk is a complete nutrition in itself. All kinds of nutrients required for life are found in milk. Similarly, honey is also made by bees to feed themselves and their offspring. The bees desiccate the juices of various flowers for making honey inside the self-made hives.

The bees devour the self-made honey before departing from those hives. Various types of sugars, such as fructose, glucose, sucrose, etc. are found in balanced quantities in the honey. Nowadays, honey is being prepared artificially. Honey is also a complete meal in itself. Many people consume honey during fasting. Pure water should be drunk in sufficient quantity to maintain proper efficacy of body. That is why water is called 'life' because all the metabolic activities of the cells take place in the aqueous medium.

DEFENSE FROM THE KRIMIS BY MORAL - KNOWLEDGE – PHYSICAL STRENGTH

The body can be saved from the aggression of the Kṛmis by making life strong through strengthening the body, mind, force and light in life. According to Vedas, Dyu Loka is considered as a mental form and Earth as a physical form.

ओते मे द्यावापृथिवी ओता देवी सरस्वती।
ओतौ म इन्द्रश्चाग्निश्च क्रिमिं जम्भयतामिति।।

(अथर्ववेद 5.23.1)

Ote me dyāvāpṛthivī otā devī Sarasvatī.
Otau ma Idraścāgniśca kṛmiṁ jambhayatāmiti.

(Atharvaveda 5.23.1)

[The heaven and earth (*dyāvāprithivi*) have graced me (*me ote*), the symbol of knowledge Goddess (*devi*) saraswati (*sarasvatī*) has graced me (*otā*), the God of my strength and light (*indraḥ agni ca*) have reciprocally graced (*otau*) me. Hence (*iti*), May they destroy the wasting disease (*krimiṁ jambhayatāmiti*)]

Scientific Explanation- Many constellations have an effect on the body from birth to death. The electromagnetic waves emanate from these constellations that affect the body and mind. For example, on the full moon day, there is excessive tide (rise and fall of sea level) in the sea and high waves come and eve. On the full moon day, there is more excitement in the mind. The intensity of insanity is greater on this day. Therefore, electromagnetic waves emitted from the Dyu loka have more effect on body, mind and brain. May my body, nurtured by the Dyu loka (means the sun, the stars and the electromagnetic waves emanating from the constellation), the earth's fertility, illuminated by the wisdom of the goddess Saraswati, overwhelmed by the gods of power and glory, be free from all ailments eliminating all the germs. This means that the soil fertility provides nutrients to nourish our body. All the nutritional ingredients are derived from the soil. On attaining the light of knowledge, individuals realize perfect action and duty. The person perfect in action falls under the category of Yogis (*Yogaḥ karmaṣu kauśalaṁ*- Śrimad Bhagavadgītā 2.50). On achieving the physical strength and vigour, the body spreads shining, and radiance virile. Disease-resistant increases in the body of such persons and they always become disease-free.

People should be alert towards food and edible material, water and mil. Any person not getting food on time and having infected food can become unwell and fall ill. Unknowingly, people fall ill quickly after consuming all kinds of contaminated water, milk and un-pure buttermilk, etc. According to Vedic concept, the king should make the people aware of food and food-based products so that they may be healthy and happy.

1. Virility (Vīryamaṇi) and Health

Virility increases in a man due to having safe Vīryamaṇi in the body; therefore both the enemy and the disease automatically leave it place. As a result, Vīryamaṇi completely eradicates the enemies and the dreaded Vātarogas. It transmits strength-providing bio-chemicals to each organ. In the Atharvaveda (19.34.5) this Vīryamaṇi is called 'Jaṅgiṇa'. This Vīryamaṇi makes the people brave, powerful, stunning, longevity, fearless and healthy. Hence Jangid is referred to as a medicine. Safe Vīryamaṇi is the most important medicine in the body to remove all diseases. Virility can protect the person from Vāta, Pitta and Kapha (Atharvaveda 19.34.10). Therefore, every person should protect health by paying special attention to their health. Hence, every person should always try to live a healthy and long life. Virile can be protected by keeping a benign life and conquering the senses. Therefore, everyone should protect virility in order to live a beautiful and healthy life living as a continent. Atharvaveda (5.26.11) mentions a similar desire to the Supreme God.

इन्द्रो युनक्तु बहुधा वीर्याण्यस्मिन्यज्ञे सुयुजः स्वाहा।

(अथर्ववेद 5.26.11)

Indro yunaktu bahudhā vīryāṇyasminyajñe suyujaḥ svāhā.

(Atharvaveda 5.26.11)

[May the inspiring (*suyujaḥ*) Lord (*Indraḥ*) use (*yunaktu*) his various vigour or virility (*bahudhā vīryāni*) in this sacrifice (*asmin yajñe*) of life. We all offer our sacrifice to him (*svāhā*)]

Scientific Explanation- Life is a Yajña in itself, where offering of sacrifice of various actions are given regularly. In this hymn, the idea of dedicating oneself to Indra has been expressed by wishing to connect various types of virility with life. Our sages expressed such views in many hymns and prayed to the Supreme God that you are virile, lustrous and powerful; so you provide us virility, luster and power to me also (*Tejo,si tejo mahi dhehi, vīryamasi viryaṁ mahi dhehi, balamasi balaṁ mahi dhehi*- Yajurvaveda 19.9).

2. Place of Vīryamaṇi

The effect of 'safe Vīryamaṇi' is seen in the form of radiance and luster throughout the body. But it is located in the middle of the body and keeps moving. The pathogenic Kṛmis do not have immediate effect due to its predominance.

वी३दं मध्यमवासृपद्रक्षेहामीवचातन्।
अमीवाः सर्वाश्चातयन्नाशयदभिभा इतः।।
(अथर्ववेद 19.44.7)

Vi,daṁ madhyamavāsṛpadrakṣeh amīvacātan.
Amīvāḥ sarvāścātayannāśayadabhibhā itaḥ.
(Atharvaveda 19.44.7)

[Body vigour (*idaṁ*) moves (*avasripaṭ*) in the midst of body (*madhyaṁ vi*), protects by destructing germs (*rakṣohā*), cures the diseases (*amīvacātayan*), vanish all kind of germs (*sarvāḥ amīvāḥ cātayan*) and may destruct (*nāśayaṭ*) all writhen (*abhibhā*) from it (*itaḥ*)]

Scientific Explanation- Vīryamaṇi is equally situated in the central part of the body. Stomach is present in the middle part of body and food digestion occurs in the stomach. All the elements in the digested food are depleted by the middle part i.e. intestines and continue to expand throughout the body via blood vessels. Therefore, the middle part of body is very important from the point of view of the nutrition and preservation of nutrients. All the organs of the body continue to work well by the nutrients. The center of all those elements is the middle part of body and the same is also the center of Vīryamaṇi. With proper nutrition, the body gets energy, luster, strength and the ability to fight against all germs and diseases that they cause. The microorganisms cannot infect due to strong body. Therefore, our sages have wished for the destruction of all the Kṛmis and for good health by safe Vīryamaṇi.

3. Protection from Amīvā by Vīryamaṇi (Jaṅgiṇa Medicine)

In the Veda, the safe Vīryamaṇi has been referred to as an Auṣadhi and termed with a word 'Jaṅgiṇa'. Virility increases anti-disease ability in the body and any person has no disease caused by pathogenic microorganisms. The verses of the Atharvaveda (19.34.9) state to destroy all kinds of diseases and germs by the medicine 'Jaṅgiṇa'.

उग्र इत्ते वनस्पत इन्द्र ओज्मानमादधौ।
अमीवाः सर्वाश्चातयं जहि रक्षांस्योषधे।।
(अथर्ववेद 19.34.9)

Ugra itte vanaspata Indra ojmānamādadhau.
Amīvāḥ sarvāścātayaṁ jahi rakṣānsyoṣadhe.
(Atharvaveda 19.34.9)

[O ! plant vigour (*vanaspate*) certainly (*iṭa*) your are resplendent (*ugraḥ*); the Lord Indra (*indraḥ*) has put in (*ādadhau*) you (*te*) luster (*ojmānaṁ*); O ! Vigour drug (*oṣadhe*) thrusting away (*cātayan*) all maladies (*sarvāḥ amīvāḥ*) destroy (*jahi*) all injurious microbes for your protection (*rakṣānsi*)]

Scientific Explanation- In this verse, the idea of establishing plant vigour in the human vigour has been expressed. But question is, how does a plant contain virile? If it is an idea of sage then it must have happened. Science also acknowledges that plants also haves disease-resistant potential. The biochemicals found in plants also provide the ability to fight diseases. All of these biochemicals are commonly called 'prohibitins' or 'phytoalexins', such as pisatin in peas, capsidiol in chilies, lycomarasmin in tomatoes, etc. Like humans, plants also suffer from many diseases, such as late and early blights of potato, plant wilt, root rot, stem rot, leaf curl, leaf roll, etc. It is essential for plants to get free from these diseases. The biochemicals are found in very low amount or are absent in diseased or sick plants. That is why the vigour of a perfectly healthy medicinal plant bestows vigour (virility) in all living beings that depend on plants for nutrition. This virility in plants is provided by their secondary metabolites (such as polyphenols, phenolic acids, protocatechuic acids, catechol, etc.) produced and stored in certain plant tissues/ organs.

KSUDRAROG IN HUMANS (JAUNDICE, MUMPS AND SMALLPOX)

The word Kṣudraroga consists of two words, Kṣudra (means small, trivial or less important) and Roga (means diseases). Kṣudrarogas have been described almost by all Ācāryas their treatise, such as Caraka Saṁhitā, Suśruta Saṁhitā, Madhavnidāna, Bhāvaprakāśa Saṁhitā, etc. either as a separate chapter or within a chapter. For example Acārya Sushruta has described 44 Kshudrarogas in 13th and 20th chapters, respectively. But Acārya Caraka did not mention Kshudraroga in detail in separate chapters but he has mentioned Kṣudraroga in different chapters.

Kṣudrarogas are such diseases the causal agents of which can hardly be assessed and cured. Viral diseases are one of them. It may develop in any part of body. For example, if liver inflammation occurs due to infections or other reasons, it does not function properly. Consequently, there develop 'Pāndu Roga' (similar to anemia) leading to 'Kāmalā' (jaundice) at the later stage. General symptoms of jaundice is discoloration (pallor, yellowish, greenish and whitish) of the body in skin, face, lips, eyes, nails, urine, feces, etc.

Measles (Romantikā) is characterized by small eruptions distributed all over the body and associated with fever, burning, thirst, itching, anorexia and excess salivation. It is also caused by imbalanced Pitta and Kapha. Herpes zoster (Kaksya) shows numerous blisters arranged like sacred thread and caused by Vāta and Pitta. Vishphotaka (early stage of Masūrikā) and Masūrikā (smallpox) have been described in Caraka Saṁhitā- Cikitsā Sthān (6.12.90-93).

Masūrikā (like lentil seeds) (smallpox) was a dreadful disease since Vedic period to mid of 20th century. It may be difficult for the well off people of the 21st century to experience the anguish of a family of millions of people living with the devastating effects of smallpox for thousands of years, but the scientist considers this to be the result of the invasiveness of a viral species. Yes, for more than 7,000 BCE, people of most countries were highly affected by the smallpox epidemic. At that time there was no medicine, no vaccines, no guidelines, no World Health Organization (WHO) like institutions, nothing else. Peoples were lying on the mercy of

God. If there was any support for the desire to live life, it was godliness. Millions of people died throughout the world. Considering the curse of God on the inflicted person, and its cure by certain precautionary measure with folklores by folk in India gave rise to the concept of 'Mātā Śītalā', and the 'Goddess of Smallpox' in Europe. Since then, thousands of temples of Mātā Śītalā were constructed for worship, in each and every village in India, which can be seen even today. Even in India, Mātā Śītalā is known by different names, such as Māriammā or Māriammana (in South India) and Bībī Mā or Olā Bībī (in Bangladesh).

1. Pānduroga or Jaundice (Kāmala, Pīliya)

Pānduroga is a disease described in Caraka Saṁhitā (Cikitsā Sthān 16.1-140) that highly resembles with the clinical symptoms of anemia. Depletion in body of Rasa Dhātu causes to develop this disease; consequently, production of Rakta Dhātu is affected. In Āyurvedic, the Pāndu is described in three forms, Pāndu in disease form, Pāndu in complication form, and Pāndu in form of symptoms of several diseases. Globally, anaemia is very prevalent deficiency disorder caused by malnutrition or infection resulting in low level of haemoblobin. Pānduroga (jaundice or Kāmala) is a fatal disease that occurs due to infection of the liver or its malfunction. Consequently, anemia occurs in sick people and the skin, eyes and urine become yellow in color. Hence, such diseased persons suffer from hepatitis, physical weakness, black skin, thoracic pain, fever, and burning sensation. Sometimes the skin appears as greenish yellow in color. Finally, jaundice occurs due to lack of immunity in the body. Greenish yellow coloured Pānduroga has been mentioned in the Atharvaveda (19.44.2).

यो हरिमा जायान्योंगभेदो विसल्पकः।
सर्व ते यक्ष्ममंगेभ्यो बहिर्निर्हन्त्वांजनम्।।
(अथर्ववेद 19.44.2)

Yo harimā jāyānyongbhedo viṣalpa..aḥ.
Sarva te yakṣmamangebhyyo bahirnirhantvānjanam.
(Atharvaved 19.44.2)

[Whatever jaundice (*yo harimā*), tuberculosis leading to weakness (*jāyānyaḥ*), aching and splitting the limbs (*angabhedaḥ*), varying skin diseases (*visalpakaḥ*), may vigour (*ānjanaṁ*) eliminate (*bahiḥ nirhantu*) those wasting diseases (*saravaṁ yakṣamaṁ*) from your limbs (*te angebhyaḥ*)]

Scientific Explanation- The functions of the liver in vertebrates are- to dissolve toxic metabolites, protein-synthesis, synthesis of essential biochemicals in food digestion, secretion of bile-juice, exchange of glycogen storage, decomposing red blood cells, secretion the necessary hormones, conversion of galactose into glucose, producing antigens and antibodies, etc. Individuals suffering from jaundice are more affected. Due to the weakening of the liver, other organs of the body are also affected. As a result, immunity in such individuals is reduced. It is but natural for such sick people to develop dermatitis and anemia. Therefore, the Vīryamaṇi removes all these diseases related to liver from all the organs of the body.

2. Types of Jaundice

Caraka Saṁhitā (16.2-43) mentions about the types, causes and diagnosis of Pāndu disease. Jaundice develops because of consumption of alkaline, salty, sour and hot, meat, oil of sesame and infected and anti-health food materials. It is also due to the odd weather or the antidote. Due to the above reasons, the bile gets aggravated and spreads throughout the body through the arteries. As a result, it becomes permanent in skin and muscles and develops many colors, such as Haridrā (yellow color), green color and light yellow (Pāndu Varna)

पाण्डुरोगाः स्मृताः पंच वातपित्तकफैस्त्रयः।
चतुर्थः सन्निपातेन पंचमो भक्षणान्मृदः।।
(चरक संहिता– चिकित्सा स्थान 16.3)

Pāndurogāḥ smṛtāḥ pañca vātapittakaphaistrayaḥ.
Caturthaḥ sannipāten pañcamo bhakṣṇānmṛdaḥ.
(Caraka Saṁhitā- Cikitsā Sthān, 16.3)

[Joundice (*pandu rogāḥ*) occurs due to five reasons (*pañca smritāḥ*), first Vat (*vāta*), second bile (*piṭta*), third cough (*kaphaiḥ trayaḥ*), forth sannipata (simultaneous effect of Vat, Pitta and cough) (*caturthaḥ sannipāten*) and fifth eating soil (*pañcamaḥ bhakṣaṇāṭa mridaḥ*)]

Scientific Explanation- In addition to soil-eating, the efficiency of the liver decreases due to the above four reasons. Vāta, Pitta, phlegm and Sannipāta occur in those individuals with weather changes that affect the smooth functioning of the liver. Important functions of the liver have been described previously. In addition to these four reasons, soil-eating is also an important cause of jaundice because many types of microorganisms like viruses, bacteria fungi, etc. are found in the contaminated soil. Moreover, the young children also have a habit of eating soil because they have no knowledge of cleanliness and hygiene. The same soil also consists of jaundice causing viruses, such as hepatitis virus A, B, C, D and E which infect the liver and destroy the cells and tissues. According to modern science, there are many causes of jaundice, such as viral infection and non-viral one. Non-viral jaundice includes alcoholism, chemicals affecting the liver, microbial toxins, accumulation of fat in the liver and impaired immunity in a sick person. According to virology, hepatitis virus A, B, C, D and E infect the liver and kill the cells. Hepatitis B virus adjacent to human lymph cell is shown in Figure 5.4.

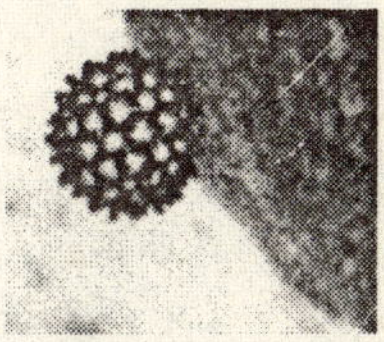

Figure 5.4. Contact of hepatitis B virus with human lymph cell.

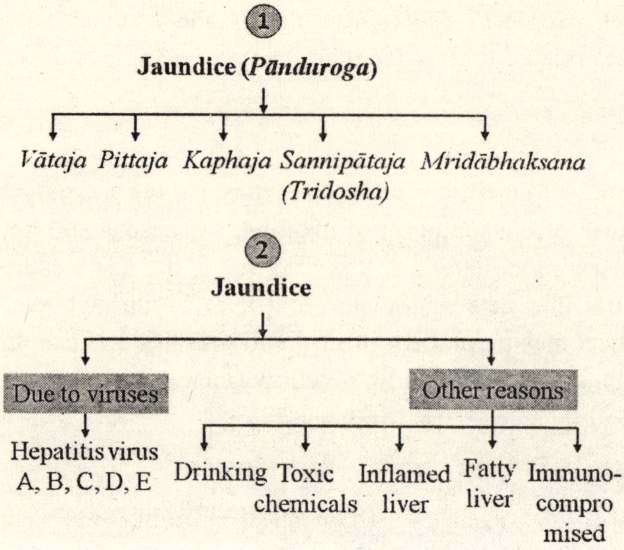

Figure 5.5. Types of jaundice. 1- according to Caraka; 2- according to modern science.

Consequently, the dead liver cells become unable to function smoothly. Therefore, the blood-forming capacity in such persons is reduced and the blood cells are broken down to form two yellow pigments (bilirubin and biliverdin) which accumulate in the skin, eyes and nails, as well as in urine and faeces. Therefore, the color of faeces and urine, nails, eyes and skin appears yellow. The digestive power of the sick person is impaired, so they experience physical weakness. Jaundice is a fatal disease. Sick person dies due to not being diagnosed in time. There are five types of Pāndu diseases, caused by Vāta, Pitta (due to increased bile), Kapha (caused by the effects of phlegm), Sannipāta (joint effect of Vāta, bile and phlegm) and soil-eating (Figure 5.5).

3. Smallpox (Masūrikā, Śītalikā, Mātā Śītalā)- an Infectious Disease

There has been the maximum death worldwide due to a fatal epidemic disease called Masūrikā. Due to lentil seed like appearance only on the skin, Caraka and Suśruta calling it as 'Masūrikā' put in the category of 'minor disease' (Kṣudra roga). It was called Masūrikā due to lentil-shaped copper-coloured blisters scattered throughout the body with intense fever, burning sensation and painful symptoms (Figure 5.6). Even other scholars, after extensive study, put Masūrikā in the category of 'fatal disease'. In western countries also there was more outbreak of this disease, which people used to call 'smallpox' and worshipped as the Goddess of Smallpox. Known by different names in scientific era, this disease occurred due to only one reason, viral infection. In due course of time, Masūrikā was called smallpox throughout the world.

Figure 5.6. Symptoms of smallpox.

विष्फोटकाः सर्वशरीरगास्तु स्फोटाः सदाहज्वर तर्षयुक्ताः ।।90।।

(चरकसंहिता– चिकित्सा स्थान, 6.12.90)

Viṣphotakāḥ sarvaśarīragāstu sphotāḥ sadāhajvara tarṣayuktāḥ.

(Caraka Saṁhita- Cikitsā Sthān, 6.12.90)

[Erupted blisters (*sphotāḥ*) on one portion or entire body (*sarva śariragāstu*) with thirst, fever and redness (*sadāhajvara tarṣayuktāḥ*) are called 'visphotaka (*viṣphotakāḥ*)]

या सर्वगात्रेषु मसूर मात्रा मसूरिकाः पित्तकफात् प्रदिष्टाः ।
विषर्प शान्त्यै विहिताः क्रिया या ता तेषु कुष्ठे च हिता विदध्यात् ।।

(चरकसंहिता– चिकित्सा स्थान, 6.12.93)

Ya sarvagātreṣu masūra mātrā masūrikāḥ pittakaphāt pradiṣtāḥ.
Viṣarp śāntyai vihitāḥ kriyā yā tā teṣu kuṣthe ca hitā vidadhyāt.

(Caraka Saṁhita- Cikitsā Sthān, 6.12.93)

[That (*ya*) lentil-shaped eruptions (*masūra mātrā*) coming out (*pradiṣtā*) on the entire body (*sarva gātreṣu*), due to effects of bile and phlegm (*pitta kaphāt*), are called 'Masurikā' (*masūrikā*). For the peace of erysipelas disease (*viṣarpa śantyai*) in these eruptions, the appropriate action (*vihitā kriyā*) be taken, and (*ca*) the medicine said for leprosy (*kuṣthe*) be beneficial (*hitā vidadhyāt*)]

Scientific Explanation- Pock means 'a rash of pimples becoming pus-filled that after healing leaves pockmarks on the skin. The viruses causing such disease are called 'poxviruses' and have been known for centuries in human societies. It known that ancestor of the poxviruses existed approximately 0.5 million years ago. Though this disease has been described during Vedic period yet smallpox is supposed to have originated in India about 1400 BCE and in China during 1200 BCE. The disease spread in the European countries in 710 A.D. and was transmitted to America by in 1520, where approximately 3.5 million Aztecs died in within 2 years. There are about 9 different poxviruses that cause disease in humans, but variola virus and vaccinia are the best known viruses. The strains of variola virus are divided into two major groups- 'variola major' (death rate 25-30%) and 'variola minor' (similar symptoms but less than 1% death rate).

Erysipelas is a cutaneous disease where blisters, filled with viral particles and fluid, develop due to infection. Viṣphotaka and Smallpox (Masūrikā) develops on skin due to ill effect of Vāta and Pitta. The symptoms of smallpox are small blisters like lentil (Masūra) seeds. It is called Masūrikā (named after Sanskrit name 'Masūra', i.e. lentil (*Lens culinaris*) seeds because of being as copper-coloured. Due to climatic changes, malnutrition, unhygienic conditions and weakness there develops impaired immunity that causes dysfunction of body organs leading to contagious diseases, one of which is the smallpox. Acute, aggressive, recurrent and fatal disease like smallpox is referred to erysipelas. The blisters of smallpox are full of aqueous oozing material containing numerous viral particles that upon shedding from blisters spread the disease again. The aqueous oozing material serves as inoculums and is enough to spread the disease in new individuals. There are different serotypes of smallpox; some of them are so dangerous that they enter inside the vital organs and make dysfunctional causing internal injuries.

Kangal (1969) in his edited and translated book 'the Kautilya Arthaśastra' describes eight divine pandemics (fire, flood, marriage, famine, Masūrikā, wild animals, snakes and devils) as described by Ācārya Cāṇakya; these also ruins the empire of a king. Possibly, diseases like smallpox would be considered as a divine wrath and kept in painful misdeeds (Yātudhāna). Up to 1960s, smallpox was an epidemic in India, Nepal, Bangladesh, Pakistan, Singapore, Turkey, England, Africa and many other countries. In order to liberate the families from this epidemic, smallpox was accepted as a divine wrath and worshiped as the 'Mātā Śītalā', i.e. 'the goddess of smallpox'. In India, folklore created Mātā Śītalā who was propitiated to protect the population from the scourge. Mātā Śītalā results in the burning sensation of blisters after infection of this virus (Dubey, 2018).

1. Mumps (Galagaṅda)

Galagaṅda is called the mumps that arises due to inflammation in one or both paratoid glands. Due inflammation the surrounding tissues of near the throat becomes compressed and solid (Figure 5.7). The pre-symptoms of mumps are low-level fever, headache and abnormal health. Thereafter, one or both of the paratoid gland(s) becomes inflamed, which lasts for a week. The other symptoms of mumps are difficulty in speaking, dryness of mouth, loss of appetite, wound in face or ear, etc. After inflammation in paratoid glands, even in 15–40% of adult males a scrotum is inflamed. There is a high probability of mumps in children and adults.

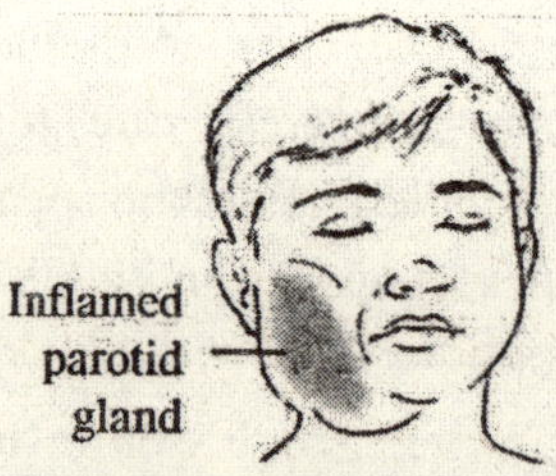

Figure 5.7. Symptom of Galagaṅda (mumps).

अपचितां लोहिनीनां कृश्णा मातेति शुश्रुम।
मुनेर्देवस्य मूलेन सर्वा विध्यामि ता अहम्।।
(अथर्ववेद 7.74.1)

Apacitāṁ lohinīnāṁ kṛśṇā māteti śuśruma.
Munerdevasya mūlen sarvā vidhyāmi tā aham.
(Atharvaveda 7.74.1)

[Of the red (*lohinīnāṁ*) glandular swelling (*apaciāṁ*), the black one (*kṛṣnā*) is the mother (*mātā*) as we have heard (*iti śuśruṃ*). With the root (*mūlen*) of divine pliers plant (*devaṣya mūne*), I pierce (*vidhyāmi*) all of them (*tāḥ sarvāḥ*)]

Scientific Explanation- The paratoid means 'adjacent to the ears'; the paratoid glands are located below both the ears. The parotid glands are the largest salivary glands that secrete serous saliva. Saliva is helpful in digesting starch and swallowing food. These glands are infected by a special type of virus called mumps virus (now called *Rubulavirus*) that results in inflammation of one or both glands which is known as 'mumps'. The mumps virus has been placed in the family

'Paramyxoviridae' and genus *Rubulavirus*. It is an RNA-containing virus that is highly contagious and infectious globally. This virus spreads through respiratory droplets from infected persons to healthy individuals upon direct contact. After 16–18 days of infection, the affected individuals show prodromal symptoms. Mumps does not reoccur once it has occurred, as the immunity against Rubulaviruses increases in affected individuals.

In mumps, arteries appear red and veins blue or light black. Due to flow of oxygenated blood in the arteries and the unoxygenated blood in the veins, they appear red and blue coloured, respectively. Due to the blackish blood in veins, it is also called impure blood. *Rubulavirus* is spread throughout the body via the infected blood and affects paratoid glands causing mumps.

The mumps can be treated by using the root extract of pliers' plant (Tesu or Palāśa) (*Butea monosperma*). Palāśa extracts has anti-inflammatory and antibacterial properties. The flower extract of Palāśa has anti-chickenpox properties and the root extract has analgesic property. That is why the use of root extract of Palāśa in the treatment of mumps has been mentioned in Veda so that inflammation and pain can be reduced in the sick people. 5-6 out of 10,000 people affected by mumps die. Nowadays, a vaccine called 'MMR' has been developed for the prevention of goiter, which uniformly prevents 'Mums-Measles-Rubella' (MMR) viruses.

2. Types of Mumps

In the Atharvaveda (7.74.2), Galgaṁda is divided into three parts- highly virulent (Doṣa Prakarṣa), moderate (Doṣa Sāmya) and normal mumps (Alpadoṣa). The characteristic features of all the three types vary.

विध्याम्यासां प्रथमां विध्याम्युत मध्यमाम्।
इदं जघन्या मासामा च्छिनद्मि स्तुकामिव।।
(अथर्ववेद 7.74.2)

Vidhyāmyāsāṁ prathamāṁ vidhyāmyut madhyamām.
Idaṁ jaghanyā māsāmā cchinadmi stukāmiva.
(Atharvaveda 7.74.2)

[Of these glandular swellings (*āsāṁ*), I pierce (*vidhyāmi*) the first of them (*prathamāṁ*) and (*ut*), I pierce the midmost of them also (*madhyamāṁ*). To this (*idaṁ*), I destroy (*acchinndmi*) the hindermost (*jaghanyāṁ*) glandular swelling (*āsāṁ*) like a knot of wool (*stukāṁ iva*)]

Scientific Explanation- Mumps is caused by *Rubulavirus* whose virulence is not uniform in all patients. Differences have been found in virulence of serotypes of Rubulaviruses; therefore, the symptoms of mumps differ. The highly virulent serotype of virus causes the first type of symptom called Doṣa Prakarṣa, the virulent serotype causes symptoms of moderate mumps, and the normal serotype results in normal mumps (Alpadoṣa). Hence, mumps differs in all the infected people.

3. Therapy of Mumps

In advanced stage when mumps have large sized eruption and become painful, its cure has been desired to through the rays of sun, moon and use of medicinal plants. Its cure has also been described earlier with the use of root extract of pliers' plant (Ṭesū or Palāśa).

अपचितः प्र पतत सुपर्णो वसतेरिव।
सूर्यःकृणोतु भेषजं चन्द्रमा वोऽपोच्छतु।।

(अथर्ववेद 6.83.1)

Apacitaḥ pra patata suparṇo vasateriva.
Sūryaḥ kṛnotu bheṣajaṁ caṅdramā vo,pocchatu.

(Atharvaveda 6.88.1)

[O! malignant tumour (eruption) (*apacitaḥ*), may you fly away (*pra patata*) like an eagle (*suparno*) from its nest (*vasateriva*). May the sun (*sūryaḥ*) produce (*kṛnotu*) medicinal remedy (*bheṣajaḥ*) and the moon (*caṅdramā*) dislodge you (*vo,pocchatu*)]

Scientific Explanation- There eradication of mumps from the infected persons has been desired to disappear like an eagle from the nest. There must not be any remains of the virus in the form of inoculum. Since radiation of sun comprises of rays of different wavelengths and colours; therefore, it was desired by the sun to act as the medicine for the patients. Sun rays like X-rays, ultraviolet rays, gamma rays and infrared rays have germicidal properties. These rays of different wavelengths at varying energy levels break the phosphor-diester bonds between two nucleotides and thus kill the viruses and other microorganisms. The moon light impart soothing experience; therefore, moon has been desired to sooth the inflamed paratoid glands so that the patients should be happy.

MICROBIAL DISEASES

The microorganisms/germs were evolved several million years before the emergence of humans. Therefore, microorganisms are the most archaic in terms of origin and development. They are found in many types of environments and places, such as water, soil, air, inside and outside plants, inside and outside animals, on the body of humans and within. Many of these types of microorganisms thrive well at temperature ranging from −80°C to 120°C. Many of these beneficial microorganisms are used in industries such as yogurt microorganisms (species of *Lactobacillus* and others), disease-causing microorganisms on plants (*Fusarium udum, Pseudomonas solanacearum, Alternaria solani, Phytophthora infestens*, etc.).

Many types of microorganisms, inside and outside the human body, produce deadly diseases, such as *Aspergillus niger* (in the ear and lungs), *Mucor* species (eye, nose, etc.), *Mycobacterium tuberculosis* (tuberculosis in the lungs), *Mycobacterium leprae* (leprosy in the hands and toes), species of *Neisseria* (disease in the brain and uterus) and species of *Trichophytones* and *Microsporum* (dermatitis, eczema etc.), hepatitis B virus (jaundice), coronavirus (***S***evere ***A***cute ***R***espiratory ***S***yndrome; abbreviated as SARS). The story of the

Pāndavas, suffering from acute jaundice, and Kuntī is known to all. The species of some important bacteria and fungi are given in Figure 5.8.

Plasmodium *Entamoeba* *Aspergillus* *Neisseria* *Trichophyton*

Figure 5.8. Some important protozoan, bacteria and fungi.

Even in the Vedic period, all these microorganisms affected human health making the people sick. The number of people who have escaped from Masūrikā (smallpox) as much as death and fear of it has not happened due to any other disease. Most deaths and migrations arising from death-fear have occurred in Europe, India and Africa. However, people left the villages and fled elsewhere due to Masūrikā disease (Dubey, 2018).

It has become clear from the previous sections that innumerable microorganisms are present in the environment including the pathogenic, oppurtunistic and normal ones besides the presence inside and out side the organs of any living organisms. However, many of the normal microflora have no harm on health because they adher on body surface and derive nutrients secreted through saliva, sweats, faeces, etc. The normal microflora become resident on the external and internal surface of body organs. In addition, the opportunistic microorganisms depending on nutritional status and host's susceptibility cause diseases on different parts of body, for example *Candida albicans*. On the other hand, the pathogenic microbes are found on external/internal sucfaces of body entering from many sources and pose a great threat to health resulting in death at the end, for examle viruses (like coronavirus, deangue virus, smallpox virus, encephalitis virus, H1N1 virus, etc.), bacteria (*Neisseria meningitis, Yersinia pestis*), fungi (*C. albicans Aspergillus niger, Mucor* sp., *Trychophyton* spp.,), protozoa (*Entamoeba histolytica*) and helmenthes (*Ascaris, Taenia solium*), etc. The numbers of microrganisms present on different parts of human body are given in Table 1.

Table 6.1: Number of microbes on different parts of body.

Organs	Bacterial cells/cm^2
Hands	1000
Forehead	1 million
Scalp	1 million
Nose mucus	10 million
Armpit	10 million
Saliva	100 million/g
Faeces	100 million/g

There are several microbiomes within the human body. One of the important microbiomes are the 'gut microflora' that has 10-fold more bacteria that the total number of cells inside the body. It is approximately 1-1.6 kilogram. Besides, there are epigenetic bacteria that turn genes ON and OFF. Further, the gut bacteria trigger our immunity; therefore, every form of pure food materials including milk, gheee honey and water (*Pāvamānīryo adhyetriṣibhih sambhṛtaṁ rasaṁ. Tasmai Sarasvatī duhe kṣīraṁ sarpirmadhūdakaṁ.* Sāmaveda- 10.82, see Chapter 5 for scientific explanation) should be consumed to make the body pious.

PANDEMIC / EPIDEMIC DISEASES DURING VEDIC PERIOD

Global pandemic/epidemics has been occuring since the Vedic time; that is why some fatal diseases have been mentioned in the Vedas, Manusmṛti, Caraka Saṁhitā, Suśrut Saṁhitā,

Purāṇas and many different antient Indian tesxts. During that period also substantial numbers of death would have been caused by mcrobial diseases like tuberculosis, smallpox, mumps, plague, yellow ferver, flues, and recenty voronavirus. So far smallpox has resulted in the maximum mortality globally. During that period there were no medicine, no therapeutic methods, nothing else. People survided from the diseases only through taking precautions.

1. Viral Diseases and its Cure

In 2020, you became aware of the term 'social distancing' after the spread of '*C*hina *O*riented *V*iral *D*isease 2019 (COVID-19). However, during the Vedic time, the viral and other unknown diseases were put under 'kṣudraroga', for example mumps, measles, smallpox, etc. In India, home sanitation, isolation and proper care of the patients (for example social distancing, keeping the patients in isolation, i.e. quarantine) and praying the Gods / Goddess assuming as the incarnation of divinity, such as the deity of smallpox (Mātā Śītalā), deity of madness (hydrophobia or rabies caused by *Rhabdovirus*) and folklores helped the families and societies to prevent these deadly diseases by creating awareness and taking precautions.

(a) **Mumps (Galagaṅḍa) and Smallpox (Masūrikā, Śītalikā, Mātā Śītalā)**- Mumps caused by *Rubulavirus* (grouped in Paramyxoviruses) has been mentioned in the Atharvaveda (7.74.1) with the name 'Apacita' and in Skandha Purān and Caraka Samhita as 'Galagaṅḍa'. Mumps has been described in detail in Chapter 5.

Apacitāṁ lohinīnāṁ kṛiśnā māteti śuśrum.

Munerdevasya mūlen sarvā vidhyāmi tā ahaṃ.

(Atharvaveda 7.74.1)

This hymn has been explained scientifically in Chapter 5.

गलस्य पार्श्वं गलगण्ड एकः स्याद् गण्डमाला बहुभिस्तु गण्डैः।

(चरकसंहिता–चिकित्सा स्थान 6.12.79)

Galasya pārśva galagaṇḍa ekaḥ syād gaṇḍamālā bahubhistu gaṇḍaiḥ.

(Caraka Saṁhita- Cikitsāsthān 6.12.79)

[One bulge of swelling (*ekaḥ syād*) in side of pharynx (*galasya pārśvaṁ*) is Galagaṅḍa (*galagaṅda*) and many bulges of swelling (*bahubhistu gaṅdaiḥ*) on the same side are called 'Gaṅḍamālā' (*gaṅḍamālā*)].

Mumps and smallpox have also been described in the Skandha Purāṇ- Śītalāṣtakaṁ (7) with the same name 'Galagaṅḍa' and 'Viṣphotaka', respectively.

गलगण्डग्रहा रोगा ये चान्ये दारुणा नृणाम्।
त्वदनुध्यान मात्रेण शीतले यान्ति संक्षयम्।।7।।
अष्टकमं शीतलादेव्या यो नरः प्रपठेत्सदा।
विष्फोटकभयं घोरं गृहे तस्य न जायते।।10।।

(स्कन्धपुराण–शीतलाष्टकम् 7, 10)

Galagaṇḍagrahā rogā ye cānye dārunā nṛṇāṁ.
Tvadanudhyānamātreṇ śītale yānti saṅkṣayaṁ.
Aṣtakaṁ Śītalādevyā yo naraḥ prapaṭhetsadā.
Viṣphotakbhayaṁ ghoraṁ gṛhe tasya na jāyate.
(Skandha Purāṇ, Śītalāṣtakaṁ- 7, 10)

[O Śītla Mātā! (*Śītale*), mumps (*galagaṅḍa*) and other dagger diseases (*cānye dāruṇā rogā*) that clog the throats (*grahā*) of humans (*nṛiṇāṁ*) are destroyed (*sankṣayaṁ yānti*) only by meditating on you (*tvadanu dhyāna mātren*). Those persons (*yo naraḥ*) who always read (*prapaṭhet sadā*) Śītalā Devi Aṣtak (*aṣtakaṁ Śītalādevyā*) do not have (*na jāyate*) the fear of a terrible disease called 'eruptions' (*ghoraṁ viṣphotak bhayaṁ*) in his house (*gṛhe tasya*)].

Scientific Explanation- Mumps (Galagaṅḍa) is one bulge of swelling on one/both side of pharynx affecting the inflammation of paratoid gland. Consequently the patients feel difficulty in swelling of saliva, water, milk and any food material due to acute pain and stiffness. Mumps is caused by a (–) RNS virus called *Rubulavirus*. Symptoms, type and cure of mumps have been described in Chapter 5.

Furthermore, Vishphotaka (early stage of Masūrikā) and Masūrikā (smallpox) have been described in Cikitsā Sthān of Caraka Saṁhitā. Viṣphotakā is a disease which is characterized by erupted blisters on entire body with redness, fever and thirst (*Viṣphotakaḥ sarva śarīragāstu sphotāḥ sadāha jwara tarṣayuktāḥ*- Caraka Saṁhitā- Cikitsā Sthān 6.12.90). Masūrikā is characterized by lentil-sized eruptions scattered all over the body which upon burst oozes out liquid material full of viral particles. In turn, these particles upon contact with healthy persons spread to others. It is caused by imbalanced Pitta and Kaph. The pain-causing effect and its relief have been mentioned by worship of Mātā Śītalā (Caraka Saṁhitā- Cikitsā Sthān 6.12.93) with proper sanitation and making social distancing with the affected persons. Human society could be rescued through worshing the Goddess of smallpox in folklures and avoiding the contact with other new and health individuals. Forelures can be considered as an act of making people aware about the occurrence of smallpox and educating them about the ways and means of its rescues.

Role of Temples of Mātā Śītalā

Mātā Śītalā also called Māriammā had become a symbol of smallpox. Temples of Mātā Śītalā were established throughout India with different names which played a key role in protecting the lives of infected persons by making social distancing so that the viral particles of smallpox could not spread further in the society. It was the biggest role of making temples of Mātā Śītalā during those days before the discovery of its causal agent as smallpox virus.

The author does not claim about the smallpox therapy by folklores or worship of Mātā Śītalā but appreciate the attempts made to prevent the spread of smallpox through folklores creating awareness about the diseases. However, there seems the breaking of chain of dissemination of viral particles by making the then 'social distancing', that really worked in all villages of India.

The precautions taken during those days in the homes of smallpox-infected persons were: *(i)* watching the symptoms on the entire body of an individual not feeling well during March and April months, *(ii)* isolating the infected persons and putting them in a separate room, *(iii)* maintaining hygiene in the home, *(iv)* putting cloths and bed sheet in boiling water daily and avoiding shavings, *(v)* application of paste of cow milk cream and clove (*Syzygium aromaticum*) with Neem (*Azadirachta indica*) leaves on the oozing eruptions, *(vi)* avoiding the contact of other healthy persons and entertaining the guests as well as beggars, and *(vii)* spreading the information to others and worshiping of Mātā Śītalā with folklores, and taking seven round of their villages assuming seven serotypes. Generally, smallpox could be cured up to 7-9 days.

2. Expression of Respect Vs Social Distancing

People live in a society and work together, enjoy together, celebrate rituals and festivals together, and worship together, and so on. The Vedas also mentions the leading of life together- *Saṅgacchadhvaṁ saṁvadadhvaṁ saṅg vo manānsi jāntāṁ. Devā bhāge yathā purvo sajjānānā upāsate* (Ṛgveda 10.191.2). Every family of the society has persons of different age groups, such as children, young and aged persons including both male and female. They have teachers and gurus in the educational cantres and temples. They respect each other by prostration (Sāṣtāṅga Praṇām), touching elder's feet, folding hand with saying Namaste, and other's ways (only by saying Namaste, Praṇām, Rām Rām, Jai Śri Rām, Rādhe Kṛśna, Rādhe Rādhe, etc). Moreover, the expression of such respect varies in every state as India is a big country with linguistic and cultural diversity of. But in other countries such expression is quite different. They do it by hand shaking and kissing; it has also influenced in Indian society in recent years. In Indian culture, this expression does not touch human-to-human but in other's culture human-to-human touch is possible. Therefore, during the time of SARS-CoV2 (COOVID-19) pandemic, the mark of respect 'Namaste' was adopted throughout the world.

(a) **Prostration (Sāṣtāṅga Pranām)-** Prostration is a gesture of expression of respect, devotion and dedication to the Supreme father, teachers (Gurus) and deities where body is placed in submissively prone position on the ground. This gesture involves the touching of ground with six body parts (sa + aṣta + aṅga = Sāṣtāṅga) namely head, eyes, hands, chest, thighs and legs) with words and pure Mānas. This gesture has been the highest level of offering the respect and worship since the Vedic time. Sri Krishna told to Arjuna that the seers and knowledgeable persons will preach you after going to them by performing Sāṣtāṅga Praṇām, by putting questions and rendering undesired services (*Tadviddhi praṇipāten paripraśnen sevayā. Upadeśyanti te jñānaṁ jñāninaḥ tatva darśinaḥ.* Śrimad Bhagavadgītā 4.34).

Figure 6.1. Namaste in Añjali Mudrā.

(b) **Namaste-** Saying Namaste or Namaskār is another way of expression of respect to the elders or seniors and old persons. In Hinduism, this gesture of Namaste is called 'Añjali Mudrā' or Praṇām Āsana. Literally meaning of Namaste is 'I bow down to you', where 'to you' refers to the 'divinity present in you' because none can be alive without the divine power. Therefore,

divinity keeps every organ functional and every organism alive. That is why the divinity has been regarded respectfully saying Namaste. Approximately 70% Indians follow this gesture of Namaste. But there have been gradual behavioural changes in human society in due course of time, who express the respect in other ways without folding the hands in this gesture. Añjali Mudrā is not a new gesture; it millenniums old tradition being following since ancient time. Añjali Mudrā can be seen in stone pieces made in many temples in India (Figure 6.1). Even the classical dances like Bhārat Nāṭyaṁ start with Añjali Mudrā.

PRECAUTIONS FOR SPREAD OF INFECTIOUS MICROORGANISMS

Diverse types of numerous microorganisms are present in the environment but great threats arise from the infectious ones. They are found in air, water, our hands, cloths, edibles, etc. Therefore, we must be cautious about the infections received from other internal and external sources including animals and humans. Microbiologically, humans have many bad habits in talking, eating, clothing, and behaving that can spread the infections. However, we can escape from infections by taking certain precautions and changing our bad habits. During the time of spread of COVID-19, World Health Organization, and the Ministry of Health, Government of India released many advisories right from lockdown to unlock periods, such as stay at home, work from home, use of mask and sanitizers, frequent hand washing for 20 second, 14 days quarantine, travelling on Government pass, corona testing, and regular taking of immunity boosters, etc. Some of the issues related to our daily life and prevention from infection, with regard to ancient texts of Indian culture as suggested thousand years BCE, are discussed in this section.

1. Changes in Eating Habit

Since centuries ago, any society of the world has been following the rituals and cultures of its own country. But during some decades, there has been mixing in traditions and culture throughout the world. The old persons still follow the culture somehow but the youngsters do on their own wish as influenced by their own working society like friends and colleagues. In Ancient Indian texts much has been described and suggested on eating habits, some of them are given below:

***(a)* Washing of Hand, Feet and Mouth before Eating:** Few decades ago, persons used to change the cloth and wash the hands before going to dining table for taking food, only by sitting on pure and clean ground, but today's scenario is far different. The modern society has ignored and forgotten the traditional advices. However, such practices are still being followed in the villages of India only by the old persons that also have been helping in preventing the contagious and infectious diseases. Washing of hands, feet and mouth before eating the food is not a new practice but these are the centuries-old and have been mentioned in different ancient Sanskrit texts of India; few of them are as below:

हस्तपादे मुखे चैव पन्चाद्रे भोजनं चरेत्।।

(पद्मपुराण– सृष्टि. 51.88)

Hatapāde mukhe caiva pañcādre bhojanaṁ caret.

(Padma Purāṇ, Sṛṣṭi. 51.88)

[Washed (*pancādre*) hand, feet and mouth (*hata pāde mukhe ca eva*) be used to eat food (*bhojanaṁ caret*).

नाप्रक्षालित पाणि पादो भुन्जीत् ।।

(सुश्रुत संहिता– चिकित्सा 24.98)

Nāprakṣālita pāṇi pādo bhunjīt.

(Suśrut Saṁhitā- Cikitsā 24.98)

[Unwashed (*aprakshālitaṁ*) hands and feet (*pāṇi pādo*) not (*na*) be used for eating food (*bhunjīt*)]

Scientific Explanation- What happens after washing of hands, feet and mouth before eating? If these organs are not washed then what will happen with us? Certainly something happens, which most of non-microbiologists could not understand properly. Obviously, microbes are present everywhere in all environmental conditions congenial for growth and multiplication of microorganisms. These microbes reside on each and every parts of our body (Table 6.1). Palms of hands consist of approximately 1000 bacterial cell/cm^2 (Figure 6.2). If you take or touch any things substantial numbers of microorganisms are transferred to that objects. If you eat food before washing the hands, feet and mouth certainly microorganisms adhered on palms, fingers and mouth will enter the gastro-intestinal tract and can cause disease, if pathogens are present. Therefore, our sages and Ṛṣis were aware of health and they have mentioned in the Sanskrit texts and advised not to eat food before washing the hands, feet and mouth.

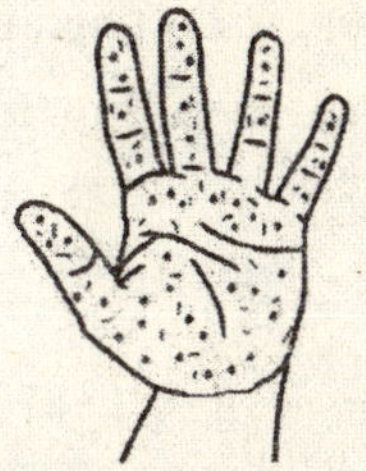

Figure 6.2. Germs on palm of hand.

***(b)* Avoidance of Touching the Edible Materials with Bare Hands-** Fingers and hands are the important organs of human body. It is used for all kinds of works. Persons without fingers and hand suffer a lot to lead the life. Many difficulties arise in the life of such persons. However, fingers are better than the spoon to eat the food materials; it is a biological sensor that does not hold too hot/cold food materials. Nobody can eat too hot/cold food if using the fingers not the spoon. Spoon users can not assess the level of temperature. However, the finger users must take precaution while taking out the edibles from the vessels and serving to others.

लवणं व्यन्जनं चैव घृतं तैलं तथैव च।
लेह्यं पेयं च विविधं हस्तदत्तं न भक्षयेत् ।।

(धर्मसिन्धु 3 पूर्व आह्निक)

Lavaṇaṁ vyañjanaṁ caiva ghṛtaṁ tailaṁ tathaiva ca.

Lehyaṁ peyaṁ ca vividhaṁ hastadattaṁ na bhakṣyet.

(Dharma Sindhu 3 Purva Ānhika)

[Salt (*lavaṇaṁ*), food materials (*vyanjanaṁ*), and (*ca*) ghee (*ghṛtaṁ*), oil (*tailaṁ*), licking materials (*lehyaṁ*) and (*ca*) different (*vividhaṁ*) drinkables (*peyaṁ*), such as water, milk, whey and others, served with bare hands (*hasta dattaṁ*), not be eaten (*na bhakṣayet*)]

Scientific Explanation- You eat food and drink water, milk and/or juice every day with little changes in items like sweats, fruits, etc. Food material is prepared by using salt, ghee, oil, and spices along with licking materials, such as pickles. This couplet (Śloka) emphasizes that all these edibles and drinkables should not be served with bare hands. If somebody takes out salt with unwashed and bare hands or glass of water by putting fingers into it, there are chances of entering the germs in water and in turn in the gastro-intestinal tract leading to stomach troubles, for example gastric, vomiting, loose motion, etc. This is because of presence of numerous germs on the palm and fingers of our hands which possibly may enter through edibles inside our body (Figure 6.2). Therefore, such habit must be changed.

***(c)* Avoiding to Touch Body Organs Without any Reason-** All the organs of our body possess a variety of microorganisms the number of which varies before and after sweetening. They may infect the depending upon opportunity, virulence of microorganisms and host's susceptibility. They spread by our bad habits of touching the secret parts without any reason. Manusmṛti (4.144) and other Vedic texts mention for avoiding such bad habits.

अनातुरः स्वानि खानि न स्पृशेदनिमित्ततः।

रोमाणि च रहस्यानि सर्वाण्येव विवर्जयेत्।।

(मनुस्मृति 4.144)

Anāturaḥ svāni khāni na spṛśedanimittataḥ.

Romāṇi ca rahasyāni sarvāṇyeva vivarjayet.

(Manusmṛti 4.144)

Pain-less *i.e.* healthy persons (*anāturaḥ*) should not touch ((*na spṛśet*)) his (*svāni*) all (*sarvāni*) organs (*khāni*), covered hairs (*romāni*) and genitals (*rahasyāni*) without any purpose (*animittataḥ*). This is completely forbidden (*vivarjayet*).

Yo akṣau parisarpati yo nāse parisarpati.

Datāṁ yo madhyaṁ gacchati taṁ kṛmi jambhayāmasi.

(Atharvaveda 5.23.3)

This hymn has been explained in detail in Chapter 4, *Origin and Prevalence of Germs*.

Figure 6.3. Nail-cutting with teeth.

Scientific Explanation- Both of the above examples clearly mention that the germs reside in our eyes, nose, crevices of teeth, mouth, tongue, gastro-intestinal tract and other organs in varying numbers (Table 6.1). Unnecessarily, we should not touch our body organs because numerous microorganisms adhere on the surfaces of these organs. However, if we touch these organs the microorganisms get attached to our fingers and palm. In turn, on putting the fingers in mouth, nail-cutting with teeth, putting fingers in nose and ears and again in mouth, or putting fingers in mouth after touching any external objects, transfer numerous microorganisms in the mouth, eyes, and other parts, leading to contagious infectious diseases (Figure 6.3). Besides, such precautions have also been mentioned in many Sanskrit texts but only two examples are sufficient to understand the precautionary measures suggested several thousand years BCE.

2. Changes in Clothing Habit

Āryans developed a civilised community since the ancient time. They are credited to give birth to Veda, the most ancient and first text of the world as well as Purāṇas, Saṁhitā, etc. However, there should be some manner and precautions while wearing the cloths. The Sutra related to all rituals at home (Gṛhya), such are marriage, Yajña and others are referred to as Gobhila Gṛhya Sūtra. Gobhila Ṛṣi is supposed to have relation with Sāmaveda. The Sutras mentioned by the Ṛṣi Gobhila in this section of Sāmaveda is called Gobhila Gṛhya Sūtra. There are seven Grihya Sūtras in Kṛṣṇa Yajurveda. Wearing the cloths for covering the body is must for every person but with some precautions.

***(a)* Avoid the Use of Wet Cloths-** Wearing of wet or moistened cloths is prohibited. But in human society such habit is found everywhere that the common men wear wet cloths when they are in hurry, for example being late for goring to offices, picking up trains and buses, when they lack sufficient cloths. India is a highly populated country. Several decades ago there was scarcity in having proper cloths. Even in the time of British rule proper cloths were not available but now India is exporting the cloths. Moreover, people have developed the habit of wearing wet or moistened cloths when undergarments are not dry, particularly in the rainy and winter seasons. In the hilly districts of Himalaya, there is problem of drying the cloths due to prolong continuous rain. Therefore, people not having sufficient cloths wear the wet undergarments.

न आद्रं परिदधीत्।।

(गोभिलगृह्य सूत्र 3.5.24)

Na ādraṁ paridadhīt.

(Gobhila Gṛhya Sūtra 3.5.24)

[Wet cloths (*ādraṁ*) should not (*na*) be worn (*paridadhīt*)]

Scientific Explanation- Do you know what happens on wearing the wet undergarments or garment? Every organism including microbes requires water for proper function of body organs through metabolism. In the presence of substantial amount of water, microorganisms grow very fast and occupy the substratum utilizing the available nutrients. Therefore, the wet cloths (for example socks, under wears, shirts, dhoti, turban, shoes, etc.) also have large numbers of microorganisms adhered to it. If you wear the wet cloths the microbes attach to the skin and grow

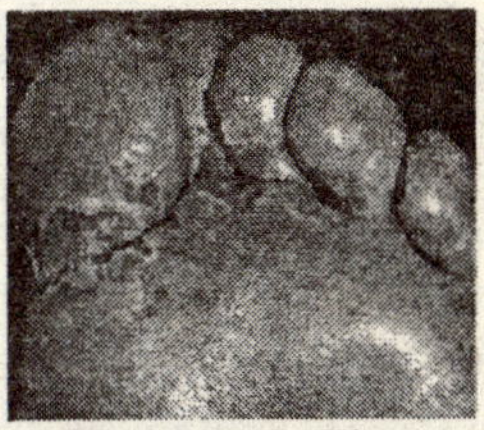

Figure 6.4. Tinea pedis on a foot fingers.

on the surfaces fast utilizing the materials discharged on the skin of our body. Eventually they cause skin diseases such as ringworm, eczema, dandruff, and different types of mycoses (chromoblastomycosis, entomophthoromycosis, onychomycosis, candidiasis, tinea corporis tinea barbae, tinea pedis, etc.). The microbes associated with such diseases are- *Candida albicans, Blastomyces dermatitidis, Aspergillus fumigates, Trichophyton rubrum, T. mentagrophytes, Epidermophyton floccosum,* and *Microsporum grisea.*

(b) **Avoiding the Use of Other's Cloths-** One must always were the own well-washed and dry cloths. Others cloths should not be worn. Generally, one family member likes brothers, sisters, son and father, grandmother and grandfather, students living in hostels or classmates, exchange their cloths, if their own cloths are not dried or any other reasons. This practice is wrong. It must be discouraged if being followed by anybody. Such precautionary measures have been mentioned in our ancient texts.

न धारयेत् परस्यैवं स्नान वस्त्रं कदाचन।।

(पद्मपुराण, सृष्टि0 51.86)

Na dhārayet parasyaivaṁ snnāna vastraṁ kadācan.

(Padmapurāṇ] Sṛṣti. 51.86)

[Never (*kadācan*) wear (*nā dhārayet*) the other's (*parasyaivaṁ*) used cloths for bathing (*snnān vastraṁ*) and drying your body]

विपर्यं न कुर्वीत वाससो बुद्धिमान् नर :।। 85।।

तथा न अन्यधृतं धार्यं न चापदशमेव च।। 86।।

(महाभारत, अनुशासन 104.85–86)

Viparyaṁ na kurvīt vāsaso buddhimān naraḥ. (85)

Tathā na anyadhṛtaṁ dhārye na cāpadaśameva ca. (86)

(Mahābhārat, Anuśāsan 104.85-86)

[The wise person (*buddhimān naraḥ*) should not exchange (*viparyaṁ na kurvīt*) the both wearing cloths (*vāsaso*), *i.e.* the long scarf (*dupattā*) as dhoti and *vice versa*. Not (*na*) wear clothes (*dhāryaṁ*) worn by others (*anya dhṛtaṁ*) and not (*tathā na*) the cloths with torn edge (*cāpadaśameva ca*)]

Scientific Explanation- Why the use of others cloths is prohibited? What happens if a person uses the cloths of his brothers, relatives or classmates? There should be no harm in using the cloths of friends or family members. Answers of these questions need to explain in detail. The persons who discourage the use of others cloths are wise. Suppose if anybody, such as your friends, classmates or family members, have skin disease and you wear their cloths, the chances of transfer of microorganisms through worn cloths on others skins get increased. Eventually, the users of others cloths become infected by such microorganisms leading to serious skin diseases. Therefore, others cloths should not be worn and such practices must be prohibited.

(c) **Avoiding the Reuse of Own Used Cloths-** You have the habit of using the same worn cloths for several days without any wash. It should not be practiced like this because it is a bad habit. Upon using the cloth one time it becomes wet and moist due to secretion of sweat glands. The sweat contains salt and other wastes of body that spoils the purity of cloths.

नाप्रक्षालितं पूर्वधृतं वसनं बिभृयाद् ।।

(विष्णु स्मृति 64.13)

Nāprakṣālitaṁ pūrvadhṛtaṁ vasanaṁ bibhṛyād.

(Viṣṇu Smṛti 64.13)

[Unwashed (*aprakṣālitaṁ*) and pre-worn (*pūrvadhṛtaṁ*) cloths (*vasanaṁ*) not (*na*) be worn again (*bibhṛyād*)]

Scientific Explanation- Once you wear a cloth substantial numbers of microorganisms become attached with the cloths due to direct contact with the skin. You know that the skin, after metabolic actions, discharges waste material through the pores that get adhered on it. Microorganisms propagating on the surface of skin get attached to cloths along with the waste materials and multiply by utilising the nutrition from the body wastes. When the used cloths are re-used, the microorganisms again get adhered to your skin and multiply in large numbers that may be harmful to the skin leading to disease. Therefore, the used cloths should not be used again and again without washing.

(d) **Use of Different Cloths at Different Occasions-** Different cloths should be worn at different occasions, such as while sleeping, walking and worshiping (performing Pūjā). The reasons for wearing different cloths at different time and occasions are the presence of varying numbers of microorganisms on the cloths and its adherence on the skin.

अन्यदेव भवेद् वासः शयनीये नरोत्तम ।। 86 ।।

अन्यद् रथ्यासु देवानामर्चायामन्यदेव हि । 87 ।

(महाभारत–अनुशासन 104.86–87)

Anyadeva bhaved vāsaḥ śayanīye narottama. (86)

Anyad rathyāsu devānāṁ arcāyāmanyadeva hi. (87)

(Mahābhārat- Anuśāsana 104.85-87)

[Best man! (*Narottama*) there should be different (*anyat eva*) cloths (*bhavet vāsaḥ*) for sleeping (*śayanīye*), different for walking on path (*anyat rathyāsu*) and different cloths (*anyat eva hi*) for worshiping the God/ Goddess (*devānāṁ arcāyāṁ*)]

Scientific Explanation- At the time of walking air-born microorganisms attach to the cloths, which are supposed to be impure and unhygienic. Similarly, cloths worn for about four to six hours receive microorganisms both internally and externally. Therefore, such impure and unhygienic cloths should not be re-used while sleeping and worshiping the God or Goddess. Therefore, different washed and dry cloths should be used at these occasions to avoid any type of infections.

2. Bathing Purifies the Body

Humans are the civilised persons. Āryans were aware of agriculture, environment, geography, forests, rivers, water, worship and living behavior. They developed the methods of purifying the environment and water. Pure and clean water is essential for carrying out healthy life. Water is used to clean the body and cloths, besides agriculture and drinking, so that microorganism attached to it can be washed out. It has been explained with some of the significant examples.

***(a)* Bathing after Touching Accouchee, Dead Body and Returning from Place of Cremation-** The place of cremation, dead bodies, accouchee i.e. procreant, menstruating woman, and persons working in unhygienic places are supposed to be impure an unclean because of prevailing the dirt and microorganisms adhered to his/her body and cloths. The persons who touch such individuals they also become impure. Therefore, they must take bath so that the waste materials or microbes attached to their body surface and cloths should be washed off and the persons resume normalcy. Such views have been mentioned in our ancient Sanskrit texts.

दिवाकीर्तिमुदक्यां च पतितं सूतिकां तथा।
शवं तत्स्पृष्टिनं चैव स्पृष्ट्वा स्नानेन शुध्यति।।

(मनुस्मृति 5.85)

Divākīrtimudakyāṁ ca patitaṁ sūtikāṁ tathā.
Śavaṁ tatspṛṣṭinaṁ caiva spṛṣṭvā snānen śudhyati.

(Manusmṛti 5.85)

[Bathing purifies (*snanen śudhyati*), the persons disposing of corpses (*divākirtiṁ*), menstruating women (*udakyāṁ*), unhygienic persons (*patitaṁ*), accouchee *i.e.* recently delivered woman (*sutikāṁ*), dead body (*śavaṁ*), and person touching (*sprisṭvā*) that (*tat*) dead body]

शवस्पृशं च स्पृष्ट्वा रजस्वलाचाण्डालयूपांश्च।

(विष्णु स्मृति 22.69)

Śavaspṛśaṁ ca spṛśṭvā rajasvalācāndālayūpāṅśca.

(Viṣṇu Smṛti 22.69)

[On touching the dead body (*śava spriśaṁ*) and (*ca*) touching (*spriśtvā*) the menstruating woman (*rajasvalā*), and (*ca*) the stick (*pāṅśaḥ*) of person disposing corpses (*cāndāla*), one should bath]

चिताधूमसेवने सर्वे वर्णाः स्नानं आचरेयुः।।

(विष्णु स्मृति 22.66)

Citādhūmasevane sarve varṇāḥ snānaṁ ācareyuḥ.

(Viṣṇu Smṛti 22.66)

[After being affected (*sevane*) by smokes of burning dead body (*citā dhuma*), at the place of cremation, persons of all sects (*sarve varṇāḥ*) of society should take bath (*snānam ācareyuḥ*)]

Scientific Explanation- The place of cremation always remains unhygienic because of burning of dead body and presence of waste material which are subjected to microbial decomposition. The smokes emanating after burning of dead body fall on body surface present at that place rendering them impure. The persons disposing of corpses (Cāndāl) and their sticks, used for turning over the fire and touching the dead body, are also impure. The persons who work at unhygienic conditions are also supposed to be impure. The dead body or the persons who touch the dead body are also become impure. The women recently delivered babies (Sūtikā) in home or in hospitals are also impure because of the presence of unhygienic conditions at all such places. Women in menstrual periods are called 'menstruating women' or 'Rajasvalā'. During these days they should not touch anything or else nobody should even touch to them. Because, due to continuous discharge of sloughed off cells and tissues along with blood make them impure. Therefore, touching to anybody and edible materials are prohibited as precautionary measures. The menstruating woman become pure and clean after taking bath on the 4th day of period (*Rajasvalā caturthe,nhi snānāṭ śudhyati.* Viṣṇu Smṛti 22.72). But in recent period these things are being ignored because of many problems associated with the family, and living in hygienic ways.

(b) **Taking Bath after Hair Every Cut-** In the ancient period there would have not been the concept of hair cutting and shavings. In due course of time scissors and razors were discovered for these two things. Establishment of the shops of saloons and beauty parlors is of recent origin. Millenniums ago, taking bath after every hair cut was advised by our seers and Ṛṣis.

श्मश्रुकर्मणि कृते च।।

(विष्णु स्मृति 22.68)

Śmaśrukarmaṇi kṛte ca.

(Viṣṇu Smṛti 22.68)

[After shaving and hair cutting (*śmaśru karmaṇi kṛte ca*) every person should take bath (*snānaṁ ācareyuḥ*)]

Scientific Explanation- Taking a bath after every haircut has been advised in the ancient Sanskrit texts, even during those days where there were no saloons and beauty parlors. At these places, the barbers cut the hairs of several persons in one day, after rapping the body so that cut hairs should not enter inside the cloths of the customers. The same cloth is used again and again on many customers. Nobody knows how many microbes would have been attached on the covering cloth of the barbers? How many types of microbes are associated with the tools used for hair cutting and shaving as well as on the palms and fingers of barbers, table tops and chairs kept in the shops? Whatever microorganisms are present at these surfaces, they are transmitted to the persons sitting for hair cut or shavings. A skin disease called barber's itch or tinea barbae, one of the examples of fungal disease that spread from the saloons (Figure 6.5). Hence, as precautionary measure, after hair cutting one

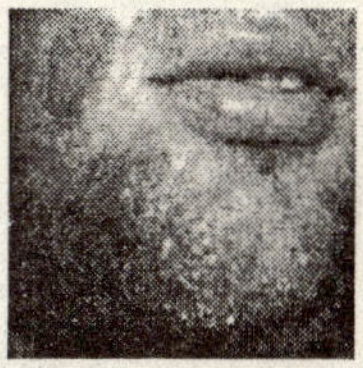

Figure 6.5. Tinea barbae on chin.

must take bath so that the microbial contaminants must be washed off and body surface may become clean and pure.

सर्वेष्वेतेषु स्नानेषु वस्त्रं नाप्रक्षालितं बिभृयात्।

(विष्णु स्मृति 22.71)

Sarveṣveteṣu snāneṣu vastraṁ nāprakṣālitaṁ bibhṛyāt.

(Viṣṇu Smṛti 22.71)

[Among all these (*sarveṣveteṣu*) baths (*snāneṣu*) unwashed (*aprakṣālitaṁ*) cloths (*vastraṁ*) should not be worn (*na bibhṛyāt*)]

Scientific Explanation- It may be concluded that in these entire cases one must take bath and wear washed and clean cloths so that the body may be pure and clean and no microbial infectious disease may occur. The infectious diseases may be prevented by adopting the aforesaid suggestions and precautions.

Elimination of Pathogens by Sun Rays

7.

The evolution of microorganisms took place millions of years before human origin. It took millions of years for human development. Microorganisms found in the environment, such as on animals, humans, and plants. Nothing is left uninfected by the microbes. They infect each and every person through various modes, such as water, air, soil, many foods (milk, ghee or any milk made food), hand shaking, kissing, skin to skin contact, blood contact, sneezing, coughing, as well as having weak immunity. Thereafter, they start living permanently and become resident on those organs by entering inside and outside the body. The resident gastro-intestinal microflora that reside permanently inside the intestines play an important role in keeping the body healthy by helping in digestion of food. They also fight against infection of any external microorganism through biocontrol mechanisms. Microorganisms present on external surface of human body have been described in the previous Chapter 6, *Prevention from Infection of Pathogens*. The Atharvaveda describes the infection and destruction of such microorganisms.

ANNIHILATION OF MICROBES OF VARIOUS COLOURS

There are always a myriad of different types of germs present on the surface of the earth. Their number goes on changing according to the season that affects their growth and development. In places where there is more air pollution, other types of microorganisms are found. These microorganisms vary in form, color, shape and prevalence. Some microbes are more active during the winter months and some in the rainy and summer seasons. The microbes found in rainy season will now be able to grow in winter season and vice versa. However, there are some other types of microbes that are always present in the environment. In addition some bacterial pathogens, normal human microflora of different body organs, always reside within the body for example *Escherichia coli*. Trillions of bacteria are the habitants of our intestine but we do not know. Their disease-causing capacity increases more as the seasons change. Hence, any person gets infected by the microorganisms quickly and can suffer from various diseases, such as flu, cough, fever, head ache, ringworms, dermatitis, etc. The Atharvaveda describes many types and colours of various, painful, skin-disease causing and vibrating fluorescent germs, and the annihilation of their offspring.

येवाषासः कष्कषास एजत्काः शिपवित्नुकाः ।
दृष्टश्च हन्यतां क्रिमिरुतादृष्टश्च हन्यताम् ।।

(अथर्ववेद 5.23.7)

Yevāṣāsaḥ kaṣkaṣāsa ejatkāḥ śipavirnukāḥ.
Dṛṣtaśca hanyatāṁ kṛmirutādṛṣtaśca hanyatām.

(Atharvaveda 5.23.7)

[Fast moving (*yevāṣāsaḥ*), pain-causing (*kaṣkaṣāsa*), vibrating fluorescent germs (*ejatkāḥ*) and spreading on skin (*śipavitnukā*) are the various types of microbes (*kṛmiḥ*). Let all such seen and (*dṛṣtaḥ ca*) unseen (*adṛṣtaḥ ca*) microbes (*kṛmi*) be killed (*hanyatāṁ*)]

Scientific Explanation- A variety of microorganisms is found in the atmosphere, out of which many are moving, some shining, and some vibrating. Such germs spread to the other places by infecting the skin. Some germs are visible (Dṛṣta) and some are invisible (Adṛṣta). Here, many types of visible and invisible germs have been mentioned with different nature and spreading on the skin. In this hymn, the Vedic sages desired to destroy the germs of diverse nature that produce the skin diseases called dermatitis. The modern microbiologists accept that after infection at one place on the skin, microorganisms spread to the other places as well. The infected persons feel as if something is crawling on the skin, hence they feel etching. For example, ringworm is produced on the skin, almost all part of the body, due to the invasion of three different types of fungal species, such as *Trichophyton rubrum, Microsporum* spp., and *Epidermophyton* spp. Hence, the affected persons feel crawling on the skin. Therefore, the sick person repeatedly itches on the affected skin.

Generally, symptoms appear within 4-14 days after the infection when the skin of an individual comes in contact with the ringworm-causing fungi. The other symptoms of ringworm are itchy skin, ring-shaped rashes, red-coloured, scaly and cracked skin, and hair loss. Ringworms are named differently depending on the body organs affected, such as scalp, around the groin, inner thighs and buttocks, nails, fingers, feet, etc. The disease appears as circular rings on the skin growing from centre to outside (Figure 7.1A).

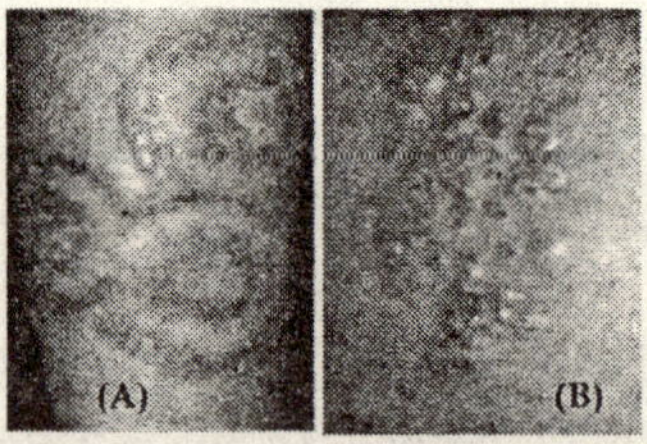

Figure 7.1. Ringworm (A) and herpes (B) on skin.

Similarly, there is another deadly and painful contagious skin disease called herpes (means to crawl) that occurs due to the infection of herpes simplex virus (HSV) on the skin. The HSV is of two types- HSV-1 and HSV-2. HSV-1 is transmitted mainly through oral-to-oral contacts and cause oral herpes (generally known as cold sores). HSV-2 is a sexually transmitted and causes genital herpes. But HSV-1 can also cause genital herpes. After infection, the patient feels pain as the HSV spreads through nervous system; therefore the patient experiences that some invisible organism is moving on the skin. Herpes spreads throughout the body by the nervous system. The location where it is affected causes excessive rashes (bathing and disseminating) (Figure 7.1B). These rashes contain herpes viruses which again infect the new place. In both these instances, the disease appears, but due to the subtlety of the disease, it remains invisible. They can be seen only through microscopic or electron-microscopic. In 2016, approximately 3.7 billion people of the age 50 had oral or genital infection globally. Africa had the highest prevalence of infection and America the lowest.

1. Destruction of Progeny of Microorganisms

The number of microbes in the environment keeps increasing gradually, and decreases after completion of life as they die. However, they are able to spread and cause the disease due to high numbers. Therefore, most of the microbes are the cause of many diseases. By destroying these germs, the problems arising from them can be solved. The hymns of Atharvaveda (2.32.4 and 5.23.11) mention the destruction of the germs.

हतो राजा क्रिमीणामुतैषां स्तपतिर्हतः।

हतो हतमाता क्रिमिर्हतभ्राता हतस्वसा।।

(अथर्ववेद 2.32.4)

Hato rājā kṛmīṇāmutaiṣaṁ stapatirhataḥ.

Hato hatamātā kṛmirhatabhrātā hatasvasā.

(Atharvaveda 5.32.4)

[The king of microbes (*rājā kṛmīṇāṁ*) has been killed (*hato*), and his chieftain (architect) (*uṭ yeṣāṁ stapatiḥ*) has also been killed (*hatāḥ*). The microbes (*kṛmi*) have been killed (*hato*), his mother has been killed (*hatamātā*), and also its brothers (*hatabhrātā*) and sisters (*hatasvasā*) have been killed (*hatā*)]

Scientific Explanation- Wherever the germs are found, their mother cells are divided to form many cells which are called progeny cells or 'daughter cells'. It means that the progeny cells are produced from mother cells (Figure 7.2). Originally, all cells are related to each other due to being born from a single cell. Like human relationships, these cells are also someone's mother, and someone's sister and brother. The most dominant of these cells is like a king, which is effective on all cells. Cells that survive even in the extreme conditions are called 'endospores'. Any cell can be converted into an endospore. The endospores can survive for many years. On the return of the favourable conditions, these endospores germinate again and form many cells. Therefore, endospores are also the basis of life of bacteria. After the death of the endospores, the origin of all the microbes is destroyed and then no new ones are born. Here it must be noted that the endospores are only the survival structure in adverse conditions; the other microorganisms like fungi also produce different types of surviving structure named by different names, such as chlamydospore (in *Fusasium udum*), sclerotia (in *Sclerotium rolfsii*), zygospore (in the species of *Rhizopus, Mucor*, etc.

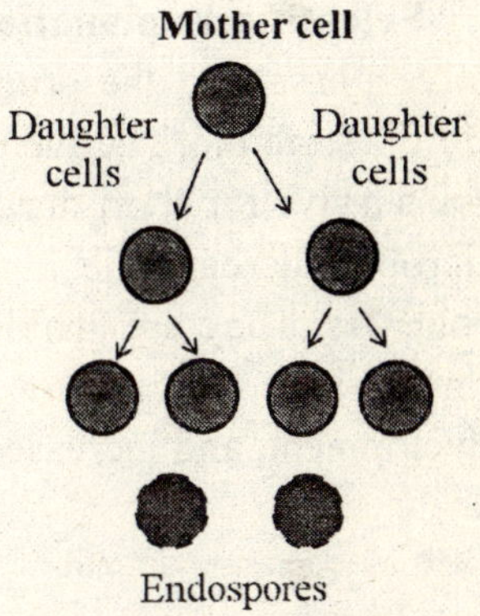

Figure. 7.2. A mother cell producing daughter cells and endospores.

2. Destruction of Active and Inactive Microorganisms

All the crimes remain in dormant (Susupta) or active (Sakṛya) phase of life. The active phase has favourable conditions for their growth, multiplication and reproduction. In this phase of life, these microbes increase their numbers and some of them cause many types of diseases.

Infection is merely a mode of nutrition from plants, animals, soil, water, milk, etc. In human, they derive nutrients from different parts of organs of human such as skin, eyes, intestine, mouth, etc. In human society, all types of infectious diseases have been noticed since the Vedic period. In the Atharvaveda (5.23.8), there is mention of killing all types of germs that are in the dormant and active phases.

हतो येवाषः क्रिमीणां हतो नद निमोत।
सर्वान् च मष्मषाकरं दृषदा खल्वां इव।।
(अथर्ववेद 5.23.8)

Hato yevāṣaḥ kṛmīṇām hato nada nimota.
Sarvān ca maṣamaṣākaraṁ dṛṣdā khalvāṁ iva.
(Atharvaveda 5.23.7)

[Among the microbes (*kṛminām*) the dormant one (*evāṣaḥ*) has been killed (*hatāḥ*) and (*uṭ*) vibrating microbes (*nada nimota*), that are in active phase also have been killed (*hatāḥ*). I have crushed (*maṣmaṣākaraṁ*) all those (*sarvān*) to pieces as (*iva*) the stones (*dṛṣadā*) crush the grains (*khalvān*)].

Scientific Explanation- In this hymn, two stages of the microorganism are described, the active phase and the dormant phase. The active phase of the microbes is the state when the microbes are more active due to the presence of favourable environmental conditions. However, they survive for short duration by various vegetative propagules like conidia, spores, etc. All the microbes increase the numbers of their species by producing their own progeny and onward progenies. They are unable to adjust themselves in the changed environment due to increase in atmospheric temperature, lack of nutrients, moisture or water required for growth and development, and increased microbial community of their progenies.

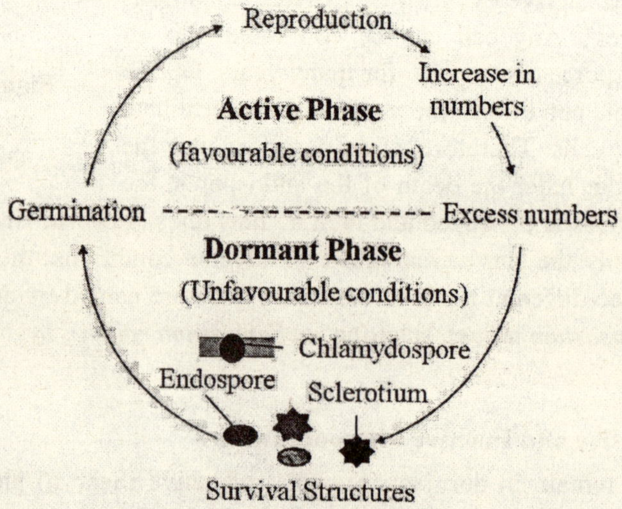

Figure 7.3. Active and inactive phases of microorganisms.

Consequently, their reproductive ability is reduced and eventually completely inhibited. Therefore, in adverse conditions, they produce a variety of survival structures, such as endospores, chlamydospores, sclerotia, etc. which on return of favourable condition the survival structure germinate and then they reproduce normally (Figure 7.3). Through these structures, they can survive for many years. On the return of favourable conditions, these structures germinate and enter into the active phase of life. The nature can completely destroy all these microorganisms as well as their surviving structures.

ELIMINATION OF MICROORGANISMS BY SUN RAYS

The sun rays have full potential to destroy the microorganisms through its energy-rich radiations. In the Vedas, the Sun that rises in the east kills all the non-visible microorganisms and demons. Rays of various intensities fall on the ground in sufficient quantity from sunrise to sunset. The sun kills the disease-causing invisible microorganisms living on the land by its rays that have electro-magnetic properties. The therapeutic application of disease control, by the rays of the rising and setting sun, has been described in the Atharvaveda.

1. Germicidal Properties in the Rays of the Rising and Setting of Sun

People think that the latitudinal position of the sun is always the same and the rays fall on the earth surface in the similar ways and the effect of the rays always remains the same, as in the morning and evening, but it is not so. Thousands of years ago, the ancient sages had mentioned that the rising and setting sun bears the property of destroying the microorganism, whatsoever present on surfaces of earth, plants, animal like cows, human, etc.

उद्यन्नादित्यः क्रिमीन्हन्तु निम्रोचन्हन्तु रश्मिभिः। ये अन्तः क्रिमयो गवि ।।

(अथर्ववेद 2.32.1)

Udyannādityaḥ kṛmīnhantu nimrocanhantu raśmibhiḥ. Ye ant kṛmayo gavi.

(Atharvaveda 2.32.1)

[May the rising sun (*udyan ādityaḥ*) kill the microbes (*kṛmīn hantu*) with his rays, and also while setting sun (in evening) let them kill (*nimrocan hantu raśmibhiḥ*); let these rays destroy the microbes that reside within the cows (*ye kṛmayo gavi antaḥ*)]

Scientific Explanation- The colours of rising and setting of the sun are different from the colour of the sun shining brightly at the noon. The sun appears red in the morning and evening but the sun in the noon appears always bright yellow. However, the intensity of light varies according to the season and climatic conditions. This variation is not due to the sun but because of seasons, climate and weather. In the noon, the rays of the sun have more brightness. It must be noted there that at the time of sunrise and sunset, the sun is on the horizon (the meeting place of the earth and the sky). Dust molecules always fly from the surface of the earth towards the sky, meaning that the dense layers of dust particles remain in the horizon forming a gradient from the earth surface toward the sky. If we observe the sun in the morning and evening, it appears reddish in colour. This is because, at the time of sunrise and sunset, its rays have to travel and cross the long path of air after hitting the dust particles flying in the sky. Due to the long air way, the nitrogen molecules are present in large quantities. When the photons of the sun's rays collide with the nitrogen molecules, then the nitrogen molecules repel the photons by desiccating them. The process of absorption and exclusion is called light scattering.

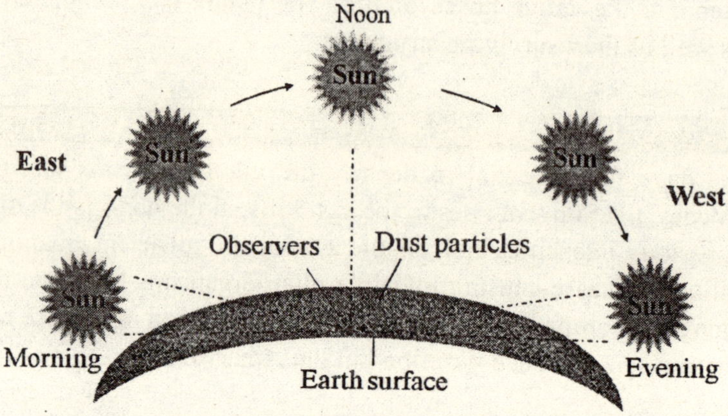

Figure 7. 4. Position of the sun during rise and setting.

The wavelength of red coloured sun rays is the longest and that of the blue rays are the shortest. Therefore, shortest wavelength sun rays, of blue, yellow and other colours, are scattered in the sky after colliding with the dust particles and smokes near earth surface. Consequently, all these rays do not come near us at sunrise and sunset due to its easy scattering. But because of having the long wavelength, the red coloured sun rays are not scattering. Therefore, these rays reach near us during sunrise and sunset. That is why the sun appears as red colored at sunrise and sunset (Figure 7.4). Therefore, one should not look, with the naked eyes, towards the sun at sunrise and sunset, because the red colored sun rays are basically the infrared rays which badly affect the eyes by damaging the lens and cornea. It may be noted that infrared rays also get absorbed in water, carbon dioxide and ozone. Therefore, in Atharvaveda (2.32.1) the red rays of the sun have been desired to kill the microorganisms present on the surface of the earth and on the cows.

2. Sun Rays kill Toxin Producing Germs

The toxin-producing germs have a very adverse effect on the health of the living organism including human due to its capacity to produce high amount of toxic secondary metabolites. The sun rays have the ability to destroy such types of invisible germs.

उत्पुरस्तात्सूर्य एति विश्वदृष्टो अदृष्टहा।
अदृष्टान्त्सर्वान्जम्भयन्त्सर्वाश्च यातुधान्यः।।
(ऋग्वेद 1.191.8)

Utpurastātsūrya eti viśvadṛṣto adṛṣtahā.

Adṛṣtāṅtsarvān jambhayantsarvāśca yātudhānyaḥ.

(Atharvaveda 1.11.8)

[The sun (*sūryaḥ*) rises in (*uṭ ēti*) the east (*purastāṭ*), seen by all (*viśvadṛśto*) and killer of the unseen (*adṛśtahā*), kills all the unseen (*adṛśtān sarvān*) and also kills (*jambhayān*) all the pain-causing microbes (*sarvā ca yātudhānyaḥ*)].

Scientific Explanation- The ability to destroy the germs by the red coloured rays coming from the sun rising and sun setting has already been discussed earlier. The sun rays destroy the toxin-producing pathogenic microorganisms. It is known that microorganisms are both unicellular and multicellular. Because of being in minutest sizes the unicellular microorganisms are invisible. They can be observed by using a microscope or electron microscope. There are some microorganisms of special class (for example photosynthetic bacteria and cyanobacteria, members of chlorophyceae, etc.) which contain photosynthetic pigments and carryout photosynthesis but microorganisms of other class do not, for example, protozoa, fungi, etc. Therefore, such microorganisms survive for a long period even in dark conditions. Hence, visible and invisible germs are all destroyed by the intense red-coloured (i.e. infra red) sun rays.

उत्पुरस्तात्सूर्य एति विश्वदृष्टो अदृष्टहा।

दृष्टांश्च घ्नन्नदृष्टांश्च सर्वांश्च प्रमृणन्क्रिमीन्।।

(अथर्ववेद 5.23.6)

Utpurastātsūrya eti viśvadṛṣto adṛṣtahā

Dṛṣtānśca nghannadṛṣtānśca sarvānśca pramṛṇankṛmīn.

(Atharvaveda 5.23.6)

[The sun (*sūryaḥ*) rises in (*ut ēti*) the east (*purastāt*), seen by all ((*viśvadṛśto*) and killer of the unseen (*adṛśtahā*), killing the visible (*dṛśtān*) as well as the invisible (*adṛśtān ca*), and crushing all sorts of microbes (*sarvān ca kṛmīn*) with his rays (*pramṛṇan*)]

Scientific Explanation - This hymn of Atharvaveda (5.23.6) has scientifically been explained in the other hymn of Ṛgveda (1.191.8) because both hymns have more-or-less similar meaning.

3. Viricidal Property in Sun Rays

There are many microorganisms that cause heart disease (myocarditis) and jaundice (Pīliyā, Harimā, Pānduroga, Kāmlā) and mumps (Galgand, Gandamālā). These diseases are caused by different viruses. Jaundice is caused by hepatitis B virus, but heart disease is caused by many viruses, such as adenoviruses, coxachievirus B, rubell virus, etc. The sun rays of varying wavelengths have a viricidal property that has been mentioned in the Atharvaveda (1.22.1) thousands of years ago.

अनु सूर्यमुदयतां हृद्द्योतो हरिमा च ते।
गो रोहितस्य वर्णेन तेन त्वा परि दध्मसि।।

(अथर्ववेद 1.22.1)

Anu sūryamudayatāṁ hṛdyoto harimā ca te.
Go rohitasya varṇen ten tvā pari dadhmasi.

(Atharvaveda 1.22.1)

[May your (*te*) heart-sickness (*hṛdyotaḥ*) and (*ca*) yellowness (*harimā*) disappear (*uda āyatāṁ*) when exposed to the sun (*anu sūryaṁ*). We have enclosed and surrounded (*pari dadhmasi*) you (*tva*) with these ruddy radiations (*rohitasya ten varṇen*) of the sun (*go*)]

Scientific Explanation- The germicidal properties of the sun rays and its effect on the mechanism of the liver function are described in the preceding section. The scientific interpretation of the infrared rays of the sun, appearing red in colour (Lohita Varṇa) at sunrise and sunset, has already been done earlier. The infrared sun rays have a therapeutic property. Therefore, in recent years, the infrared rays are being used in many types of treatments like eczema, etc. Daily exposure of sunrays, for about 30 minutes to 1 hour in the morning, causes the conversion of cholesterol present in the skin into cholecalciferol due to the ultraviolet-B rays. Later on, cholecalciferol forms vitamin-D. Further, vitamin-D is stored in the liver and preserves the efficiency of the liver function as well as calcium absorption. We know that calcium is an important macronutrient required for body. There are certain metalo-proteins, for example 'calmodulin', that complex with calcium for its proper function. It is required for bone, muscles, heart, and other organs of the body. In the cases of calcium-deficiency, the bones become weak and chances of heart attack get increased. Calcium is needed for the myocardial muscle for its proper function. There are more chances of coronary disease due to its deficiency. Therefore, daily exposure of sun rays makes the liver healthy and functional and there shall be no calcium deficiency due to synthesis of vitamin-D in bones. Therefore, daily exposure of red coloured sun rays in morning does not cause heart disease and jaundice.

4. Elimination of Tuberculosis by Sun Rays

It has becomes clear from the previous discussion that the electromagnetic radiations of sun light poses both positive and negative effects on animal life. All the microbes present on skin are killed due to positive effect. Relief in cough, headache and joints pain has been noticed in persons exposed to sun rays. Also patients get relief from arthritis and liver-related diseases after taking pure air from the medicinal plants growing in hills.

मुन्च शीर्षक्त्या उत कास एनं परुष्परुराविवेशा यो अस्य।
यो अभ्रजा वातजा यश्च शुष्मो वनस्पतीन्त्सचतां पर्वतांश्च।।

(अथर्ववेद 1.12.3)

Muñca śīrṣaktyā ut kāsa enaṁ paruṣparurāviveśā yo asya.

Yo abhrajā vātajā yaśya śuṣmo vanaspatīntsacatām parvatāṇśca.

(Atharvaveda 1.12.3)

[O Sun! set him free (*muñca uṭ enaṁ*) from headache (*śīrśkṭyā*) and that cough (*yaḥ kāsaḥ*) which has entered (*āviveśaḥ*) in his every joints (*asya parusparuḥ*). May the disease, that is caused by cloud (*yaḥ abhrajā*), wind (*vātajaḥ yaḥ*) and by heat or bile (*yaḥ ca śuṡmaḥ*) be cured by consuming medicinal herbs from hills (*vanaspatīna sacatāṁ*) and pure air from mountains (*ca parvatān*)].

Scientific Explanation- In this hymn, the sun has been prayed to liberate the Agnihotra performing persons suffering from diseases, such as headache, cough, rheumatism, phlegm, and bile disorder by the use of pure air of mountains and plants. There is a power to cure disease by the smoke released from healthy medicinal and aromatic plants used in Agnihotra, sun rays, and pure air coming from the mountains. In Indian traditions, worshiping sun (Suryopāsanā) is being practiced by most of the persons daily or on special occasions. Suryāsana has also been recommended for those who perform daily Yoga during sun rise to keep the good health. The synthesis of vitamin D1 - D3 through the exposure of sun rays has already been discussed earlier. The liver, heart, muscles and bones function properly when there is sufficient amount of vitamin-D. Therefore, no person suffers from rheumatism, headache, gout and gall bladder disease who following this tradition. Due to vitamin-D synthesized by the sun rays, the disease-preventing ability (immunity) in the body increases. Infectious diseases occurring in the liver and lungs can be overcome by healthy medicinal plants. Pneumonia and cough disease can be eliminated with the use of these plants in performing oblation to fire (Agnihotra, Hawan, Homa).

Due to deficiency of vitamin D, any person can have multiple sclerosis (in brain, nervous system, lungs, chest, urethra, etc.) and inflammatory bowel disease. Hence, vitamin D keeps all body organs functional and healthy. It is interesting to note that after exposure of infra red rays for a week on the skin of vitamin D-deficient persons by an 'infrared B lamp' illuminating the ultraviolet B rays (300 nanometre), the diversity and numbers of gastro-intestinal bacteria get changed due to synthesis of vitamin D in such patients. This change in number and diversity of bacteria in patients treated by infrared rays has been found similar to those given vitamin D supplements. It is only because of similar ways of vitamin D supply through the skin treatment by infrared rays as well as dietary supplement of vitamin D. This change in gastro-intestinal bacteria is only because of the effect of vitamin D. A gradual increase in the numbers of fermicutes and proteobacteria, and a decline in the numbers of bacteroids in the gastro-intestinal tract of patients have been noticed after infrared B rays treatment. The mechanism of increase in the numbers of microorganisms is not fully understood. But the effects of this increased numbers certainly influence the microorganism of gastro-intestinal tract and finally on human health. No burning sensation on skin is experienced upon exposure of rays from infrared B lamp (Bosman *et al.*, 2019).

GERMICIDAL PROPERTIES IN THE SUN RAYS

Small, large uncountable illuminated planets and stars exist in the universe. Together they make the galaxies. The solar system is very large and 4.5 billion years old, which has 1 sun, 8 planets, 5 dwarf planets, 181 moons, 555 meteorites and 3 thousand comets. All of them are linked together due to the gravity of the sun and continue to revolve around the sun. The Sun is the largest star whose rays of different intensity fall on the Earth and other planets in the form of electromagnetic radiations. The sun rays falling on the earth are the basis of all creatures. These rays illuminate and appear in seven colors of different intensity, called electromagnetic radiation spectrum (Figure 5.5).

The sun rays are only a part of electromagnetic radiation that fall on the earth. However, the rays of low energy and long wavelength include gamma rays, X-rays, ultraviolet (UV) rays, visible and infrared rays (IR), microwaves and radio waves (RW). These rays are filtered through the earth's atmosphere before reaching the earth. Electromagnetic radiation in the sun light has both positive and negative effects on animals, such as the synthesis of vitamin D-3 and mutations in chromosomes.

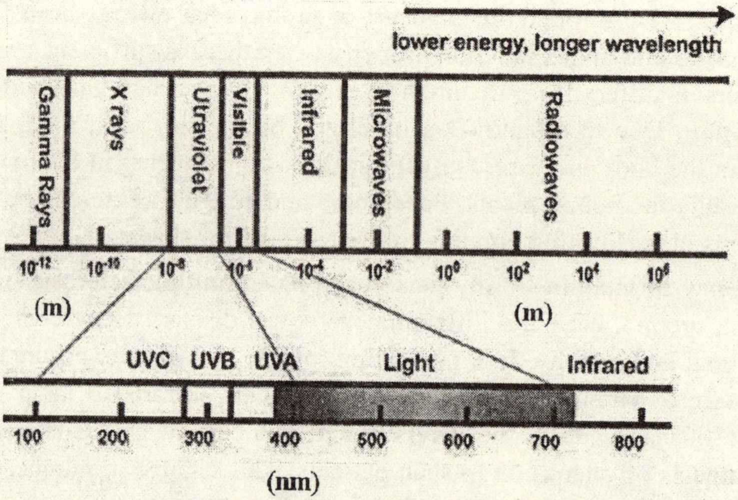

Figure 5.5. Spectrum of electromagnetic radiation.

1. Solar Heat Treatment Method (Luthra and Sattar Experiment)

Luthra and Sattar (1953) for the first time used this method to eliminate the wheat smut occurring in India. In this method, the wheat seeds are treated for 4 hours in cold water in the morning (8-12 AM) and after 4 hours of soaking the seeds are re-treated in sun light for 4 hours in the afternoon (12-4 PM). During this period, temperature-sensitive fungi are destroyed at this temperature because of more sensitivity of fungi to the temperature than the resistance. Thereafter, the dried seeds are treated with fungicides and stored properly. This method is called 'solar heat treatment' or the Luthra and Sattar experiment.

2. Soil Solarization in Agriculture

This is an Israeli technique applied for control soil-borne plant pathogens and used for the first time in India by Dubey and Dwivedi (1986) at Banaras Hindu University, Varanasi. This method is used in the month of May-June when the intense sun rays fall on the top surface of the soil in the fields for 12-14 hours. First of all, the agricultural field is ploughed and soil is well leveled and duly suppressed by flattening the top surface of the soil. Thereafter, a sheet of transparent polythene (25 micrometers thick) is spread over the soil surface in that field in such a way that the entire field is covered with the polythene sheet. If polythene is torn by an animal, it must be sealed by an adhesive tape (Figure 7.6).

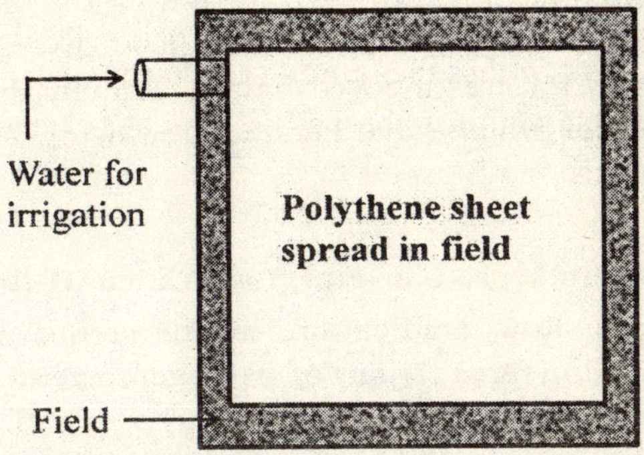

Figure 7.6. Method of soil solarization.

Then the corners of the sheet are covered with soil from the all four sides. The field is irrigated from one side so that sufficient moisture should remain in the soil. The open space is also covered with soil after irrigation so that the steam created by moisture does not evaporate. In this way, all treated fields are left for 30-40 days. During this period, due to the highest temperature and long duration of the sun, the moisture of the field is converted into steam inside the polythene sheet that remains for a long time. Due to the highest temperature of steam, the soil temperature of the treated fields is raised to about 10-15°C higher than the normal temperature. Due to prolonged high temperature, all types of pathogenic bacteria, fungi, and nematodes die and the fertility of the soil increases. After the removal of polythene sheet, the number of other beneficial and antimicrobial bacteria and fungi increases which kills any microbes present in the soil by bio-control mechanisms. Therefore, this method is highly beneficial for small groups and marginal farmers where there is problem of soil-borne plants diseases.

Eradication of Pathogens by Medicinal Plants

The mankind has been bestowed by the 'mother earth' providing hundreds of medicinal plants bearing the capability to cure many ailments of human. Since the Vedic period this unique characteristics of plants have been known to our sages. According to the World Health Organization (W.H.O.), over 80% population of the world meets out their needs only through the traditional plant-based medicines. The plants that possess potential secondary metabolites and are used for curing the diseases as drugs are called 'medicinal plants'. India is 8th country in the world in plant diversity where over 7,500 plants are used as medicinal plants for treatment of many human diseases. There are numerous microbial and viral diseases which have been treated using several medicinal plants; few of them are described below:

1. Apāmārga (Ciracitā, Latjīra, chaff-flower) (*Achyranthus aspera*)

Due to eradication, by the eternity-derived knowledge persons through abstersion or cleansing (apamārjan) of pathogenic germs, the herb has become the best and has been called Apāmārga (*Achyranthus aspera*) or 'chaff-flower'.

यददो देवा असुरांस्त्वयाग्रे निरकुर्वत।
ततस्त्वमध्योषधेऽपामार्गो अजायथाः।।
(अथर्ववेद 4.11.4)

Yadado devā asurānstvayāgre nirakurvat.
Tatastvamadhyoṣadhe,pāmārgo ajāyathāḥ.
(Atharvaveda 4.11.4)

[Because (*yat*) in that (*adaḥ*) ancient time (*agre*), the knowledgeable men of devotion (*devāḥ*) through you (*tvayā*) had removed (*nir kurvat*) the pathogenic germs (*asurān*), due to which (*tataḥ*) you (*tvaṁ*) got on top (*adhi ajāyathā*) of all the medicines (*oṣdhe*) and your name became Apāmārga (*apāmārgaḥ*)]

Figure 8.1. A plant of *Achyranthus aspera.*

Scientific Explanation- Apāmārga is an herb belonging to the family Amaranthaceae and found everywhere. The plant begins to sprout at the beginning of the rainy season. It thrives in cold weather and grows completely in summer. Its flowers are green with pink buds and seeds are like rice. Its leaves are elliptical, somewhat pointed and very small, and covered with white follicles. Its leaves are used in worship of Gaṇeśa on the day of Gaṇeśa Caturthī, which is generally called 'Gaṇeśa Patra Pūja". There are mainly two species of the plant, e.g. white and red types, which are used in medicine. It contains microscopic and thorny seeds which are like small black grains of light black colour.

It bears many medicinal properties and hence used as Āyurvedic medicines for treatment of cough, tooth ache, urinary disease, skin disease (boils and pimples), dyspepsia, etc. Daily use of the root of *A. aspera* is said to cure toothache, gingival weakness, and the bad smell of mouth. It is also used for treatment of bronchitis, diabetes, dysentery, asthma, hypertension, rheumatism and malarial fever. The methanol, acetonitrile, chloroform and n-hexane-soluble extracts of *A. aspera* herb have been investigated for *in vitro* antimicrobial activity against *Escherichia coli, Salmonella typhi, Staphylococcus aureus* and *Bacillus subtilis*. These extracts have been reported to inhibit the growth of *E. coli, S. typhi, S.aureus* and *B. subtilis* at varying levels. The extracts of *A. aspera* plant consist of several potential bio-chemicals, such as glycone, ecdysterones, triterpenoid saponins, long chain alcohols, oleanolic acids, etc. and possess many therapeutic properties, such as anti-microbial, anti-asthmatic, anti-inflammatory, anti-oxidant, anti-arthritic, and wound healing (Naidu *et al.*, 2006).

अपामार्गोऽप मार्ष्टु क्षेत्रियं शपथश्च यः।
अपाह यातुधानीरप सर्वा अराय्यः।।
(अथर्ववेद 4.18.7)

Apāmārgo,pa mārṣtu kṣetriyaṁ śapathaśca yaḥ.
Apāh yātudhānīrapa sarvā arāyyaḥ.
(Atharvaveda 4.18.7)

[May this Apāmārga (*Apāmārga*) remove (*apamārṣtu*) the infectious diseases (tuberculosis, leprosy, etc.) (*kṣetriyaṁ*) and (ca) remove the diseases which (*yaḥ*) are suffering from anger (*śapathaḥ*). It must (*ahaṁ*) remove (*apa*) painful diseases (*yātudhāni*) and remove (*apa*) all (*sarvāḥ*) sleeplessness (*arāyyaḥ*)]. That is, the ailment sickness makes the body health-free for all types of patients.

Scientific Explanation- Apāmārga acts against infections occurred locally as well as ailment in other parts of body. The medicinal properties found in the plant have been explained earlier.

2. Ajaśṛṅgī (Utaran, trellis-vine) (*Pergularia daemia*)

Ajaśṛṅgī belongs to the family *Asclepiadaceae*. Its fruits look like 'goat's horn'; therefore, it is called *Aja* meaning 'goat' and *Śringi* meaning 'horns bearer'. It is found in India, Pakistan, Afghanistan, Burma, SriLanka, Arabia and Egypt along the roadsides, fringes of riparian forests and in woodland.

त्वया वयमप्सरसो गन्धर्वांश्चातयामहे।
अजशृङ्गयज रक्ष सर्वान् गन्धेन नाशय।।
(अथर्ववेद 7.37.2)

Tvayā vayamapsaraso gandharvānścātayāmahe.
Ajaśṛṅgayaja rakṣa sarvān gandhen nāśaya.
(Atharvaveda 7.37.2)

[O ! Ajaśṛṅgī (*Ajaśṛṅgī*) through you (*tvayā*), we destroy (*cātayāmahe*) the vibrating germs (*gandharvān*) who moving in the water (*apsarasā*). Ajaśṛṅgī ! Remove these germs (*aja*), destroy (*nāśaya*) all the Kṛmis (*sarvān rakṣa*) with your smell (*gandhen*)]

Scientific Explanation- Several chemical, such as flavonoids, sterols, terpenoids and cardenolides, have been screened from different parts of Ajaśṛṅgī plant, e.g. leaves, stems, roots, seeds and fruit. It is used for the treatment of diarrhoea of infants, malarial fevers, toothache and common colds. The leaves and young stems possess analgesic, anti-diabetic, anthelmintic, hepatoprotective, antifertility and laxative properties. Decoction of roots is used for cure of muscular pain, rheumatism, asthma, arthritis, and venereal diseases. Its leaf extract also shows antioxidant activity. This plant also possesses antiviral properties. Methanol-soluble extract of aerial parts bears potential properties against rhinovirus, poliovirus, influenza virus, herpes simplex virus and many other viruses.

Figure 8.2. Ajaśṛṅgī fruit resembles a goat's horn.

Besides, Ajaśṛṅgī plant extracts have been found to possess a wide spectrum of potential activity against some Gram-positive bacteria (*Staphylococcus aureus, Staph. pyogenes,* and *Bacillus substilis*) and Gram-negative bacteria (*Escherichia coli, Vibrio harveyi, Pseudomonas aeruginosa, Aeromonas hydrophila* and *Klebsiella pneumoniae*). Though there are many microbial diseases and several medicinal plants used for its treatment yet only two human diseases, tuberculosis and leprosy, are being dealt with in this chapter with reference to Vedic hymns.

OCCURRENCE AND PREVENTION OF YAKṢMA

Tuberculosis (Kṣaya, Tapedic, Yakṣmā) has been a highly infectious disease since Vedic period. Tuberculosis eradicating hymns (Yakṣmanāśan Sūtra) have been seriously dealt with in Atharvaveda (3.31.1-11) and have been desired to be eradicated from the diseased persons. In Vedas, tuberculosis has been described at many places.

वि देवा जरसावृतन वि त्वमग्ने अरात्या।
व्य१हं सर्वेण पाप्मना वि यक्ष्मेण समायुषा।।

(अथर्ववेद 3.31.1)

Vi devā jarasāvṛtana vi tvamagne arātyā.
Vya,haṁ sarven pāpmanā vi yakṣmen samāyuṣā.

(Atharvaveda 3.31.1)

[Gods (*Devā*) are not affected even in old age (*vi jarsāvṛtana*). O! Agnideva (*Agne*) you (*tvaṁ*) should keep it away from kindness and enmity (*vi arātyā*). I (*ahaṁ*) should be free from all (*vi sarven*) painful sins (*pāpmanā*) and tuberculosis (*vi yakṣmen*) and get longevity (*samāyuṣā*)]

Scientific Explanation- This hymn indicates that persons become diseased in old age but the Gods and Goddess are not affected by any ailments including tuberculosis even in old age because Agni Deva (the great knowledgeable and powerful king of all Devas) have blessed them. Secondly, tuberculosis has the present in human societies since the Vedic period. Therefore, our Ṛśis have mentioned it at many places and prayed the medicinal herbs for its cure.

Tuberculosis is caused by *Mycobacterium tuberculosis*. Tuberculosis is one of the top 10 causes of global death due to any bacterial infection. However, there are large numbers of medicinal plants that have been described in the Vedas. These plants bear antimicrobial, immuno-modulatory, anti-viral, antioxidant and many more properties. However, there exist several harmful human pathogenic microbes in nature and they are also associated with several ailments. For example, tuberculosis and leprosy are known since the Vedic period. These two diseases are caused through infection of two different species of *Mycobacterium*. Tuberculosis is caused by *Mycobacterium tuberculosis* and leprosy by *Mycobacterium leprae*. *Mycobacterium* is a Gram-positive, spongy, and slow-growing bacterium. Its cell wall is very complex, due to the presence of mycolic acid, cord factor and Wax–D that cause slow growth, resistance to medicines and prolong survival.

Around 460 BC, Hippocrates identified tuberculosis as a disease called 'white death'. It is known that tuberculosis is a deadly infectious disease caused by *M. tuberculosis*. The patient dies due to lack of proper treatment. In the human body, this bacterium enters through many sources, affects the lungs and causes tuberculosis. The tuberculosis patient coughs with excessive phlegm and feel tired with mild fever. Evidence of tuberculosis in Egypt was obtained from Mummies in around 2400 BC, but thousands of years ago in India, people suffered from tuberculosis.

Table 8.1: Cases of pulmonary and extra-pulmonary tuberculosis.

Types of tuberculosis	Cases (%)
Pulmonary tuberculosis[1]	50-52
Extra-pulmonary tuberculosis[1,2,3]	15-20 (due to immune dysfunction)
1. Musculo-skeletal tuberculosis	19 (of extra-pulmonary tuberculosis)
2. Bone and joints tuberculosis	8 (of extra-pulmonary tuberculosis)
3. Spinal tuberculosis	40 (of extra-pulmonary tuberculosis)
4. Buttock tuberculosis	25 (of extra-pulmonary tuberculosis)
5. Knee tuberculosis[4]	8 (of extra-pulmonary tuberculosis)
6. Immunocompromised patients[4]	15–20 (of extra-pulmonary tuberculosis)
7. Gastrointestinal (GI)tuberculosis[5]	
Oesophageal tuberculosis	0-2.0 (of GI tuberculosis)
Gastric tuberculosis	0.4-2.0 (of GI tuberculosis)
Duodenal tuberculosis	2-2.5 (of GI tuberculosis)
Jejunal tuberculosis	64 (of GI tuberculosis)
Colorectal tuberculosis	8-10 (of GI tuberculosis)

[1]Adler (2009), [2]Baydur (1977), [3]Sharma and Mohan (2015), [4]Lidder *et al.* (2009), [5]Uma Devi *et al.* (2014).

Tuberculosis is a contagious disease whose presence in the world had been first documented in India 3500 years ago and in China 2200 years ago according to written records. Tuberculosis accounts 25 percent of all death globally. Every year, approximately 2 million people suffer from this disease and 25 percent people of all cases die of tuberculosis only. India is the largest country in the world after China, where 26 percent people die of tuberculosis, followed by China and Southern Africa. There are two types of tuberculosis viz., pulmonary tuberculosis and extra-pulmonary tuberculosis (miliary tuberculosis). In pulmonary tuberculosis, the cells of *M. tuberculosis* are seen in the cells of the pleura; but in pulmonary tuberculosis, these bacterial cells appear in all parts and all organs of the body and cause many disorders. There is about 10-25% extra-pulmonary tuberculosis in the world. In 2016, the number of new pulmonary tuberculosis patients increased by about 15 percent in India. Pulmonary tuberculosis is not an infectious disease. Therefore, there is no phlegm and fever in this disease. The reasons for the rapid expansion of tuberculosis are smoking, unbalanced diet, filth, immune dysfunction, diabetes and AIDS. The prevalence of pulmonary and extra-pulmonary tuberculosis is given in Table 1.

Indian sages have mentioned the prevalence of pulmonary and extra-pulmonary tuberculosis in the Atharvaveda (2.33.1–2.33.7) over thousands of years ago. When cells of *M. tuberculosis* spread the tuberculosis by infecting the lungs via nasal ducts at the time of inhalation of air containing droplets from cough and sneeze of other sick individuals, it is called primary tuberculosis. The infectious dose is 1–200 bacilli. However, a single droplet contains 1–4000 bacilli. The bacilli reach the alveoli where the resident macrophages engulf these bacilli. In the primary tuberculosis, lymphatic nodes are also affected. The primary lesion can be seen in the affected pulmonary tuberculosis. Primary tuberculosis is cured automatically in most people. However, secondary or reactivated tuberculosis is different from primary tuberculosis. Secondary tuberculosis gradually develops in people affected by primary tuberculosis or due to reactivation of pre-tuberculosis spots. Symptoms of secondary tuberculosis are the excessive erosion of pulmonary tissue resulting from the reactivation of the tuberculous bacterial cells and the reaction of their secretions by the immune system. The cavity lesion usually occurs in the upper part of the pleura due to the internal reaction. Small-scale lesions in the lower parts of the pulmonary are called miliary lesions (Figure 8.2).

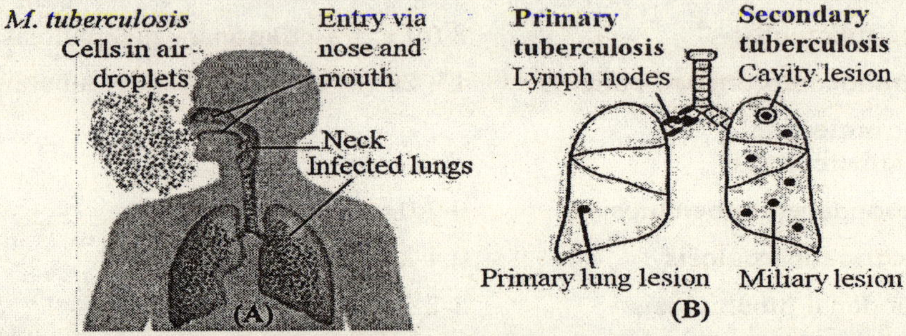

Figure 8.2: Spread of cells of *Mycobacterium tuberculosis* (A); pulmonary and miliary tuberculosis (B).

1. Tuberculosis of Upper Part of Neck

Tuberculosis is an infectious disease that spreads from infected or sick persons to the healthy people. The Ṛgveda (10.163.1) and the Atharvaveda (2.33.1) talk of annihilation of tuberculosis from the upper part of the neck.

अक्षीभ्यां ते नासिकाभ्यां कर्णाभ्यां छुबुकादधि।
यक्ष्मं शीर्षण्यं मस्तिष्काज्जिह्वाया वि वृहामि ते।।
(अथर्ववेद 2.33.1)

Akṣībhyām te nasikābhyām karṇābhyām chubukādadhi.
Yakṣamaṁ śirṣanyaṁ maṣtiṣkājjihvāyā vi vṛhāmi te.
(Atharvaveda 2.33.1)

[Out of your (*te*) two eyes (*akṣībhyāṁ*), nostrils (*nāsikābhyāṁ*), ears (*karṇābhyāṁ*) and out of your (*te*) chins (*chubukā dadhi*), brain (*mastiska*) and tongue (*jihvāyām*), I root out those (*te*) wasting disease (*vṛhāmi*) tuberculosis (*yakṣamaṁ*) seated in your head (*śirsaṣyaṁ*)]

Scientific Explanation- In the above hymn, the destruction of the tuberculosis occurring in the upper part of the neck like eyes, nose, ears, tongue, chin and brain has been mentioned. According to modern medical science, the prevalence of pulmonary (lungs) tuberculosis is very common and it is a global problem. Tuberculosis is found in human eyes, nose, ears, brain and tongue in many countries (Baydur, 1977). Approximately, 70 percent of the people are affected by pulmonary tuberculosis per annum and 30 percent of people with extra-pulmonary tuberculosis. Due to lack of proper treatment, an additional 10-15% people are affected by this disease. *Mycobacterium tuberculosis* cells causing tuberculosis reach the eyes through the air or circulatory system and affect the cornea and lens. As a result, the eyes of such patient become red and they seen blurred with black spots. Eye tuberculosis can occur in people of any age. Therefore, such individuals should take regular medicines along with nutritious diet. People suffering from pulmonary tuberculosis are more likely to have nasal tuberculosis as a secondary disease. Tuberculosis of nose, nasopharynx and para nasal sinus is very rare even in those countries which have high prevalence of pulmonary tuberculosis. Nasal tuberculosis is a rare disease that appears without symptoms in the initial stage and such patients do not experience any difficulty. Hence, nasal tuberculosis is asymptomatic disease. The outer membrane of the nose is covered with a layer of the cells of mycobacteria (Dixit and Dave, 2008).

Ear tuberculosis is a rare disease but the sufferers do not experience pain. Granulomatous disease occurs in the ear due to the proximity of the middle cell to the bacterial cells. This disease may be localised in the middle ear. As a result, in patients with attenuation of hearing loss, nasal tubes are also blocked (Lmekki and Lecanu, 2013). Meningeal (brain) tuberculosis is caused by infection of air-borne cells of *Mycobacterium tuberculosis* that also spread to other parts of the body through blood stream. When the cells of *Mycobacterium tuberculosis* cause meningitis, pain and fever by malignant meninges of the brain (the outer membrane that covers the brain), it is called tubercular meningitis or brain fever (Saleh *et al.*, 2014). The tongue tuberculosis is also a rare disease. Traumatic lesions are seen on the tongue of the afflicted persons. A biopsy of these spots is not cancerous, but tuberculous bacteria in the mucus can be visualized with the help of a microscope (Furugen *et al.*, 2009).

2. Tuberculosis of Neck, Arms, shoulders, Chest and Joints

Due to keeping the body covered, people sweat profusely. As a result, some elements get accumulated on the skin along with sweat in such parts of the body, due to which the number of microorganisms increases. Generally, these bacteria are not harmful. Those microorganisms are likely to contain tuberculosis bacteria. The Ṛgveda (10.163.3) and the Atharvaveda (2.33.2) describe to eliminate all diseases of the arms, bones and joints.

ग्रीवाभ्यस्त उष्णिहाभ्यः कीकसाभ्यो अनूक्यात् ।
यक्ष्मं दोषण्यमंसाभ्यां बाहुभ्यामं वि वृहामि ते ।।

(ऋग्वेद 10.163.2)

Grīvābhyasta uṣnihābhayah kīkasābhyo anūkyāt.

Yakṣmaṁ doṣanyamansābhyāṁ bāhubhyāmaṁ vi vṛhāmi te.

(Ṛgveda 10.163.2)

[I pluck off (*vṛhāmi*) your (*te*) tuberculosis disease (*yakṣmaṁ*) from your two muscles of neck (*grīvābhyāṁ*), veins of nape (*usṇihābhyaṁ*)], ribs of chest (*kīkasābhyaṁ*), joints of spines (*anūkyāta*), shoulders (*ansābhyāṁ*) and arms (*bāhubhyāṁ*)]

Scientific Explanation- Due to infection and ill effects of *Mycobacterium tuberculosis*, there develops swelling in the glands in the lower side of the neck, which is called neck or cervical tuberculosis. In about 80% cases of bone and joints tuberculosis, spines, hips and knee are the most suitable sites that are infected by the *Mycobacterium tuberculosis*. Consequently, joints become swollen and painful. Cells of the bacterium can be seen when the inflamed tissues are cultured or Gram-stain. After infection, cells of *M. tuberculosis* spread throughout the body via the cardiovascular system. Hence, these cells get settled there after affecting the blood vessels. As a result, there develops pain due to inflammation on the end of the blood vessel. This type of disease is called arterial tuberculosis.

In bone tuberculosis, *Mycobacterium tuberculosis* cells are transmitted after infection from air to the bones, joints and spines through the blood vessels. Therefore, there develops stiffness, swelling and severe pain in the backbone, long bones and joints, causing bone deformities. Rheumatism and stiffness develop in the joints, and sometimes abscess oozes out from these places. The badly affected bone becomes crooked. It is known as tuberculous spondylitis or Pott's disease. Lover thoracic and upper lumber vertebrae are the areas of the spines that are most severely affected. In such a condition, harmful spots also appear in the spinal cord. Due to HIV / AIDS epidemic in developing countries, the number of patients of bone tuberculosis is increasing gradually. Tuberculosis of the arms and shoulders is also similar to that of bone tuberculosis. Moreover, the affected area has pain. *Mycobacterium tuberculosis* also causes musculoskeletal tuberculosis in 19% cases of extra pulmonary tuberculosis.

3. Tuberculosis of Heart, Lungs, Intestines and Kidneys

The middle part of body, below shoulders and above pelvic girdle, is very important because of the presence of all vital organs. The heart, lungs, liver, intestine and kidneys functions in well coordinated ways. Failure of any organs, due to microbial infections such as tuberculosis, certainly reduces the life span, even casing the death of infected persons. Our Vedic Ṛṣis desired for eradication of tuberculosis from these organs.

हृदयात्ते परि क्लोम्नो हलीक्ष्णात्पार्श्वाभ्याम्।

यक्ष्मं मतस्नाभ्यां प्लीह्नो यक्तनक्ते वि वृहामसि।।

(अथर्ववेद 2.33.3)

Hṛdayātte pari klomne halīkṣṇātpārśvābhyām.

Yakṣmaṁ mastanābhyāṁ plīhno yaktanakte vi vṛhāmasi.

(Atharvaveda 2.33.3)

[I destroy (*vṛhāmi*) and remove the wasting disease tuberculosis (*yakṣmaṁ*) from your heart (*hṛdaya*), from your right lungs (*pari kloma*), from your intestine (*halīkṣṇa*), from your two sides (*pārśva*), from your two kidneys (*matasna*), from your spleen (*plīhā*), and from your liver (*yaktanak*)]

Scientific Explanation- *Mycobacterium tuberculosis* has the ability to infect mostly every body organ in spite of several advancements in medical science. However, *Mycobacterium tuberculosis* rarely infects the heart. But if it infects the heart it does as the isolated pericarditis resulting in myopericarditis. Though the isolated tubercular myocarditis is very rare disease yet it suddenly causes cardiac death or 'congestive cardiac failure'. Since tuberculosis has long latent phase, it is difficult to diagnose in the heart and other body organs in an early stage. Generally, myocarditis is diagnosed at post-mortem stage. *Mycobacterium tuberculosis* can be diagnosed by acid-fast and Ziehl-Neelsen staining of the biopsy of surrounding lymphatic tissue or lymph nodes based on positive staining results and presence of giant cells that invade the cardiac myocytes later on (Cowley *et al*., 2017).

Similarly, tuberculosis of lungs, intestine, spleen and kidney (renal tuberculosis) and urinary tract is also troublesome and fatal. Tuberculosis of the urinary tract can be diagnosed on the basis of presence of pyuria and culture of *Mycobacterium tuberculosis* on growth medium. In the advanced stage, tuberculosis can be confirmed by seeing bladder fibrosis, ureteric strictures and calyceal distortion done through urography. Hence, the above hymn confirms the presence of cardial and renal tuberculosis since the Vedic period (Daher *et al*., 2013).

4. Abdominal Tuberculosis

Ṛgveda 10.163.3) and Atharvaveda (2.33.4) describe the destruction of causal agent of tuberculosis from places like stomach, intestines, abdomen, flanks, mesenteric layer, navel, guts, etc. In the above mentioned sites, these germs live for long time and cause tuberculosis in the immuno-compromised individuals.

आन्त्रेभ्यस्ते गुदाभ्यो वनिष्ठोरुदरादधि।
यक्ष्मै कुक्षिभ्यां प्लाशेर्नाभ्या विवृहामि ते।।

(अथर्ववेद 2.33.4)

Āntrebhyaste gudābhyo vaniṣṭhorudarādadhi.
Yakṣmai kukṣibhyāṁ plaśernābhyā vivṛhāmi te.

(Atharvaveda 2.33.4)

[I puck off (*vivṛhāmi*) your (*te*) wasting disease (*yakṣmai*) from your intestines (*āntrebhyaḥ*), guts (*gudābhyo*), your bowels (*vaniṣṭho*), your abdomen (*udaraḥ*), your two flanks (*kukṣibhyāṁ*), your mesentery (*plāśeḥ*), and your naval (*nābhyā*)]

Scientific Explanation- The intestine and its adjacent organs are the main places of extra-pulmonary tuberculosis. Therefore, removal of tuberculosis, from all the sites where the causal agent survives and spreads the disease, has been described. The abdominal tuberculosis [tuberculosis of gastrointestinal (GI) system] involves the various parts, such as oesophagus, stomach, duodenum, jejunum, intestines, mesenteric layer, colorectal area, navel and guts. More than 8.5 million people receive infection and 1.3 million deaths occur every year. The mechanism of development of tuberculosis is similar to that of above symptoms.

Peritoneal tuberculosis is of three types: *(i)* wet sciatic type (has free or loculated fluid in abdomen), *(ii)* fibrotic type (involves mesentery, it is less common), and *(iii)* dry plastic type (characterised by fibrous peritoneal reaction, peritoneal nodules and presence of adhesion) (Uma Debi *et al.*, 2014). Tuberculosis occurring in different parts of the gastrointestinal system is summarized (see Table 8.1).

5. Tuberculosis of Thighs, Hips, Knees and Feet

The Rig Veda (10.163.4) and the Atharva Veda (2.33.5) describe tuberculosis from the lower part of abdomen of human body and its removal.

उरुभ्यां ते अष्ठीवद्भ्यां पार्ष्णिभ्यां प्रपदाभ्याम्।
यक्ष्मं भसद्यं श्रोणिभ्यां भासदं भंससो वि वृहामि ते।।
(अथर्ववेद 2.33.5)

Urubhyāṁ te aṣṭhivadbhyaṁ pārṣṇibhyāṁ prapadābhyām.
Yakṣmaṁ bhasadyaṁ śroṇibhyāṁ bhāsadaṁ bhaṅsaso vi vṛhāmi te.
(Atharvaveda 2.33.5)

[I take out (*vṛhāmi*) your (*te*) wasting disease (*yakṣmaṁ*) from your two thighs (*urubhyāṁ*), two knees (*aṣṭhibhyāṁ*), two heals (*pārṣṇibhyāṁ*), forefeet (*prapadābhyāṁ*), hips (*bhāsadat*), loins or waist (*śroṇibhyāṁ*) and around anus (*bhaṅsasaḥ*)]

Scientific Explanation- Thigh tuberculosis is a rare disease which is caused by infection of bacterial cells in the pubic area. After affecting the pubic tissue, the mycobacterial cells develop tubercular lytic lesions by causing stiffness in tissue around the thighs muscles. Consequently, there develops swelling and pain in the affected areas. Similarly, knee tuberculosis is also a painful disease. In about 8 percent adults having extra-pulmonary tuberculosis, *Mycobacterium tuberculosis* cells cause knee tuberculosis after reaching the cells to knees through the spinal cord and buttocks. Knee tuberculosis occurs in about 8 percent of individuals due to immune dysfunction (Lidder *et al.*, 2009). Hip tuberculosis is the second class of tuberculosis after spinal tuberculosis. Therefore, a large number of patients of hip tuberculosis are found throughout the globe. The hip tuberculosis is not identifiable in the initial state; therefore, getting the complete information of it is delayed. Moreover, this disease can be identified by using the modern methods on hip joints. Approximately, 15-20 percent of the tuberculosis has been found in the musculoskeletal system. The sufferers feel buttock pain; therefore, the patient cannot travel. The joint space is also reduced in such conditions.

Paw and ankle tuberculosis is a type of rare skeletal tuberculosis. In the initial stage, this disease spreads from the bones to the paws, ankles and joints resulting in stiffness in the feet. It is identified on the basis of the presence of granular tissue in biopsies as the *M. tuberculosis* is difficult to culture (Dhillon and Nag, 2002). Vertebral or spine tuberculosis causes acute back pain; the patient may also become bedridden if not treated effectively. The cells of *M. tuberculosis* reach the blood stream from the lungs and spread from here to the spines. Disorganization also occurs due to thawing of bones of the spines. People of every age group can be a victim of spinal tuberculosis. Symptoms of vertebral tuberculosis are backache, fever, vomiting, weakness, weight loss, acute and unbearable pain at night, muscular stretching, inflammation in spinal cord, and respiratory obstruction.

Rectal or anal tuberculosis is a very rare disease. About one percent of people suffering from gastrointestinal tuberculosis suffer from rectal tuberculosis. Identification of this disease is possible only through biopsy and culture of *Mycobacterium tuberculosis*. This tuberculosis occurs most likely in ileocecal region of the gastrointestinal tract. There are least chances of this disease in jejunum and appendix. Symptoms of anal tuberculosis are– hemorrhagic bumps and fissure or fistula. There is a possibility for presence of *Mycobacterium tuberculosis* in the persons suffering from fissure or fistula.

6. Tuberculosis of Bone, Marrow, Fingers

Bone tuberculosis occurs when anybody contracts *Mycobacterium tuberculosis* from the infected ones. Then it spreads from lungs to the other parts of body. Generally, bacterial inoculum of tuberculosis disseminates from person to persons via air droplets through coughing, sneezing or loud talking. Thereafter, it spread through the blood vessels from the lungs/ lymph nodes to the bones, spines or joints of the body. Spines are most severely affected by the *Mycobacterium tuberculosis*. Since the middle portions of the long bones and the vertebrae have rich vascular supply, the bone TB starts to develop from here. The patients of bone TB show some symptoms like severe back pain, stiffness, swelling and abscesses formation. The various parts of body like bones, marrow, veins, arteries, hands, fingers and fingernails have been mentioned to have tuberculosis in the Atharvaveda (2.33.6).

अस्थिभ्यस्ते मज्जभ्यः स्नावभ्यो धमनिभ्यः।
यक्ष्मं पाणिभ्यामगुंलिभ्यो नखेभ्यो वि वृहामि ते।।
(अथर्ववेद 2.33.6)

Asthibhyaste majjabhyaḥ snāvabhyo dhamnibhyaḥ.
Yakṣmaṁ pāṇibhyāmangulibhyo nakhebhyo vi vṛhāmi te.
(Atharvaveda 2.33.6)

[Out of your bones (*asthibhyaḥ*), out of your marrow (*majjābhyaḥ*), out of your sinews (*snāvabhyaḥ*), out of your blood vessels (*dhamanibhyaḥ*), out of your two hands (*pāṇibhyāḥ*), out of your fingers (*angulibhyaḥ*) and out of your nails (*nakhebhyaḥ*), I puck off your (*te*) wasting those diseases (*yakṣmaṁ vivṛhāmi*)]

Scientific Explanation- Bone pulmonary is an extra-pulmonary that can occur in the bones of any immune-compromised persons of any age. It is also known as 'Pott disease'. The cells of the *Mycobacterium tuberculosis* infect the blood through the air flow with the blood stream, affect the lungs and reach the lymph glands, spinal cord, bones and joints. Bone tuberculosis begins especially with the long bones and middle blood vessels in the vertebrae. Although bone tuberculosis is a rare disease yet its prevalence has increased in the developing countries as a result of increase in decreased immunity in HIV/AIDS patients due to certain drugs. Diagnosis of bone tuberculosis is difficult, but making free the untreated patients may lead to other problems. Symptoms of individuals suffering from bone tuberculosis are constant back pain, pimples, swelling and stiffness. In addition, such patients may also have distorted bones, paralysis, fractures and nerve complications.

Bone marrow (BM) tuberculosis is also an extra-pulmonary disease occurring in immune-compromised persons. BM tuberculosis can be studied on the basis of other tests by isolating bacterial cells from bone marrow on culture medium. BM tuberculosis is also a progressive disease due to which the death rate increases. Therefore, prompt action should be taken to treat this disease carefully. Moreover, the tuberculosis of central nervous system (CNS) is a malignant pulmonary disease that is commonly found in developed countries because it has a high mortality rate. CNS tuberculosis occurs in 1 percent individuals having pulmonary tuberculosis and 5-10 percent persons suffering from extra-pulmonary disease. Tubercular bacilli are found in the CNS. The five countries namely China, Indonesia, Nigeria South Africa and India have the highest number of CNS tuberculosis. There are many reasons for tubercular bacilli in the CNS, such as age, HIV/AIDS infection, malnutrition, alcoholism, cancer, use of drugs decreasing immunity of the body.

The possibility of artery tuberculosis and vein tuberculosis is very high in patients with 'deep-thrombosis'; because in such patients, the synthesis of anti-inflammatory cytokines and anticoagulant proteins is low and fibrogen levels are increased that help in producing these diseases. Therefore, equilibrium can be established between 'deep-thrombosis' and *Mycobacterium tuberculosis*. Hand tuberculosis is also an extra-pulmonary disease. The reason for the increase in the number of hand tuberculosis patients and the interest of the researchers on them is the increase in the number of migrants, the increase in age, and increases in numbers of immune-compromised patients. There are many types of hand tuberculosis namely cutaneous lesions, arthritis, tenosynovitis, bursitis, osteomyelitis, tuberculous hypersensitive reaction.

Metacarpals of the little finger are more affected by tuberculosis. At this place, there is pain, inflammation and fluid secretion in the form of pus, due to which there develops acute pain in the hands. Therefore, the pus is thrown out of fingers. Besides, this disease also occurs in the wrists of hands. Cells of *Mycobacterium tuberculosis* can be observed in a clinical biopsy. Due to this disease, wrists become stiff. Hence, the pus is removed from Inside the wrist. A good diagnosis of wrist tuberculosis is possible only after the quick identification of this disease. Nail tuberculosis occurs in very few individuals. In such patients, there is swelling and pain between the fingernail and the skin. Putrefaction and pus are produced due to bacterial infection in the inflamed area.

7. Tuberculosis in All Parts of the Body and its Prevention

There is no barrier for the growth and infection of *Mycobacterium tuberculosis*. Any or all parts of body can be infected and hence tuberculosis may occur. Atharvaveda (2.33.7) has mentioned the prevention of tuberculosis from all the external and internal organs of the body.

अंगे अंगे लोम्निलोम्नि यस्ते पर्वणिपर्वणि ।
यक्ष्मं त्वचस्यं ते वयं कश्यपस्य वीबर्हेण विश्वन्चं वि वृहामसि ।।

(अथर्ववेद 2.33.7)

Aṅge aṅge lomnilomni yaste parvaṇiparvaṇi.

Yakṣmaṁ tvacasyaṁ te vayaṁ kaśyapasya vībarheṇ viśvañcaṁ vi vṛhāmasi.

(Atharvaveda 2.33.7)

[Whatever tuberculosis (*yakṣmaṁ*) occurred in your (*te*) each and every organs (*aṅge aṅge*), each and every follicle (*lomni lomni*), each and every joints (*parvaṇi parvaṇi*) that wasting diseases I pluck off (*yakṣmaṁ vi vṛhāmi*). We (*vayaṁ*) pluck off (*vībarhen*) the diseases (*yakṣmaṁ*) appearing on your (*te*) skin (*tvacasyaṁ*), eyes etc. (*viśvañcaṁ*) by the person having knowledge of drugs (*kaśyapasya*), i.e. person knowing drugs)]

Scientific Explanation- In this hymn, the idea of destroying tuberculosis of all the organs of the body, follicles, joints and skin has been expressed by the Rishis. The above hymns talks of the prevalence and destruction of the tuberculosis in the all body organs. But this hymn is a summary of all types of tuberculosis arising in the body. The body of all vertebrates consists of bones of many shapes and sizes. All the bones are linked together by skeletal muscles. The middle of the bones is hollow called the marrow. Blood is produced in the marrow itself. Nerves travel via the muscles and skin throughout the body. *Mycobacterium tuberculosis* cells produce tuberculosis by travelling through the blood and nervous system throughout the body, affecting any organs, follicles or skin. Therefore, the hymn describing 'Aṅge aṅge lomni lomni' for the tuberculosis occurring on/in all parts of the body proves to be true.

MANAGEMENT OF YAKṢMA (TUBERCULOSIS)

Atharvaveda describes the use of only one plant for treatment of one disease with hymn. Some special hymn are recitation to praise the medicinal herbs, for example Kuṣṭhā (*Costus speciosus* Syn. *Saussurea lappa*), Apāmārga (*Achyranthus aspera*), Rohini, Jangiṇa (*Oroxylum indicum*), etc. Recitation of the hymns of Atharvaveda (2.33) along with using some important the medicinal herbs like Kuṣṭhā (*C. speciosus*) (Atharvaveda 5.4.9)/ Cipudru (*Pinus longifolia*) (Atharvaveda 6.127.1,3) and Arundhati (*Sida cordifolia*) (Atharvaveda 6.59.2), has been found an effective cure of Yakṣmā. Anjana is capable of removing the Yakṣmā from the limbs of human (Atharvaveda 21.44.1-2). In additions, there are some divine powers that eradicate Yakṣmā, such as Sun, Āditya, Agni, Vāyu and Sāviti (Atharvaveda 4.25.5; 5.29.13; 9.8.22). Yakṣmā has also been prevented from the infection by the causal agent by joint action of recitation of hymn, God blessings and use of medicinal plants. Moreover, combination of Varuna (*Crataeva nurula*) and Satāvara protects Yakṣmā. Besides, the scent of burning of dried Guggula (*Commiphora wightii*) gum removes Yakṣmā from the patients (Atharvaveda 6.85; 19.36; 19.38). A hymn of Atharvaveda (2.33) is very popular and effective in cure of Yakṣmā. Further, it has been wished in the Vedas that the main cause of all types of Yakṣmā, in the form of venom, be discharged with urine of the patients (Atharvaveda 9.8.10) (Prasad, 2002). This section describes about tuberculosis (Yakṣmā) in detail with scientific explanation.

1. Eradication of Yakṣmā by Guggul Fumes

Tuberculosis is a terrible disease caused by *Mycobacterium tuberculosis*. Due to pathogenic microbial infection, the lungs of individuals are more affected. In India, from the ancient times (around 3500 BCE), tuberculosis was treated by using the smoke of Guggula (Atharvaveda 19.38.1). Guggala gum is put over a fire of burning coal or cow dung, and a dense smoke emanating from Guggula is spread everywhere in the house and over the affected persons. By doing so, the microorganisms that affect the person and present in home die; also the evil spirits (Piśāca) run away from the house and also from the affected persons.

न तं यक्ष्मा अरुन्धते नैनं शपथो अश्नुते।
यं भेषजस्य गुल्गुलोः सुरभिर्गन्धो अश्नुते।।

(अथर्ववेद 19.38.1)

Na taṁ yakṣmā arundhate nainaṁ śapatho aśnute.

Yaṁ bheṣajasya gulguloḥ surabhirgandho aśnute.

(Atharvaveda 19.38.1)

[Wasting tuberculosis disease (*yakṣmaḥ*) obstruct you (*taṁ*) not (*na arundhate*), nor the cures affect him (*śapathaḥ*), whom (*yaṁ*) the soothing fragrance (*surabhiḥ gandhaḥ*) of the healing bdellium drug (*bheṣajasya gulguloḥ*) penetrates (*aśnute*)].

Scientific Explanation- No person's curse and tuberculosis have any effect on the individuals who inhale the best aroma of Guggula i.e. Indian bdellium (*Commiphora wightii*). According to plant science, Indian bdellium is a shrub or small tree of the family Burseraceae (class Magnoliopsida), which is often known as Guggula, Guggala, Gugglu and Indian bdellium. Generally, Guggala grows in a semi-arid climate in North India. A fragrant product is extracted from the bark of Guggul plants, which is a resin like gum called 'Guggul gum' or 'Guggala gum'. It contains moisture (6.7%), volatile oil (0.8%), resin (62%), bum (28.7%) and many insoluble substances (2.8%). However, over 100 metabolites have been extracted from various parts of this plant, such as leaf, stem, root and fruits. The most beneficial and effective bio-agents of this plant is Guggulsterone. Moreover, quinic acid and myo-inositol are also found in the leaves and fruits of this plant. The 'Plant Board' has started a project to cultivate Guggul plant in 500-800 hectares of land in Kutch district of Gujarat (India). The chemical structure of the Guggula plant, the Guggula gum and the guggulsterone, are given in Figure 8.3.

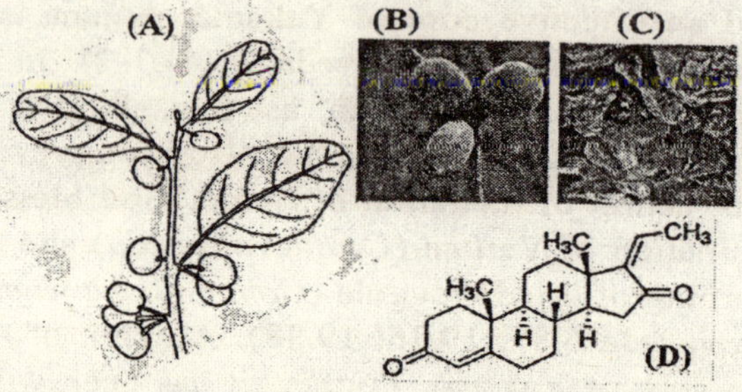

Figure 8.3: The apical part of the Indian bdellium (Guggula) plant showing leaves and fruits **(A)**, the Guggula gum **(B)** and the chemical structure of Guggulsterone **(C)**.

The main bioactive compound of Guggula gum is guggulsterone. In recent years, Guggul is used for reducing obesity, cholesterol, hypertension, arthritis and prevention of peptic ulcer, besides being used as ant-inflammatory, hepatoprotective, muscle relaxing drug (Sairkar *et al.*, 2016). Guggula is beneficial for heart, liver, kidney and skin. On the other hand, Guggula possesses antibacterial properties also and inhibits the growth of *Mycobacterium tuberculosis, Escherichia coli, Staphylococcus intermedicus, Streptococcus pyrogenes* and *Burkholderia* species. The antibacterial activity of Guggula gum extracts (prepared in methanol and dichloromethane) against six Gram-positive and four Gram-negative bacteria was carried out. It was found that that Gram-positive bacteria viz., *Enterococcus faecalis, Micrococcus luteus* and *Bacillus megaterium* were very sensitive to gum extract. But Guggula gum extract slightly inhibited the growth of Gram-negative bacteria. Moreover, some bacteria are unaffected by the Guggula gum extract. There are many antimicrobial compounds present in Guggula gum but 5(1-methyl, 1-amino ethyl)-5-methyl-2-octanone is one of the effective potential identified antibacterial bioagents (Ishnava *et al.* 2010).

ERADICATION OF MICROBES BY VACA (VACA OR BACA)

Vaca (*Acorus calamus,* Syn. *Acorus odoratus*) is known by several names, such as sweet flag, sweet root, sweet myrtle, sweet cane, sweet rush, sweet sedge, flag root, myrtle flag, myrtle grass, and myrtle sedge. *Acorus calamus* belongs to the family *Araceae* (= *Adoraceae*). It is a perennial herbaceous plant having leaves with are brown, white and spongy scars. It bears slender roots and few distichously branched alternate leaves. The plant has a long indefinite branched cylindrical, smooth, pinkish or pale green rhizome of about 3.4 inches in diameter. *Acorus calamus* is a native of India. But it is also found in Sri Lank, Myanmar, Europe, Japan, China, Southern Russia, and Northern U.S.A. In India, it is found as perennial medicinal plant in Kashmir, Manipur, Karnataka and Northeast Himalaya. It is currently declared as the extinct species and placed in this list with some other plants. It has been used for centuries in treatment of many diseases like hysteria, and recommended as memory booster, antimicrobial. It increases appetite and helps in the digestion, reduces fever, and cramps in stomach. Its rhizome is chewed as a remedy in toothache. The United States has banned on the use of its products. Several methods of killing the pathogens/disease-causing germs by Vaca plant have been described in Vedas. A photograph of Vaca plant bearing long leaves, flower and thick rhizome is given in Figure 8.4.

(A) (B)

Figure 8.4. *Acorus calamus* (A) with thick rhizome (B).

1. Prevention of All Kinds of Microbes by Vaca

Germs (Kṛmi*s*) are found inside, outside and on all parts of the body, as well as in all places because they are capable of surviving in varying environmental conditions. Eventually, they derive nutrition from the surroundings, multiply fast and increase in their numbers. Depending on host susceptibility/resistance, the pathogenic microbes infect and cause serious diseases. Elimination of all types of pathogenic germs from the body by using Vaca medicine has been mentioned in the Atharvaveda (2.31.3).

अलगण्डून्हन्मि महता वधेन् दूना अदूना अरसा अभूवन् ।
शिष्टानशिष्टान्नि तिरामि वाचा यथा क्रिमींणां नकिरुच्छिषातै ।।

(अथर्ववेद 2.31.3)

Algaṅḍūnhanmi mahtā vadhen dūnā adūnā arsā abhūvan.
Śiṣtānaśiṣtānni tirāmi vācā yathā crimīṇāṁ nakirucchiṣātai.

(Atharvaveda 2.31.3)

[I strike the germs (*Kṛmi)* resulting in itching with the great destructive weapon (*algaṇḍūn mahatā vadhen hanmi*). All the microbes (*Kṛmi*) have become without life. I destroy the lame one (*dūnā*), fast moving and sluggish ones (*adūnā arasā abhūvan*) with *vacā* herb (*śiṣtān aśiṣtān vācā ni tirāmi*) so that none may remain alive (*yathā Kṛmiṇām na kiṁ ucchiṣātai*)]

Scientific Explanation - The idea of killing the remaining microorganisms found in all places after killing them, moving and non-moving, has been expressed. The specificity of killing the germs by Vaca medicine has been explained after this mantra. In fact, there are many types of movable and non-movable germs. Many appendages such as flagella, fimbrae, and sex pili are found attached to bacterial cell wall. Microbes use flagella for locomotion, i.e. movement from one place to another. Bacterial cells are transported from one place to another in aqueous medium. But in the absence of these appendages and aqueous media, the microbial cells are not able to be transmitted. The bacterial cells, during the congenial environment, derive nutrition from the host cells or from the surrounding environment. They more through flagella and get attached to the substratum by fimbrae. They transfer fertility factors via sex pili from one cell to the other cell. They multiply by binary fission. Then non-flagellated microorganisms develop some other mechanisms of transmission. The structure of a normal bacterial cell (A) and the surviving structure called endospore (B) are given in Figure 8.5.

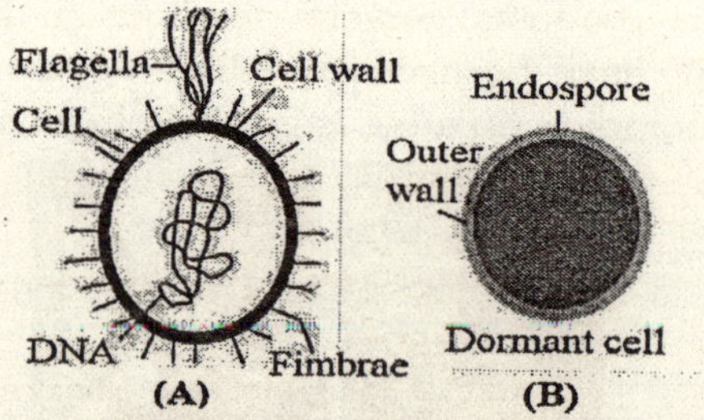

Figure 8.5. Structure of a normal bacterial cell (**A**); an endospore (**B**).

Under adverse conditions, they produce dormant endospores through which they enter into inactive phase; again they are reactivated on the return of suitable environmental conditions. Then the endospores germinate and give rise to parental type of cells. Therefore, special emphasis has been given to eliminate the pathogenic microorganisms that survive by dormant endospores and remain alive for prolong period during inactive phase of life.

अन्वान्त्रयं शीर्षण्यमथो पार्ष्टेयं क्रिमीन्।
अवस्कवयं व्यंध्वरं क्रिमीन् वचसा जम्भयामसि।।

(अथर्ववेद 2.31.4)

Anvāntrayaṁ śīrṣaṇyamatho pārṣteyaṁ Kṛmīn.
Avaskavayaṁ vyadhvaraṁ Kṛmīn vacasā jambhayāmsi.

(Atharvaveda 2.31.4)

[By using the *vacā* herb (*vacasā*), I destroy the microbes (*jambhayāmasi*) residing in intestine (*anvāyantryaṁ*), in head (*śīrṣaṇya*) or in the lungs and ribs (*atho pārṣteyaṁ*) and the creepers (*avaskavayaṁ*) and borers (*vyadhvaraṁ*) that bounce and cause severe pain in body]

Scientific Explanation- According to modern microbiologists, over 100 trillion (100 Lakh) bacteria reside in our intestine, out of which few bacterial species have been discovered so far as the rest do not grow on artificial growth media in laboratory. These bacteria are beneficial for our body and are helpful in keeping the intestines functional. But many pathogenic microorganisms entering the intestines from external sources are very harmful, such as *Escherichia coli, Staphylococcus aureus, Mycobacterium tuberculosis, Pseudomonas auriginosa, Vibrio cholerae, Klebsiella pneumoniae, Streptococcus* spp., adenovirus, and hepatitis viruses. Some microorganisms are the pathogens that cause disease by entering the body upon biting of other animals, such as hanta virus, rabies virus, Nipah virus, Japanese encephalitis virus, *Plasmodium falciparum, Yersinia pestis, Rickettsia rickettsii,* etc. All these undesirable and painful pathogenic microorganisms have been said to remove by 'Vaca' medicine.

Chopra *et al.* (1957) have reported the antimicrobial properties of aromatic oil extracted from rhizomes of *Acorus calamus* against *Mycobacterium tuberculosis*. Antimicrobial chemicals are found in the leaves and rhizomes of the *Acorus calamus*, which act effectively on different bacteria at different concentrations. For example, a methanol-soluble chemical constituent called beta-asarone inhibits the growth of *Escherichia coli* at 40–10 mg/ml concentration and *Aspergillus niger* at 80–100 mg/ml. Antibacterial activities of ethanol and methanol soluble essential oils from rhizome of *Acorus calamus* has been investigated against different bacterial strains, for example *Escherichia coli* and *Staphylococcus aureus* (Rahamoz-Haghigh *et al.*, 2014). The minimum inhibitory concentration (MIC) of these bacterial strains varied in the range of 25-100 mg/ml. Several types of chemical constituents from essential oil have been isolated, for example beta-asarone, phenyl propanoids, monoterpenes and sesquiterpenes, etc. In the future, these methanol and ethanol soluble extracts can be used for the treatment of many infectious diseases by using Vaca plant.

ERADICATION OF LEPROSY AND OTHER DISEASES

Leprosy is an infectious disease caused by *Mycobacterium leprae*. It is also known as Hansen's disease after the name of discoverer in 1873. Leprosy results in severe skin discolouration in patches, skin-sores as well as damages of nerves present in arms, legs, hands and scattered areas of skin all over the body. Initially, leprosy affects the skin, eyes, nose, outside the brain, and the peripheral nerves. Leprosy is not a new disease, rather it has been known since the ancient times in India, China, Egypt and other countries. People feared that leprosy cannot be cured. People of every continent have been affected due to leprosy outbreaks.

New and healthy persons receives the inocula of *Mycobacterium leprae* after coming in close contact repeatedly through the droplets from nose and mouth from untreated leprosy patients. Chances of getting leprosy in children are more than the adults. The damaged nerves result in muscular weakness, discolored skin patches, skin nodules, thick skin, loss of eyebrows, ulcers on the soles of feet without pain, etc. In prolong cases of disease, the fingers start rotting by twisting and automatic falling off at the end (Figure 8.6). Nowadays, medicines of leprosy are available.

(A) (B)

Figure 8.6: Symptoms of leprosy on back skin (A) and distorted fingers (B).

1. Occurrence of Kuṣṭha (Crepe Ginger) (*Costus speciosus*)

Leprosy has also been prevalent during the Vedic period; therefore, it has been described in Vedas also. Atharvaveda mentions the use of an auspicious medicinal plant called Kuṣṭhā, i.e. crepe ginger for the prevention of leprosy and other diseases. Kuṣṭha (Crepe Ginger) has been mentioned to occur on the snowy peaks of the Himalayan Mountains.

इमं मे कुष्ठ पूरुषं तमा वह तं निष्कुरु। तमु मे अगदं कृधि।।

(अथर्ववेद 5.4.6)

Imaṁ me Kuṣṭha pūruṣaṁ tamā vah taṁ niṣkuru. Tamu me agadaṁ kṛdhi.

(Atharvaveda 5.4.6)

O! Creep ginger (*Kuṣṭha*), get to my (*imaṁ me*) patient again (*taṁ pūruṣaṁ avah*), get him (*taṁ*) out of the disease (*niṣkuru*). Surely (*u*) free my man (*mey taṁ*) from disease (*agadaṁ kṛdhi*).

Scientific Explanation- Undoubtedly, Kuṣṭha is capable of removing the disease from all parts of body. Therefore, its therapeutic applications have been emphasised and rxpected for its cure in this hymn.

यो गिरिष्वजायथा वीरूधां बलवत्तमः।
कुष्ठेहि तक्मनाशन तक्मानं नाशयन्नितः।।

(अथर्ववेद 5.4.1)

Yo giriṣvajāyathā vīrudhaṁ balavattamaḥ.
Kuṣṭhehi takmanāśana takmānaṁ nāśayannitaḥ.

(Atharvaveda 5.4.1)

[O! Disease-destroying (*takmanāśana*) Kustha! (*Kuṣṭhehi*), you are very strong (*balavattamaḥ*) in all types of medicinal herbs (*vīrudhaṁ*) originating in the mountains (*giriṣvajāyathā*). You are here to destroy (*nāśayannitaḥ*) the troublesome diseases (*takmānaṁ*)]

उदङ् जातो हिमवतः सः प्राच्यां नीयसे जनम्।
तत्र कुष्ठस्य नामान्युत्तमानि वि भेजिरे।।

(अथर्ववेद 5.4.8)

Udaṅg jāto himavataḥ saḥ prācyāṁ nīyase janaṁ.
Tatra Kuṣṭhasya nāmānyuttamāni vi bhejire.

(Atharvaveda 5.4.8)

[This crepe ginger plant (*Kuṣṭha*) originates (*jātaḥ*) from the snow-capped peaks of Himalaya (*himavataḥ*) in the north (*Udaṅg*). This (*sah*) is obtained near people (*janaṁ nīyase*) in the east direction (*prācyāṁ*). They use (*vi bhejire*) there (*tatra*) the best names of Kuṣṭha (*Kuṣṭhasya uttama nāmāni*)]

उत्तमो नाम कुष्ठास्युत्तमो नाम ते पिता।
यक्ष्मं च सर्वं नाशय तकमानं चारसं कृधि।।
(अथर्ववेद 5.4.9)

Uttamo nāma kuṣṭhasyuttamo nāma te pitā.
Yakshmaṁ ca sarvaṁ nāśaya takamānaṁ cārasaṁ kṛdhi.
(Atharvaveda 5.4.9)

[O Kushtha! (*Kuṣṭha*) You are certainly the best (*uttamaḥ nāma asi*), the one who produces you (*te pitā*) is also the best (*uttamaḥ nāma*), and (*ca*) destroy all diseases (*yakshmaṁ sarvaṁ nāśaya*) and neutralize (*ca arasaṁ kṛdhi*) fever (*takamānaṁ*)].

This means that the leprosy and its snow-clad mountains are capable of eliminating both diseases. Therefore, with the use of leprosy, a sick person should go to the snow covered mountain for health benefits.

Scientific Explanation- Kuṣṭha plant does not occur everywhere, rather it prefers to grow, in the north region of country, on the snowy peaks of the Himalaya, because of its adaptation at low temperature. Low temperature may help in producing effective therapeutic biomolecules in substantial amount that would have cured the leprosy. How knowledgeable the Vedic Ṛṣis would have been who discovered Kuṣṭha and studied its preference? Occurrence and distribution of Kuṣṭha in India has been discussed in more detail in the preceding section.

शीर्षामयमुपहत्यामक्ष्योस्तन्वोऽरप।
कुष्ठस्तत्सर्वं निष्करद् दैवं समह वृष्ण्यम्।।
(अथर्ववेद 5.4.10)

Śirṣāmayamupahatyāmakṣyostanvorapa.
Kuṣṭhastatsarvaṁ niṣkarad daivaṁ samaha vṛṣṇyaṁ.
(Atharvaveda 5.4.10)

[This Kuṣṭha (*Kuṣṭhaḥ*) removes (*niṣkarad*) disease related to the head (*śirṣāmayaṁ*), the weakness of eye sight (*akṣyorapa*), all the defects of the body (tanvorapa), all of them (*tat sarvaṁ*). O sharp (*samaha*) leper ! Your strength is divine (*vṛṣṇyaṁ daivaṁ*)]

Scientific Explanation- The Kuṣṭha herb has supernatural power; therefore, head, eyes and other organs become free from defects and diseases after its application. Furthermore, it is also capable of eradicating all types of ailments including the leprosy. Therefore, the herb Kuṣṭha has been paid much attention and suggested for its use in varying types of diseases and other defects.

2. Prevention of Leprosy

Leprosy is a dangerous mycobacterial disease. Its identification in the initial stage is difficult. It has been affecting the humans since the Vedic period but it has not been completely eliminated from the human society so far in spite of several efforts. Still leprosy affected individuals are seen in the society.

एतु देवस्त्रायमाणः कुष्ठो हिमवतस्परि।
तक्मानं सर्वं नाशय सर्वाश्च यातुधान्यः।।
(अथर्ववेद 19.39.1)

Etu devastrāyamāṇaḥ kuṣṭho himvataspari.
Takmānaṁ sarvaṁ nāśaya sarvāṅśca yātudhānyaḥ.
(Atharvaveda 19.39.1)

[May the Devine (*devaḥ*) Kuṣṭhā (*kuṣṭhaḥ*) (*Costus specious*) eliminator of leprosy (*vāhi*) come to me (*ā etu*) as protector (*trāyamāṇaḥ*) from the snowy mountain (*himavataḥ pari*) and banish (*nāśaya*) all painful diseases (*takmānaṁ sarvaṁ*) and all disease-causers (*ca sarvāḥ yātudhānyaḥ*), which make life difficult]

Scientific Explanation- The God has been prayed to remove all the leprosy bacteria that make life free from the ailment by using a medicinal plant called Kuṣṭhā (*Costus speciosus*) originating in snowy peaks of northern states. The question is what are the special qualities in the Kuṣṭhā that growing in the icy states cures the leprosy? Are all these qualities not found in Kuṣṭhā that grows in other states? It may be noted that a plant has many species and varieties that can grow successfully at a particular place and synthesize secondary metabolites in a short period of time but the same plant species fails to do so due to changed environmental conditions. The climate varies from place to place which affects the metabolic reactions of the plants. This hymn signifies the Kuṣṭhā plant quickly growing in low or zero temperatures; hence it possesses the special ability to eliminate the painful disease-causing germs. Therefore, special emphasis has been laid on the use of such medicines in this hymn.

Kuṣṭhā [*Costus speciosus* (Syn. *Cheilocostus speciosus*)]- Kuṣṭhā, crepe ginger, is a medicinal plant which is distributed in the Himalayan regions (such as Himachal Pradesh, Uttarakhand, Sikkim, Darjeeling, Assam and Meghalaya), Vindhya Satpura hills, Andhra Pradesh (Eastern Ghats of) and Maharashtra, Tamil Nadu, Karnataka and Kerala (Western Ghats) and Gujarat. It is commonly known as 'Beltauri', and also known by different names in different states, for example Ketaki, Kemuk, Kaśmīra, Pushpamool, Keukand, Kostam, Kosta, Pakarmula, etc. In English, Kuṣṭhā is called by a popular a name 'crepe ginger'. It has been placed in the family Costaceae (= Gingiberaceae). This plant is found in the ditches located along roadside as well in the moist and shady places in forest where there are low-lying areas. The flowering season begins from October to December, soon after the rainy season is over. It grows very well when the climate has high humidity and low temperature. It is an important medicinal ornamental, succulent and perennial herbaceous plant.

Costus speciosus is a succulent, erect, perennial, ornamental and herbaceous plant. The roots hold tuberous or nodular 2-2.7 metre long aerial stem, which is sub-woody at the base having 120-300 cm long creeping rhizomes. The stem bears long, often branched, one-sided and spirally arranged lanceolate leaves. White or red fragrant flowers are terminally produced in clusters. There are several species of *Costus*, such as *C. chartaceus*, *C. cuspidatus*, *C. giganteus*, *C. igneus*, *C. asae*, etc. The colour and flowers of these species vary, for example *C. spiralis* pruduces red-coloured flowers and *C. speciosus* produces white-coloured flowers (Figure 8.7).

Figure 8.7. Flowers of *Costus speciosus* (Kuṣṭhā).

3. Three Names of Kuṣṭhā

Kuṣṭhā has three names viz., first Kuṣṭhā, second Nadyamāra and third Nadyāriṣa. When the water of the rivers gets collected at one place, many microorganisms start growing in it. As a result, various types of diseases spread. The plant that kills microorganisms like malaria and filaria occurring at such places has been called 'Nadyamāra'. Similarly, the term 'Nadyāriṣa' has been used for such a plant that eliminates the diseases arising due to the river water.

त्रीणि ते कुष्ठ नामानि नद्यमारो नद्यारिषः।
नद्यायं पुरुषो रिषत् । यस्मै परिब्रवीमि त्वा सायंप्रातरथो दिवा।।
(अथर्ववेद 19.39.2)

Trīṇi te Kuṣṭha nāmāni nadyamāro nadyāriṣaḥ.
Nadyāyaṁ puruṣo riṣat. Yasmai paribravīmi tva sāyaṁprātaratho divā.
(Atharvaveda 19.39.2)

[O Kuṣṭhā! (*kuṣṭha*) you have three names (*trīṇi te nāmāni*), Kuṣṭhā (*kuṣṭha*), nadyamara (*nadyamāraḥ*), nadyariṣa (*nadyāriṣaḥ*). O ! Kuṣṭhā ! (*nadya*) let this person (*ayaṁ puruṣaḥ*) be capable of eradicating the disease (*riṣataḥ*) whom (*yasmai*) I suggest to use (*tvā paribravīmi*) three times, evening, morning and in day (*sāyaṁ prātaḥ atha u divā*)].

Scientific Explanation- The Kuṣṭhā plant has three names- Kuṣṭhā, Nadyamāra and Nadyāriṣa. These three names are named according to their special characteristics. The Kuṣṭhā plant having the ability to eliminate leprosy has been called ' Kuṣṭhā'. The Kuṣṭhā plant that kills the water-borne microbial pathogens like *Mycobacterium leprae* is 'Nadyamāra'. Thus, the plant that eliminates the vectors of all such germs is named as 'Nadyamāra'. But the name of the plant that eliminates the diseases caused by the river water is called 'Nadyāriṣa'. It must be noted that in the stagnant water of rivers, the vectors of malaria, filarial and others thrive well by laying the eggs. The plant that destroys germs is named 'Nadyāriṣa'. Therefore, using Kuṣṭhā plant in the morning, afternoon and evening, leprosy can be eliminated.

जीवला नाम ते माता जीवन्तो नाम ते पिता।
नद्यायं पुरुषो रिषत्। यस्मै परिब्रवीमि त्वा सायंप्रातरथो दिवा।।
(अथर्ववेद 19.39.3)

Jīvalā nāma te mātā jīvanto nāma te pitā.
Nadyāyaṁ puruṣo riṣat. Yasmai paribravīmi tvā sāyaṁprātaratho divā.
(Atharvaveda 19.39.3)

[Due to giving you life your mother (*te mātā*) earth is known as Jīvalā (*jīvalā nāma*); due to keeping you alive your father Sun/cloud is known as Jivant (*jīvantaḥ nāma*). O Kuṣṭhā ! (*nadya*) let this person (*ayaṁ puruṣaḥ*) be capable of eradicating the disease (*riṣataḥ*) whom (*yasmai*) I suggest to use (*tvā paribravīmi*) three times, evening, morning and in day (*sāyaṁ prātaḥ atha u divā*)]

Scientific Explanation- Due to the giving birth of Kuṣṭhā, the Earth has been called 'Jīvalā' and the Sun has been called 'Jīvan' because of keeping it alive by nurturing it through photosynthesis. The plant seedlings grow in the soil and its further development takes place.

There are many nutrients available in soil to which the plants derive and maintained the life. In the same way, all plants take the sun's rays and make their food in the form of glucose by through photosynthesis in the presence of carbon dioxide (CO_2) and water (H_2O) in chloroplasts and discharge oxygen (O_2). Plants preserve glucose in the form of cellulose in leaves and other parts of the plants (Figure 8.8). This biochemical reaction can be expressed as follows.

$$CO_2 + H_2O \xrightarrow{\text{Light}} \text{Glucose} + CO_2$$

That is why the leaves of plants always appear light green or dark green. In the absence of the sun rays, photosynthesis cannot be possible in plant because sun rays are the source of energy. Therefore, such plants become thin and yellow. In this context, it is perfectly appropriate to call the earth as 'Jīvalā' (that gives birth to a life and nurtures it) and the sun as 'Jīvant' (that makes the life alive). Moreover, the earth has been regarded as the mother in all Vedic and SansKṛt text, for example 'the Earth is mother and I am the son of the earth (*Mātā bhumiḥ putro,haṁ prithivyāḥ.* Atharvaveda 12.1.12), the mother and the birthplace (i.e. mother earth) are better than the heaven (*Jananī janmabhumiśca svargādapigarīyasi.* Vālmiki Rāmāyan).

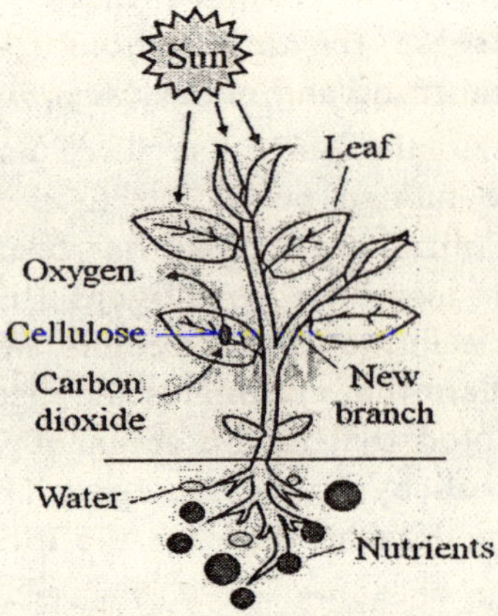

Figure 8.8. Plant nutrition, photosynthesis, and production of cellulose and oxygen.

4. Occurrence of Kuṣṭhā

Kuṣṭhā, the drug of all diseases (Sarvoṣadhi), grows on the peaks of the mountains covered with snow, after the snow melts due to the sun's light. But in the modern period many species of Kuṣṭhā have been discovered. Kuṣṭhā also grows in many other states of India.

यत्र नावप्रभ्रंशनं यत्र हिमवतः शिरः।
तत्रामृतस्य चक्षणं ततः कुष्ठो अजायत।।
स कुष्ठो विश्वभेषजः साकं सोमेन तिष्ठति।
तक्मानं सर्वं नाशय सर्वाश्च यातुधान्यः।।
(अथर्ववेद 19.39.8)

Yatra nāvaprabhranśanaṁ yatra himavataḥ śiraḥ.

Tatrāmritasya cakṣaṇaṁ tataḥ kuṣṭho ajāyat.
Sa kuṣṭho viśvabheṣajaḥ sākam somen tiṣṭhati.
Takmānaṁ sarvaṁ nāśaya sarvāśca yātudhānyaḥ.
(Atharvaveda 19.39.8)

[Where there is no slipping downwards of the Himalaya (*yatra himvataḥ śirah*) and where there is the summit of the snowy mountain (*yatra na avprabhanśanaṁ*), there is the source of immortality (*tatra amritasya*); there from the kuṣṭhā is born (*tatah kuṣṭhaḥ ajāyat*) when rays of sun fall on it (*cakṣaṇaṁ*). This kuṣṭhā (*sah kuṣṭhāḥ*) is a drug of all diseases of world (*viśva bheṣajaḥ*). It exists with Devine Elixir (*somen sākaṁ tiṣṭhati*). O ! Kuṣṭhā banish (*nāśaya*) all fever (*sarvaḥ takmānaḥ*) and all pain-causing diseases (*sarvāṁ yatudhānyaḥ*)]

Scientific Explanation- The Kuṣṭhā is born on the snowy mountains, where peaks always remain covered with snow, where ambrosial sunrays fall at height and snow melts creating suitable conditions for seed germination and growth of seedlings. Many diseases have been supposed to be cured by using the Kuṣṭhā, because it has been recommended by our sages as 'global medicine' (Viśwauṣadhi) for treatment of all diseases. Being as global medicine, Kuṣṭhā has been said to be full of Devine Elixir (Sōmaras); hence it also lustres the body of the users of Kuṣṭhā. It is possible only becuase of presence of several bio-chemical compounds in stem, roots, leaves and rhizome of the plant. Some of the known chemicals found in Kuṣṭhā leaves and rhizomes are- saponin, for example diosgenin (as a major steroid constituent), sapogenin, steroids tigogenin, alkaloids, quinones, gracillin, tricontanoic acids and α- tocopherol. Rhizome also consists of triterpenes, aliphatic hydroxyl ketones, starch mucilage, fatty acids, oxa-acids, corticosteroids and abscisic acid. Besides it also contains many more chemicals.

This 'global medicine' Kuṣṭhā has anti-cancer, anti-diabetic, anti-fungal, anti-microbial, antioxidant and liver-protective properties (Hussain and Hoare, 2006). In Ayurvedic system of medicine, rhizome of Kuṣṭhā has been recommended for treatment of several ailments, for example asthma, fever, bronchitis, rashes, and worms growing in intestine. Its rhizome and root are also used in various diseases, such as arthritic, jaundice, anaemia, meningitis, tuberculosis, snakebite, dermatitis and appendicitis. Generally, rhizomes are consumed as decoction, and have also been used for treatment of a viral disease, smallpox. Mental disorders can also be treated by using its leaves. Some of the effective biochemicals found in leprosy are sisquiterpine lactone, costunolide, eremanthin, etc. Costunolide has been found to be more effective in the control of dermatitis and microorganisms (Duraipandian *et al.*, 2012). Costunolide also decreases serum cholesterol and triglyceride with an increases serum protein, plasma insulin, and tissue glycogen. Diosgenin and eremanthin are the two very potent bioactive compounds of *C. speciosus*.

In vitro antibacterial activity of *C. speciosus* leaf and rhizomes has been reported against some bacterial pathogens, such as *Staphylococcus aureus, S. epidermidis, Bacillus subtilis, Escherichia coli, Salmonella typhimurium, Pseudomonas aeruginosa,* and species of *Salmonella* and *Pseudomonas*. It also bears antifungal properties against the species of *Trichophyton rubrum, T. mentagrophytes, Epidermophyton floccosum,* and *Microsporum grisea* (Pawar and Pawar, 2012).

5. Application of Kuṣṭhā

Our sages not only discovered the Kuṣṭhā plant that grows at varying conditions on the Himalaya but also suggested for thrice use of this medicinal plants. By using the Kuṣṭhā three times a day, the patient becomes dynamic, knowledgeable and healthy. It makes the mind, brain and body three disease-free. In means that Kuṣṭhā plant boosts up immune system of the peoples and helps in preventing the infection in human being.

त्रिः शाम्बुभ्यो अंगिरेभ्यस्त्रिरादित्येभ्यस्परि। त्रिर्जातो विश्वदेवेभ्यः।
स कुश्ठो विश्वभेषजः साकं सोमेन तिष्ठति।
तक्मानं सर्वं नाशय सर्वाश्च यातुधान्यः।।

(अथर्ववेद 19.39.5)

Triḥ śāmbubhyo aṅgirebhyastriādityebhyaspari. Trirjāto viśvadevebhyaḥ.
Sa kuṣṭho viśvabheṣajaḥ sākaṁ somen tiṣṭhati.
Takmānaṁ sarvaṁ nāśaya sarvāśca yātudhānyah.

(Atharvaveda 19.39.5)

[Thrice used kuśtha (*triḥ*) makes the person energetic (*śāmbubhyaḥ*), enables (*parijātaḥ*) sacrifice performers (*angirebhyaḥ*). This (*yaḥ*) thrice used Kuṣṭha (*triḥ*) becomes to (*jātaḥ*) Āditya and all God (*ādityebhyaḥ*). This Kuṣṭhā (*saḥ kuṣṭhaḥ*) is a drug of all diseases of world (*viśva bheṣajaḥ*). It exists with Devine Elixir (*somen sakaṁ tiṣṭhati*). O! kuśtha banish (*nāśaya*) all fever (*sarva takmānaḥ*) and all pain-causing diseases (*sarvāḥ yātudhānyaḥ*)]

Scientific Explanation- Kuṣṭhā gets offered to the Āditya and all the Gods after it's thrice use. As a result, all fever and painful diseases are eliminated. That is why Kuṣṭhā has been called 'global medicine' or Viśwauṣadhi. It is perfectly appropriate to consume leprosy thrice after offering to the God. For treatment, Vaidyas (persons skilled in medicinal herb) and doctors also ask them to consume Kuṣṭhā medicines 3-4 times a day. The reason for being Viśwauṣadhi is that various types of biochemicals are present in different quantities in this medicine; therefore, its activity and effectiveness vary accordingly. It is necessary to consume Kuṣṭhā medicines thrice so that the concentrations of its specific biochemicals could be maintained in the body consecutively for ling time. Only high concentrations of specific biochemicals affect body disorders and the sick person become quickly disease-free. Kumar *et al.* (2018) have conducted research on the metabolic profiling of *C. speciosus* plant and identified 91 metabolites, among which they also carried out quantification of 69 metabolites.

ERADICATION OF LEPROSY BY PRSNIPARNI (*URARIA PICTA*)

Pṛśniparṇi (also called Citraparnī, Durbā, Piṭhavan), scientifically known as *Uraria picta* (Syn. *Hedysarum pictum*, *Doodia picta*), is an erect and scantly branched perennial herb attaining a height of 60–765 cm. It belongs to the family Fabaceae (sub-family Papilionoidae). *Uraria picta* is found in India, Sri Lanka, Bangladesh, Africa, Philippines and Malay Islands. It is a long plant having the striped white coloured leaves. It has stem with short rough hairs, leaves imparipinnate with 5-9 leaflets; leaflets 7-25 cm long and slightly lanceolate. Leaflets are variegated, shiny and hairless above and rough hairs below. Leaves margins are entire; inflorescence is long, terminal, spike-like raceme bearing many flowers. Inflorescence is 55 cm long and covered by whitish hairs; flowers are pink, bluish or reddish.

Fruits are brown to black, 5-9 mm long and folded into 3-6 segments. It has dense, small, red or purple coloured flowers (Figure 8.9).

This plant flowers during the winter season. On flowering, its flowers look like jackal's tail. This plant is found in all the provinces of India, in grassland and forests (especially in Bengal and Himachal Pradesh). The plant is used in nasal, cough, cold, haemorrhage, catarrh, fever, phlegm, ulcers, gout, mania and urinary disease, fistula, bone-braking, stammering of children, dermatitis and debility. Since ancient time, this plant has been used traditionally, as an antidote against the venom after biting the dangerous Indian snake called *Echis carinata*. Moreover, the leaves of *Uraria picta* bear anti-anxiety activity also.

Figure 8.9. A plant of *Uraria picta.*

It is one of the constituents of 'Daśmula' which is a well established Ayurvedic formulation of Indian System of Medicine. Daśmula is a mixture of ten herbs used for treatment of fatigue, oral sores, gynecological disorders, etc. Leaves are used against gonorrhoea as it acts like antiseptics. In children the oral sores can be effectively treated by using the fruits and pods. But the use of roots against chills, fever and cough are also an effective remedy.

1. The Divinity in Pṛśniparṇi (*Uraria picta*)

Pṛśniparṇi has been called the Goddess due to the divine qualities present in it. This plant has miraculous properties due to the synthesis and storage of effective biochemical secondary metabolites. The miraculous property of Pṛśniparṇi has been described in the Atharvaveda (2.25.1).

शं नो देवी पृश्निपर्ण्यशं निर्ऋत्या अकः।
उग्रा हि कण्वजम्भनी तामभक्षि सहस्वतीम।।
(अथर्ववेद 2.25.1)

Śaṁ no devī pṛśniparṇayaśaṁ nirṛtyā akaḥ.
Ugrā hi kaṇvajambhnī tāmabhakṣi sahasvatīm.
(Atharvaveda 2.25.1)

[Pṛśniparṇi (*pṛśniparṇī*) with divine qualities (*devī*) has done good to us (*naḥ śaṁ*) and bad (*aśaṁ*) to wretchedness (*nirṛtyā aśaṁ akaḥ*). She is terrible destroyer (*ugrā hi*) of sins and roots of disease (*kaṇva jambhani*); I consume (*abhakṣi*) disease-destroying (*sahasvatīṁ*) that herb (*tāṁ*)]

Scientific Explanation- The Pṛśniparṇi has been referred to as a goddess due to possessing the divine qualities, because its effectiveness and potentiality due to presence of abundant amount of quality biochemicals. As a result, many skin diseases including leprosy are eliminated. There are many types of biochemical compounds found in the leaves, roots, and stems of *Uraria picta*, such as alkaloids, flavonoids, isoflavonoids, terpenoids, phenols, saponins, tannins, cardiac glycosides, etc. All these biochemicals are helpful in maintaining good human health while fighting many ailments (Saxena *et al.*, 2014). Flavonoids and isoflavonavides of *Uraria picta* have anti-inflammatory properties against *Staphylococcus aureus, Bacillus subtilis, Proteus vulgaris, Escherichia coli, Aspergillus niger* and *Candida albicans*. Both these biochemical compounds have anti-inflammatory and antimicrobial properties also. They also provide liver protection through the 'scavenging free radicals' method (Rahman *et al.*, 2007). Therefore, *Uraria picta* is used in the prevention of leprosy and many other diseases.

2. Pṛśniparṇi as a 'Global Medicine' (Viśwauṣadhi)

According to the Ayurveda, the Pṛśniparṇi cures fever, pneumonia, bloody diarrhoea, thrust and vomiting. Many types of blood disorders and pregnancy-related diseases are cured with its use. Leprosy can also be cured with the use of Pṛśniparṇi.

सहमानेयं प्रथमा पृश्निपर्ण्य जायत।
तयाहं दुर्णाम्नां शिरो वृश्चामि शकुनेरिव।।
(अथर्ववेद 2.25.2)

Sahamāneyaṁ prathamā pṛśniparṇya jāyat.
Tayāhaṁ durnāmnā śiro vṛścāmi śakuneriva.
(Atharvaveda 2.25.2)

[This potential herb Pṛśniparṇi (*ayā pṛśniparṇī*) able to eliminate all diseases (*sahamānaṁ*) was born first (*prathamaṁ*). With this (*tayā*) I (*ahaṁ*) cut off the head (*śirah vṛścāmi*) of inauspicious and leprosy-like diseases (*durnāmā*) as (*iva*) done the head of the birds (*śakuneḥ*)]

Scientific Explanation- Pṛśniparṇi has the first place among all medicines because the sick persons become miraculously healthy by using this medicine that is full of divine qualities. A variety of inauspicious and altruistic diseases such as viral and bactericidal diseases, leprosy, fistula, mania, bone and skin disease are eliminated by the use of Pṛśniparṇi.

Science of Agnihotra (Sacrificial Fire) 9.

Agnihotra (Sanskrit, *Agni* meaning 'fire', and *Hotra* means 'healing'), practiced in the rhythm of sunrise and sunset, is a Divine worship which is performed with oblations in burning fire (Agni) in an inverted pyramidal copper pot or a pit with bricks steps on the four edges. However, Kaṇva Ṛṣi was the first who discovered 'fire worship'/'medicinal fire worship' technology called 'Agnihotra', a divine worship performed by the sacrificing fire. Agnihotra (Syn. Yajña, Homa, Hawan) is an ancient tradition of prosperous India. In ancient times, people used to call 'Bhārat Varṣa' as 'Āryāvarta' because all people were Aryans. In the Vedic period, Aryans wanted to make the whole world 'Ārya' (*Krinavanto viśvamāryam*- Ṛgveda 9.63.5). According to western's views, during in the Saraswati-Indus Civilization around 7500 years BCE, our sages gave the first and oldest book to the world that they acquired as 'Revealed Truth', i.e. the Ṛgveda, on this holy land and the Agnihotra was started in Āryavarta for health improvement and environmental purification. Our Ṛṣis used to perform Agnihotra according to season by collecting odoriferous medicinal herbs from the forest. There is special mention of hymns related to Hawan in the Ṛgveda. All the Ṛṣis of the Vedic period and their disciples like Yājñavalkya, Pippalādi, Agastya, Kaṇva, Caitanya, Bādarāyaṇa, Gārgi, Maitreyi, Naciketā, Kaśyapa, Gautama, Atri, Vaśiṣtha, Viśvāmitra, Bharadwāja, Jamadagni, Visravā, Rāvaṇa, Rām, Kṛṣṇa and many more others had carried this tradition forward. It is well known that the Kings Daśaratha and Śrī Rām performed the Aśwamedha Yajña.

In Mesopotamia from 2600 BCE till today, the smoke of medicinal and aromatic plants have been used in the treatment of various diseases like phlegm, cold, parasitic infection, inflammation, etc. At the time of Suśruta (600-800 BCE), it was believed that evil spirits flee and the treated person gets relief from the sepsis due to smoke emanating from a mixture of mustard, butter, and salt in the operation theatre (OT). In Syria (522-486 BCE), esfand (*Peganum harmala*) and sandalwood-fired smoke were used to protect the emperor from diseases and evil spirits. Fumigation, by burning the herbs and aromatic essence, was the main prophylaxis against infectious microbial diseases during the medieval period, including the pandemic period of the bubonic plague caused by *Yersinia pestis* (Nautiyal *et al.*, 2007). Even today, in about 50 countries of the world, the smoke of one / many medicinal and aromatic plants is used in some forms to ward off many diseases and evil spirits.

In Vedic texts, Agnihotra has been mentioned as the 'supreme discipline of Yajñas', which is a science of purification of environment by using the fire as transformer or 'a process of removing the polluted environment through the fire'. The purified atmosphere has a positive effect on life forms, including microorganisms, plants, human, and all animals. Agnihotra is performed for different purposes, for example as medicine for disease control, environmental purification, agriculture, psychotherapy, and bioenergetics (Devi *et al.*, 2004).

SIGNIFICANCE OF HAWAN/ YAJÑA

Hawan has religious, spiritual and scientific importance but most people do not know about its significance. Of course, Hawan has spiritual and scientific significance. In the 19th century, Swami Dayānand Saraswati gave more importance to Vedic education by establishing Ārya Samāj. Swāmi Śraddhānand, a disciple of Swami Dayānand Saraswati, established the Gurukula Kangri Vishwavidyalaya (Haridwar) based on this principle and took the task of disseminating the Vedic education and Agnihotra in the country and abroad. Why fire and fumigation by using a variety of methods are being performed at these occasions? Does it have any significance? What do medicinal smokes do at these occasions? What is the mystery and what does science say? All these questions shall be discussed and answered in this chapter.

इयं वेदिः परो अन्तः पृथिव्या अयं यज्ञो भुवनस्य नाभिः ।

(ऋग्वेद 1.164.35)

Iyaṁ vediḥ paro aṅtaḥ pṛthivyā ayaṁ yajño bhuvanasya nābhiḥ.

(Ṛgveda 1.164.35)

[This altar (*iyaṁ vediḥ*) is the last end (*paraḥ aṅtaḥ*) of the land (*pṛthivyā*). This Yajña (*ayaṁ yajño*) is the navel of the entire universe (*bhuvanasya nābhiḥ*)].

Scientific Explanation- Fire is produced from the sacrificial fire, whose electromagnetic waves disperse throughout the universe. That is why Yajña has been called the navel of the entire universe. Life operates through fire. Due to the spread of fire energy in the body of all creatures as adenosine triphosphate (ATP), it is possible to conduct their life. Respiration, digestion, excretion, seeing, hearing, laughing, etc. are possible only due to fire. That is why in the first hymn of the Ṛgveda (1.1.1) says '*Agnimīlle purohitaṁ yajñasya devamṛtvijaṁ hotāraṁ ratnadhātaṁ*, i.e. I prays the fire (agni) that is the priest (purohitaṁ) of sacrifice (Yajña) performing at proper time (ritvija) directing to the Devas (devaṁ), who is also the priest appealing the Gods (hotāraṁ) and the providers of Ratna, i.e. good health, wealth and mind. Fire has been praised since the Vedic time and still by modern time.

1. Modified Forms of Yajña

In many countries of the world, people of all religious communities and creeds, such as Hindu, Muslim, Christian, Jain, Buddhist, Jewish and others use smoke in their houses on special occasions, such as marriage, rituals, etc. By igniting and smoking incense, lamps, incensed-sticks, candles, fragrant gum resin of Indian bdellium (Guggula), frankincense (Lohabān), they have preserved the ancient tradition of Yajña as a symbol even today. All this is a changed and modified form of Vedic Yajña, but at the root of all these is only the 'fire and fumigation' spreading odoriferous smoke in the surroundings and purifying the environment with ultimate effect on plants, microbes, animals and humans.

2. Why to Perform Yajña?

Why our Ṛṣis, sages and ancestors did perform Hawan? What happens by performing Hawan and what happens by not performing it? Several kinds of questions come to mind. In fact, people in ancient India were rich and prosperous. Over the years, due to the attack of the terrorists, looters and the subjugation, India became a poor country. Therefore, all these traditions were highly affected and destroyed. However, Hawan could be done only at the time of marriage and any special occasions or rituals. People forgot the daily Yajña. In the 19th century, Maharṣi Dayānand Saraswati again attempted to rejuvenate the Vedic traditions. But even today, there are many people who ask why one should perform Hawan and what happens with Hawan? The following explanations will definitely be helpful to remove their doubts.

ये देवा दिव्येकादश स्थ ते देवासो हविरिदं जुषध्वम् ।11।

ये देवा अन्तरिक्ष एकादश स्थ ते देवासो हविरिदं जुषध्वम् ।12।

ये देवाः पृथिव्यामेकादश स्थ ते देवासो हविरिदं जुषध्वम् ।13।

(अथर्ववेद 19.27.11–13)

Ye devā divyekādaśa stha te devāso haviridaṁ juṣadhvam.

Ye devā antarikṣa ekādaśa stha te devāso haviridaṁ juṣadhvam.

Ye devah pṛthivyāmekādaśa stha te devāso haviridaṁ juṣadhvam.

(Atharvaveda 19.27.11-13)

[O divine materials! all of you (*devāha*) in the planetary world i.e. *dyauloka* (*divi*), in space (space) (*antarikṣa*) and in the earthly world (*pṛthivyaṁ*), who (these) each have eleven gods (eleven Devas at three different places each i.e. 11 × 3 = 33) established (*stha*), they are you (*te*) Divine substance (*devaso*), take this (*idaṁ*) grain (*haviḥ*) in every world i.e. loka (*juṣdhvaṁ*)].

According to Maharṣi Dayānand Saraswati, there exist 11 Gods in the resplendent world (Dyau Loka), 11 Gods in space and 11 Gods on the earth (11×11, i.e. a total of 33 Gods; 33 Koti Devās means 33 types, not crores) (Yajurveda 7.17). Some important hymns have also been mentioned in the Yajurveda (18.28) and Atharvaveda (10.7.27) regarding the attainment of 33 types of God by praying them. There are 33 Koti of Devās; the word 'Koti' has two meanings, crore (>1 million)) and 'type' (kind, forms). In this case the world 'type' is applicable for God, not 'crore'. Atharvaveda (10.7.27) also mentions that the persons having the knowledge of Vedas know about 33 types of God who bear and nurture the world (*Yasya trayastrinśad devā ange gātrā vibhejire. Tān vai trayāstrinśad devāneke brahmvido viduḥ*. Atharvaveda 10.7.27).

In addition, the Agnihotra Yajña purifies the environment, reduces unwanted contagious pathogenic germs and insects, and improves the mind status of all sacrifice-performers. Thus, performing of Agnihotra is both the act of art and science. The act of art lies in preparation of Hawan Kuṇḍa (square-shaped pit with steps of bricks on edges, or using inverted pyramidal copper pot), selection of wood/twig pieces of plant, selection of odoriferous medicinal herbs, chanting of hymns. The science of Agnihotra lays in its action on germs, insects, plants and humans as well as on the environment. Sacred fire worship cleanses not only the atmospheric pollution but also minimises the total entropy of the body-mind-spirit (BMS) complex by influencing the eight major energy centers, the Cakras (Nair, 2017).

WHAT HAPPENS AFTER PERFORMING A YAJÑA?

Obviously, questions arise in mind that what happens after performing the daily Yajña or at certain rituals or auspicious occasions? Soon after igniting the fire during Yajña, the plant twigs and odoriferous material start burning in the presence of ghee. Here ghee intensifies the burning of these organic matters of wood pieces (*Ghritaṁ tībraṁ juhotan*. Yajurveda 3.2). It has been described that by performing Yajña, there happens an increase in spiritual and physical happiness, attainment of peace, pure environment, good rains, and running away of demonic powers.

अनवद्यैरअभिऽद्युभिर्मखः सहस्वदर्च्चति। गणैरिन्द्रस्य काम्यैः ।।

(ऋग्वेद 1.6.8)

Anavadyairabhi,dyurbhirmakhaḥ sahasvadarccati. Gaṇairindrasya kāmyaih.

(Ṛgveda 1.6.8)

[Oblation (*makh*) adores (*arcati*) irreproachable (*anavaidyaiḥ*), luminous (*abhidyubhiḥ*) and conquered powers (*sahasvaṭ*) of the king of God, Indra (*Indrasya*) with desirable properties (*kāmyaiḥ*)]

Scientific Explanation- We dedicate all our worships, Haviṣa and prayers, for the enhancing the Divine power of Indra, who eliminates the destructing demonic powers, with the help of the universally illuminated vital forces of Maruts. Here the word 'Makh' is synonym of the Yajña. Hawan performed in the fire using medicinal and aromatic materials spreads the odoriferous fumes through the air with the help of sun rays. The germ-destroying substance released from the Hawan fire by air makes all the living beings healthy and strong. In the same way, by making life sacrificial, we should pray to the Supreme Father through continuous practice.

1. Significance of Yajña

Daily and purposefully performed Yajña has much significance as it affect in a subtle manner on soil, water, air, plants, animals and humans as well as on environment. Therefore, we all should perform daily Yajña/Hawan, because of its multifarious effects; some important points of its significance have been briefly given as below:

- A person who performs the Yajña daily and eats according to his / her instinct is healthy and has longevity. Hence, everyone should perform Yajña (*Ayuryajñen kalpatāṁ prano yajñen kalpatāṁ caksuryajñen kalpatāṁ*- Yajurveda 9.21).
- Yajña is the best act, so we all should do the best work (*Yajño vai śresṭhataṁ karma*- Śatapatha Brahman 1.7.1.5).

- Life becomes better by performing a Yajña (*Asave swāhā vasave swāhā vibhuve swāhā*- Yajurveda 22.30).
- Those who wish to attain heaven should perform daily Yajña (*Swargakāmo yajet*- Tandya Brahman 16.15.5).
- The house of the Yajña performers is very attractive, full of wealth, beneficial and delightful (*Hotasadanaṁ haritam hiranyaṁ*- Atharvaveda 7.99.1). Therefore, Yajña / Hawan should be performed daily.
- The daily Hawan keeps the environment clean and the health of Yajña-performers (Yajñik) is also good. Therefore, to keep the environment clean and to keep your health good, the sacrificial fire oblation should be performed daily in the morning during sunrise (7 - 8 am) and also during sunset.

2. Yajña Embodies the Supreme Power

All the living beings on this earth are undoubtedly fed with food. Trees, plants, animals, etc. are the source of all kinds of edible materials required for small or big organisms. But their source is also soil and water. All kinds of nutrients are available in the soil. Plants derive nutrients from soil, and animals from plants, etc. Plants carry out photosynthesis in the presence of light, chlorophyll and water. But the animals do not carry out photosynthesis due to absence of chlorophyll pigments. Therefore, the animals ingest the plants materials and secrete enzymes that break down the complex form of nutrients locked up in cells. On the other hand, the source of food of fungi and bacteria are both, the animals and plants, on which they grow and derive nutrition by decomposing the complex organic materials and absorb the nutrients released from them. Water is required for all these organisms for their growth and development. But the water is possible only through rains after sacrificial fire. That is why, it is necessary to perform a Yajña. All these are described in the Śrīmad Bhagavadgītā (3.14–15).

अन्नाद्भवन्ति भूतानि पर्जन्यादन्नसम्भवः।
यज्ञाद्भवति पर्जन्यो यज्ञ कर्मसमुद्भवः।।
कर्म ब्रह्मोद्भवं विद्धि ब्रह्माक्षरसमुद्भवम्।
तस्मात्सर्वगतं ब्रह्म नित्यं यज्ञे प्रतिष्ठितम्।।

(श्रीमद् भगवद्गीता 3.14–15)

Annādbhavanti bhūtāni parjanyāt annasambhavaḥ.
Yajñādbhavati parjanyo yajña karṃasamudbhavah.
Karm bramhodbhavaṁ viddhi brahmākshar samudbhavaṁ.
Tasmātsarvagataṁ bramha nitye yajñe pratishitaṁ.

(Śrīmad Bhagavadgītā 3.14-15)

[All being *(bhūtāni)* are evolved from food *(annādbhavanti)*; food production (*anna saṁbhavaḥ*) depends on rain (*parjaṅyo*); rain ensues from sacrifice (*yajñādbhavati parjanyo*);

and sacrifice is rooted in action (*yajña karma samudbhavaḥ*). Prescribed action (*karma*) originates from Vedas (*brahmodbhavaṁ*), and the Vedas proceeds from indestructible (*braḥmākṣara samudbhavṁ*); therefore, all the pervading (*tasmāt saṛvgataṁ*) infinite (*nityaṁ*) is always present in sacrifice (*yajñe pratiṣṭhitaṁ)*]

Scientific Explanation- Śrīmad Bhagavadgītā very rightly describes the chronology of Yajña in well ordered way. Obviously, the animal's life is possible only due to plants and plant's life is possible only because of water through rain. As we know that animals cannot derive the nutrients as plant do through photosynthesis. Animal cells lack chloroplast, i.e. the machineray of photosynthesis. During photosynthesis, energy derived from light foming from the sun in the resence of water in plant's chloroplast is stored, and utilised by all animals as food including humans. Thus the digestive system of animals that has may cells/single cell of unicellular organims ingest the food and breakdown enzymatically to derive energy and nutrients like proteins, fats, carbohydrates, vitamins, minerals, etc. Therefore, animal's life is not possible without the plants. In contrast, the plant prepare their food materials through photosynthesis in the presence of water because photolysis of water results in oxygen that is necessry for all aerobic morganisms.

$$2H_2O \rightarrow 4H^+ + 4e + O_2 \uparrow$$

Here two photons from light are required for electron (*e*) flow through electron transport system from one molecule of water (H_2O) with the evolution of one molecule of oxygen (O_2). All the initial metabolic activities of plants occur within the chloroplast in aqueous environment. Therefore, plant's life is not possible without water. Further, water comes through clouds that bring the water. The clouds are formed only after Yajña, a mechanisms that creates temperature gradient and help in evoporation of water and formation of clouds in the sky. The sacrifice (Yajña) is rooted in action that originates from the Vedas which itself have emerged from the Supreme Father. Hence, that OMnipresent as OM is pervading in the pious scrifice and all of us should perform Agnihotra.

METHOD OF DAILY YAJÑA (SACRIFICE)

Before starting the Yajña, the Yajña-performer (Yajñik) should be ready after bath in the morning and be prepared with a pure mind. Daily Yajña is performed in a Yajñaśālā (Figure 9.1) or at some other fixed place. For performing Yajña, the book, Hawan Sāmagri (mixture of aromatic and medicinal plant materials), Samidhā [wood pieces of mango (*Mangifera indica*), Bel (*Aegle marmelos*), cedar (*Cedrus deodara*), cowdung, coconut (*Cocos nucifera*), or other plants], copper Hawan Kuṇd and copper vessel, etc. should be collected in advance.

The daily Yajña is completed in two stages, in the first phase the Sandhyopāsanā mantras are recited and in the second phase, the sacrifice is offered through various hymns (mantras) narrating the word 'Swāhā'. Different types of mantras to be recited in Sandhyopāsanā are Ācamana Mantra, Anga Sparśa Mantra, Iśvara Prayer Mārjana Mantra, Prānāyām Mantra, Agamarṣaṇa Mantra, Manasāparikramā Mantra, Upsthana Mantra, Gāyatri Mantra, Samarpaṇa

Mantra and Namaskār Mantra. Similarly, chanting mantras are Āchman Mantra, Anga Sparś Mantra, Iśvara Stuti Prārthopāsanā Mantra, Agnayādhān Mantra, Agni Pradipta Mantra, Samidhādāna Mantra, Ghritāhuti, Jal Prasecana Mantra, Āghārāvājyāhuti Mantra, Ājyābhāgāhuti Mantra, morning-evening Mantras, Vyāhrityāhuti Mantra, Swishtakridāhuti Mantra, Prajāpatyāhuti Mantra, Ājyāhuti Mantra, Aṣtājyahuti Mantra, Purṇāhuti Mantra. Help can be taken from books written for performing Yajña.

Figure 9.1. Yajñaśālā of Gurukula Kangri (Deemed to be University), Haridwar.

1. Material used in Daily Yajña

Two types of material are used in daily Yajña, first Samidha i.e. thick pieces of bark-containing wood which are ignited in fire, and second is the incense material which contains aromatic and medicinal herbs. Some of the following other material used are mentioned in brief.

- **Hawan Kuṅḍa (Inverted Pyramidal Copper Pot)-** An inverted pyramidal copper (ICP) pot called Hawan Kuṅḍa (top 29 × 29 cm, bottom 10.5 cm × 10.5 cm, height 12.5 cm or its half sized pot used at small level) is used for daily Agnihotra. The size of copper pot may increase or decrease according to the requirement. Traditionally, Hawan Kuṅḍas were used to prepare by digging pits of various sizes and depths.
- **Samidhā (Small Twigs with Bark)-** According to the shape of Hawan Kuṇḍa, small twigs (approximately 25 cm long) with bark or wood pieces are used, such as sandalwood (*Santalum album*), cedar (*Cedrus deodara*), mango (*Mangifera indica*), Palās (*Butea frondosa*), grapevine (*Vitis vinifera*), Vata (*Ficus bengalensis*), Pipal (*Ficus religiosa*), śami/Ghaf (*Prosopis cineraria*), etc. are used as per size of Hawan Kuṅḍa. Dried cake made of cow dung is also used for such work.
- **Hawan Sāmagri (Odoriferous Medicinal Herbs used as Oblation to Fire)-** The main aromatic plants used in oblation material are agar (*Aquilaria agallocha*), tagar (*Tabernaemontana coronaria*), powder of sandalwood (*Santalum album*), saffron (*Crocus sativus*), mace/Jāvitri (*Myristica fragrans*), camphor (*Cinnamomum camphora*), rice (*Oryza sativa*), barley (*Hordeum vulgare*), gram (*Cicer aeritinum*), peas (*Pisum sativum*), etc.
- **Medicinal Plants-** The main medicinal plants used in incense materials are– Giloy (*Tinospora cardifolia*), water hyssop or Brāhmī (*Baccopa monnieri*), Śankhpushpī

(*Convolvulus prostratus*), Mulethī (*Glycyrrhiza glabra*), Lālcandan (*Pterocarpus marsupium*), Harada (*Terminalia chebula*), Baherā (*Terminalia bellirica*), etc.

- **Ghee or Oil-** Ghee or oil and sesame seeds (*Sesamum indicum*) or linseed (*Linum usataticimum*) are used in the incense.
- **Other Ingredients-** In addition to the above, sugar or sugarcane product, jaggery i.e. Khāṇa or honey are also used.

2. Variations in Incense Contents

Different types of incense are made in different seasons. For example, the Hawan contents in the spring, summer, rainy, autumn and winter seasons vary in quantity and number. Medicinal plants found in North India and Himalayas are not found in South India. Similarly, most of the herbs and aromatic plants found in South India are not found in North India because the climate of both the regions is not the same. Probably, there is abundance of medicinal and aromatic plants in the Himalayan regions. That is why, when Lakṣmaṇa was fainted by Meghnāth's arrows, Mahābalī Hanumān came to the Himalaya to bring Sanjīvanī for saving the life of Lakṣmaṇa. Therefore, there are variations in the medicinal plants used in North India and South India, as well as in the other parts of the country. Hence, medicinal and aromatic herbs to be used as Hawan Sāmagrī (fire oblations materials) should be selected on the basis of availability in the particular areas.

For the said work, care is also taken for the accessibility and purpose of the material. Different types of fire oblation materials are chosen for different purposes at different rituals and seasons. The place where fire offering is to be started must be clean and hygienic and all materials should be collected in advance. An inverted pyramidal copper (IPC) pot and the copper vessels are shown in Figure 9.2.

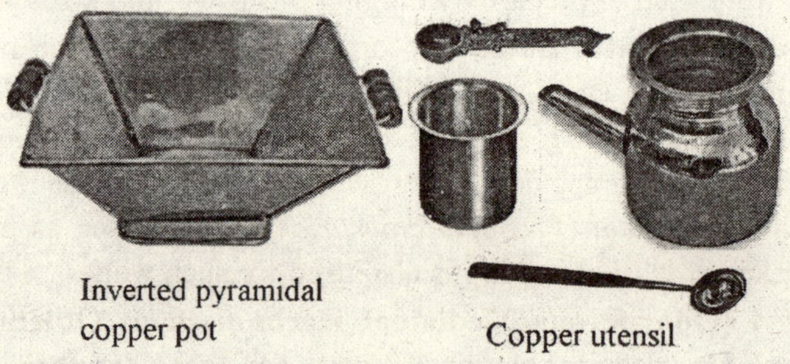

Figure 9.2. An inverted pyramidal copper (IPC) pot (Hawan Kuṅḍa) and copper vessels.

In a study, the conventional fire oblations (cow dung cake and unpolished rice), plus 2-3 pieces of copra (coconut endosperm) and nine types of grains (Navadhānya), were spread sparsely in the shade at room temperature. The oblations were not dried under direct sunlight because its heat/light sensitive chemicals may be denatured. Then the dried oblations were powdered by using a blender/grinder. The powdered samples were analyzed within three months

(Nair, 2017). After burning fire in the IPC pot, the exact amount of incense made from odoriferous medicinal herbs was offered to fire, along with narration of the Vedic hymns ending with the word 'Svāhā'. Use of Navadhānya is described in South India. Offering 2-3 pieces of coconut endosperm and the Navadhānya in the burning fire increases the intensity and efficiency of the fume that spread all around the place of sacrifice (Nair, 2017).

Nine Types of Grains (Navadhānya)

Wheat (*Triticum aestivum*), rice (*Oryza sativa*), black sesame (*Sesamum indicum*), red lentils (*Lens culinaris*), green gram (mung) (*Vigna radiata*), black gram (*Vigna mungo*), Bengal gram (*Cicer arietinum*), horse gram (*Macrotyloma uniflorum*) and white bean (*Phaseolus vulgaris*).

2. Why to Take Yajñaśeṣa?

Many times, people ask whether it is necessary to take Yajñaśeṣa (food items made up grains and ghee left over after sacrifice) after completion of Agnihotra. It should be completely clear what happens if you take or not take the Yajñaśeṣa? What is the significance of Yajñaśeṣa? Why are the products made of food, vegetables and butter used in the Yajña? This is all a matter of consideration. In the Śrīmad Bhagavadgītā (3.13), taking or not taking of the Yajñaśeṣa has been mentioned.

यज्ञशिष्टाशिनः सन्तो मुच्यन्ते सर्वकिल्बिशैः।
भुन्जते ते त्वघं पापा ये पचन्त्यात्मकारणात्।।

(श्रीमद् भगवद्गीता 3.13)

Yajñaśiṣthāśinaḥ saṅto mucyaṅte sarvakilbiśaiḥ.
Bhuñjate te tvaghaṁ pāpā ye pacaṅtyātmakāraṇāt.

(Śrīmad Bhagavadgītā 3.13)

[The devotees (*santo*), who eat (*āsinaḥ*) of what is left over after sacrifice (*yajña-śiṣtā*), are absolved (*ucyaṅte*) of all kinds of (*sarva*) sins (*kilbiṣaiḥ*). But (*tu*) those (*te*) sinful ones (*pāpā*) who (*ye*) cook the food (*pacaṅtyaṭ*) for the sake of nursing their bodies alone (*ātma-kārṇāt*), partake (*bhuñjate*) of grievous sins (*aghaṁ pāpāḥ*) only]

Scientific Explanation- In the operation of creation and nurture of living beings, five kinds of beings are related, such as Goddess and God, Ṛṣi s, Pitṛgana (died forefathers), humans and other beings. With the help of these five being, everyone is nurtured. Gods and goddesses are to everyone in the world offered according to will. Ṛṣi gives knowledge to all. The forefathers want the welfare of all. Humans serve everyone through their actions and offer themselves to animal, birds, trees and all as a means of happiness. But the responsibility of all these duties is on the humans. Therefore, man serves everyone by the classical method. Pañca Mahāyajña (Brahmayajña) is performed by the classical rituals. These Pañcamahāyajña are- reciting Veda, Vedānga and Śāstras (Brahman Yajña or Ṛṣi Yajña), Hawan (Deva Yajña), guest service or hospitality (Atithi Yajña), serving parents with reverence (PitṛYajña), and serving every being through the sacred sacrifice to Balivaiśvadeva (BalivaiśvaYajña) (*Pātho homaścātithinām saparyā tarpanam baliḥ, amī pañca mahāyajñā brahmayajñādi nāmakā*). Whatever a man earns, he receives from the cooperation and blessings of all. Therefore, the person who eats the leftover food after giving it to everyone after his sacrifice is called the 'nectar eater' (Amritāśī). But the one who does not do this and by taking away the self of others, earns and pleases only for himself, in fact he eats sin. This is because, without sacrificing in the fire of cooked grain, the Gods, Goddesses and Balivaiśvadeva do not become happy. Hence, Hawan and Balivaiśvadeva are given more importance here. Therefore, those who enjoy the Yajñaśeṣa have been referred to as 'Yajñaśiṣtāśinaḥ Santo'.

It is necessary to understand here the word 'sin'. What is sin, and how does it take place unknowingly? In order to sustain life, all of us do some form of the violence, such as the violence of ants and insects including microorganisms, the violence of individuals in serving the citizens and war, in the practice of life, in the cultivation during ploughing, trade and crafts. Many germs and insects die due to our daily activities; hence, daily violence takes place in the place of keeping stoves (Culha), broom (Jhāṇu), pestle (Okhli), and water-containers (Udkumbhī) in houses (*Kandni peṣani culli udkumbhī ca mārjani. Pañca sūnā grihastasya vartante,harahaḥ sadā*). Therefore, after being free from all laxity and neglect, to provide happiness to all the living beings for public service, and after offering the sacrifice of Pañca Mahāyajñādi and Balivaiśvadeva, the person taking the cooked Yajñaśeṣa becomes free from sin. Therefore, because of being the wealth and earning as sinful, the enjoyer is a 'sinner' and his pleasures are called 'sin' (*Agham sa kevalam bhungakte yaḥ pañcatyatmakāraṇat*- Manusmṛti-3.118).

3. Effect of Soma Yajña

In Vedas, Soma is conceptualized as a spiritual principle and cosmic power, which is present in all plants (Ṛgveda 10.97.7), in water of rivers originating from the Himalaya (Ṛgveda-7.49.4), every form of fire (Agni) as well as throughout the universe. Becoming immortal and attaining physical strength and the Devine Light by consuming Soma have been mentioned in Ṛgveda (8.48.3). Moreover, Soma Yajña plays a great role in refining the human minds and life process according to the Nature. It is performed to bestow the prosperity of human and restore equilibrium in the Nature. There are many plants that have been described to have the Soma, namely three species of ephedrine-yielding *Ephedra* (*Ephedra gerardiana*, *E. intermedia* and *E. major* var. *procera*), similar to 'Haoma' as mentioned in Avesta texts. R.G. Wasson suggested the presence of Soma in a mushroom called *Amanita muscaria*. But Merlin (2008) has mentioned a similarity between the Soma and a narcotic plant, *Papaver somniferum*.

According to Abhang (2015), the purpose of Soma Yajña is different from that of ordinary Yajña. This term is derived from a ceremony where fresh and green stalk of Soma or Somāwalī (species of *Ephedra*) is used. In Soma Yajña, the plants are used are the stalk of Somāwalī, twigs of banyan (*Ficus bengalensis*), Pīpal or sacred fig (*Ficus religiosa*), mango (*Mangifera indica*) and many others. Both types of Yajña (Soma Yajña and daily Yajña) are performed to purify the environment and control the cycle of six seasons. But both the Yajñas differ from each other with respect to purpose, time, odoriferous medicinal herbs, cost and public participation at a time.

SCIENTIFIC VALIDATION OF AGNIHOTRA

There are mainly two types of energy in the physical world, thermal energy and sound energy. Both types of energy are produced at the time of Hawan- sound energy through chanting of Vedic hymns and heat energy through sacrifices after fire combustion. In the fire ignited in Hawana Kuṇḍa, fumigation, vaporisation and subtlisation of substances of specific incense material occur as a result of a scientific process that produces ions and energy consisting of sonic waves of Vedic hymns, influencing the Yajña performers (Yājñik). Therefore, for the involuntary, physical and spiritual benefit, both types of energies need to be blended with Brahman energy, which can only be achieved through the oblation of odoriferous medicinal herbs as oblation in sacrificial fire.

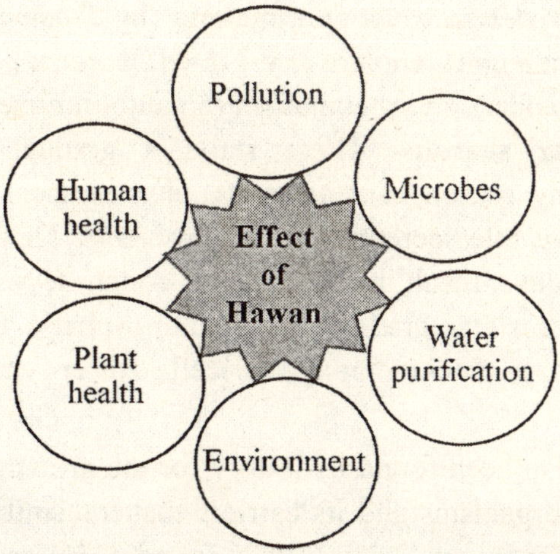

Figure 9.3. Effect of Agnihotra on environment, plants and human health.

1. Impact on the Environment

Many scientists have worked on the effect of Agnihotra Yajña on environment, plants and human health, and have also advocated the validity of the effect of Yajña (Figure 9.3). It is not possible to describe the experiments of everyone here. Therefore, only some scientific results have been briefly described. With the change in the climate, temperature, wind, precipitation, rains and biodiversity, several environmental changes occur resulting in the changes in growth, development and destruction of the microbial biodiversity. Therefore, we must change our food habit and living style according to climatic changes. Moreover, our sages used to perform

Agnihotra during Vedic period at the time of changes in seasons to purify the environment by applying odoriferous medicinal herbs.

2. Impact on Microorganisms

Microorganisms are one of the most ancient species evolved on the planet Earth. They are ubiquitous in distribution. They grow fast and adapt with the changes in the environment. But their numbers and diversity vary with the seasonal changes; the number of pathogens may be low or high in a particular season. Accordingly they cause diseases in plants, animals and humans. Different kinds of diseases occurring in different seasons can record be recorded as below:

- **Summer season-** There remains high temperature in summer season. Hence, the effect may be sun stroke, body parts burning, heart problem, constipation, hyper pigmentation, etc.
- **Rainy season-** In rainy season, there is excessive moisture in the environment and water-logged conditions causing congenial environment for the growth of insects and microorganisms. The most prevalent diseases of rainy season are- itching (ringworm) in body, scabies (by *Corynebacterium* sp.), malaria (by *Plasmodium falciparum*), typhoid (by *Salmonella typhimurium*), cholera (by *Vibrio cholerae*), pneumonia (by *Klebsiella pneumoniae*, staphylococci), and rheumatism (an autoimmune disease).
- **Autumn and winter seasons-** There starts a gradual increase/decrease in the temperature after rainy season causing many physiological disorders, bile fever, and other several excessive bile secretion-related problems. Dews and fog/smog in winter, persisting for several days, result in cold, sneeze, cough, fever and headache.
- **Spring season-** There starts gradual rise in atmospheric temperature, which causes measles (Morbillivirus), chicken pox (Varicella-zoster virus), small pox (smallpox virus), etc.

Besides, Agnihotra has also been found inhibitory for the growth and multiplication of both normal and pathogenic microorganisms and its carriers that transmit the aetiologic agents from diseased person to the healthy persons. Tilak (1982) found a decrease in the number of fungal species by about 70 percent after performing the Hawan. Nautiyal *et al.* (2007) conducted a detailed study on the effect of medicinal smoke used in incense burns on the bacterial composition and changes in its numbers in an artificial chamber. The scientific and ancient knowledge of Agnihotra, on the changes in composition and number of airborne microorganisms in the environment by sacrificed smoke, emanated after burning of 52 odoriferous medicinal plants, in the sacrificial fire, used in the incense procured from the Gurukula Kangri Pharmacy (Haridwar), could be validated based on the basis of Biolog Microplate and Microlog database studies. Compared to the untreated chamber, most pathogenic bacteria were not found in the treated room for about one month after 24 hours of the Hawan. The absence of bacteria was only due to smoke alone.

After performing the Hawan, the smoke spreads far enough through the air and affects the air-borne bacteria. Such pathogenic bacteria are either eliminated or their numbers are reduced on the plant. Approximately, over 94% decline in population of aerial bacteria was recorded after 1 exposure of medicinal smoke. Moreover, the smoke was capable to purify and maintain the environment clean for 24 h in the closed experimental room. All the pathogenic bacteria that existed before the sacrificial fire were eliminated after using the oblation material containing of odoriferous medicinal herbs used in Hawan. The pathogenic bacteria, absent for 30 days. were *Bacillus megaterium, Clevibactor agropyri, Corynebacterium urealyticum Staphylococcus lentus, Staphylococcus xylosus, Enterobacter aerogenes.* The bacterial species present for 30 days after offering the oblation material to Sacrificial fire were *Bacillus cereus, Cellulomonas turbata, Flavobacterium johnsoniae, Leifsonia aquatic,* etc. The fungi eliminated even after exposer of medicinal smoke for 12 hours were *Alternaria Alternata, Aspergillus terreus, Cladosporium herbarum, Rhizopus oryzae,* etc. (Table 1).

Table 1. Effect of Fumes of Agnihotra on microorganisms*.

Names of Microorganisms	Before start of Hawan	12 hours after Hawan
Bacteria (Gram-positive and Gram-negative)		
Bacillus megaterium	+	+
Burkholderia glumae	+	-
Clavibacter agropyri	+	-
Corynebacterium urealyticum	+	+
Enterobacter aerogenes	+	-
Kocuria rosea	+	-
Pseudomonas syringae	+	-
Sphingomonas yanoikuyae	+	-
Staphylococcus lentus	+	-
Staphylococcus xylosus	+	-
Xanthomonas campestris	+	-
Fungi		
Alternaria Alternata	+	-
Aspergillus terreus	+	-
Cladosporium herbarum	+	-
Curvularia lunata	+	+
Rhizopus oryzae	+	-

*Based on Nautiyal *et al.* (2007), Gupta (1996), Navneet *et al.* (2011)

Several pollutants, such as sulfur and nitrogen oxides, hydrocarbons and pathogenic microorganisms are always present in the environment. In 2017, Pranay *et al.* (2015) conducted a detailed study of the beneficial effects of ash of Agnihotra on the environment and plant growth. They found that the microbial load and sulfur oxide levels, near the odoriferous smoke emanation area of the Agnihotra, decreased by 89 percent, but the level of nitrogen oxides increased slightly, though it was below the desired level. Treatment of Agnihotra ash increased the seed germination and seedling growth of black gram (*Vigna mungo*) with neutralization of genotoxic effects. Therefore, these experiments prove that daily/weekly incense burns kill pathogenic bacteria, the number of normal bacteria is almost eliminated, the environment becomes clean and the sacrifice performers remain healthy.

2. Work done on Agnihotra in Gurukula Kangri (Deemed to be University), Haridwar

In 1996, Ganga P. Gupta studied the effect of Agnihotra Yajña smoke on the number of bacteria, fungi and actinobacteria, in the Department of Botany and Microbiology. He found that the number of microorganisms, as mentioned earlier, decreased considerably due to the effect of the smoke of the Yajña. In 1998, Navneet, in the same department also found, in the Yajña experiments performed in the Prayer Hall of the University, that most of the microorganisms present in the Prayer Hall before the Hawan were killed after the Hawan and the microbial load decreased in the room. After the sacrificial fire, the fully eliminated fungi were *Aspergillus niger*, *Aspergillus terreus*, *Cladosporium herbarum*, *Rhizopus oryzae*, etc. But the number of *Curvularia lunata* was completely reduced after 12 hours of Hawan (Navneet *et al.* 2011).

3. Work on Agnihotra Yajña by Ārya Pratinidhi Sabha (Delhi)

A scientific study, on Hawan under the auspices of Ārya Pratinidhi Sabhā (Delhi) under the guidance of Vedācārya Śri Sanata Kumar, was conducted at two different places to reduce microbial load in air and water. All the pre- and post-Hawan tests were done in famous laboratories, such as Sigma Test and Research Center (Delhi), ITRI Innovation (London), F.I.C.C.I. Research and Analysis Center (New Delhi), and CSIR-NEERI (Nagpur). Pre- and post-incense analyses resulted in the reduced microbial loads (both fungi and bacteria) in air and water (sewage and tap). The decrease in MPN index of water is a sign of decreasing bacterial load.

After 10 days of Hawan outside the chamber, the concentration particulate matter (PM) i.e. PM-10 in the air gradually reduced from 465 microgram/mL to 180 microgram/mL and that of PM-2.5 decreased from 229 microgram/mL to 95 microgram/mL. Similarly, the concentration of carbon dioxide was reduced from 479 ppm (parts per million) to 360 ppm, and that of carbon monoxide from 11 ppm to 1 ppm. But after burning the oblation in fire in the chamber, the amount of carbon dioxide was reduced from 1280 ppm to 471 ppm. If carbon dioxide is released slowly, the concentration of oxygen has little effect. This proves that by performing the Hawan, the environment becomes clean and purified. After incineration, a many essential elements are left in the ash, such as sodium, aluminum, phosphorus, silica, sulfur, calcium, magnesium, iron, nickel , Copper, gink, selenium, etc., which are necessary to increase the fertility of the soil, All these elements are also required in plant nutrition.

4. Water Purification by Using the Ashes of Incense

Pranay *et al.* (2015) used the ashes obtained after Hawan for purification of contaminated water. They prepared a column of glass and filled the ashes of the incense in it and allowed to flow slowly the non-potable contaminated water. Purification of polluted water using the Hawan ash is show in Figure 9.4. The filtered and collected water was analysed according to the guidelines of the Central Pollution Control Board (CPCB) (New Delhi) (2005-2008). It was found that the polluted water filtered through the ash in glass column complied with completes minimum levels of all the standards of potable water (for example, BOD, COD, TDS, TSS, MPN, SPC, etc.) set by the World Health Organization. Therefore, contaminated water treated in this way becomes potable. This experiment proves that the ashes of Hawan can be used to increase fertility of soil, seed germination and plant growth as well as purification of contaminated water.

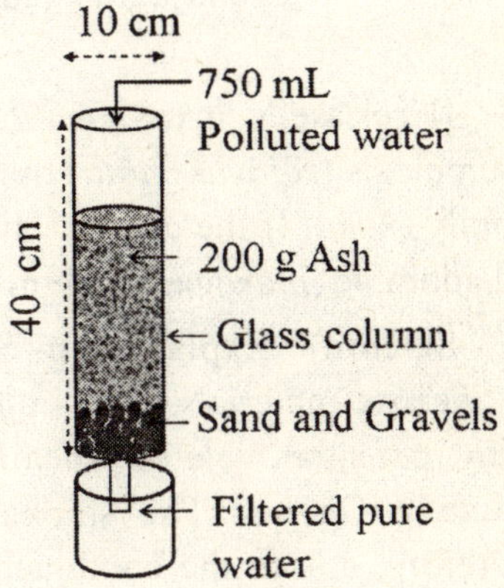

Figure 9.4. Purification of polluted water using the Hawan ash.

EFFECT OF AGNIHOTRA ON HUMAN HEALTH

According to the Ayurveda, about 22 types of diseases can effectively be controlled by the Agnihotra. For the best curative and preventive powers of Hawan, use of a combination of 17 medicinal herbs mixed with the 10 plants has been suggested (Tripathy, 1953). These specific 10 plants, having the prophylactic and therapeutic properties are against all diseases, are- Agara (*Aquilaria agallocha*), Tagara (*Tabernaemontana coronaria*), Caṅdana (*Santalum album*), Lāl caṅdana (*Pterocarpus marsupium*), Devadaru (*Polyalthia longifolia*), Guggal (*Commiphora candata*), Jāiphala (*Myristica aromaticum*), Launga (*Syzygium aromaticum*), Cirāyatā (*Swertia chirayita*), and Aśwagaṅdha (*Withania somnifera*).

Before studying the effect of Agnihotra on human health, knowledge of some of the basic organs of humans and their esoteric secrets is essential, such as different types of waves operating in the brain and the concept of the eight Cakras (energy centres), their location and function.

1. Cure of Tuberculosis by Hawan

The fumes of odoriferous medicinal herbs emanated during Hawan spread around the nearby area and affect the environment including plants, animals and humans. The sick person becomes disease-free by offering the oblation to the in fire, Agnihotra. All the unknown diseases like tuberculosis are overcome by Hawan and sun rays. Such views are expressed in the Atharvaveda (3.11.1) and Ṛgveda (10.161.1).

मुन्चामि त्वा हविषा जीवनाय कमज्ञातयक्ष्मादुत राजयक्ष्मात्।
ग्राहिर्जग्राह यदि वैतदेनं तस्या इन्द्राग्नी प्र मुमुक्तमेनम्।।

(ऋग्वेद 10.161.1)

Muñcāmi tvā haviṣā jīvanāy kamajñāta yakṣmādut rājayakṣmāt.
Grāhirjagrāh yadi vaitdenaṁ tasyā indrāgnī pra mumuktamenaṁ.

(Ṛgveda 10.161.1)

[I release you (*tvā muñcāmi*) from the unknown wasting disease (*ajñāt yakṣmāta*) and tuberculosis (*rajayakṣmāta*) by the use of proper diet (*haviṣā*) and live for a long time (*jivanāy*) happily (*kaṁ*). If the grip has siezed (*yadi tvā enaṁ yetaṭ jagrāh*), may you, O! God resplendent and adorable (*indrāgni*) set him free from it (*pramuktaṁ*)].

Scientific Explanation- Several aromatic medicinal herbs are used along with Guggal in the incense materials used in Agnihotra. All these medicinal plants have curative properties. Many potential volatile chemicals are released in the form of smoke of medicinal plants including Guggal. The smoke emanated after burning in fire in Ghee also antimicrobial. Therefore, due to the combined effect of these volatile chemicals on the bacterial cells of the *Mycobacterium tuberculosis*, the chance of cure of tuberculosis becomes high. That is why a person suffering from tuberculosis can get rid of disease by performing regular Hawan using odoriferous medicinal herbs containing Guggal gum.

2. Effect of Hawan Smokes on Brainwaves

Brain is the master organ of human body; hence it is a mainstay of life-force. All the actions are controlled only by the nervous system of the brain consisting of about 10 billion nerve cells. Therefore, it can also be called as an 'electrochemical organ'. Along with being the main point of the nervous system, it is also a center for various other types of energy. Energy is always released by the brain and distributed throughout the body. Energy reaches various parts of the body in the form of subtle waves. It has been speculated that a completely functioning brain in a human is capable of generating approximately 10 watts of electricity. Furthermore, if all 10 billion nerve cells interconnected to each other discharge at one time, 5-50 millionths of a volt of electricity can be recorded by an electrode that may flash a light bulb. In addition, the electrical pulses emerging from the brain proceed as brainwaves. There are seven types of brainwaves having the highest level to the least level of activity. Brain generates beta waves when a person is engaged in mental activities, delivering a lecture, a talk or a speech. But the mu waves are generated when body of a person is at rest.

Brain produce seven types of waves of different lengths called 'wavelength', which perform many functions. Therefore, before performing the Hawan, one should pray with enthusiasm to the Supreme Father i.e. the Supreme Soul, so that the mind can concentrate and be fully devoted to speech and action to the Brahman. By doing so, equilibrium is established between the brainwaves and the cosmic waves. At the time of Hawan, the brain waves are affected due to good idea and peace in mind. During Hawan period, mind, hatred, deception, deceit, etc. should not be kept in mind towards any person. Due to having any type of misconception against any person at the time of Hawan similar types of brainwaves are produced (Table 9.2).

Table 9.2. Type and function of brainwaves.

Brain waves	Frequency (Hertz)	Function of brainwaves
Gamma waves	Maximum	Gamma waves have the maximum frequency and play a key role carrying out functions by different areas of brain and making coordination among them. They have relation with intelligence and memory coordination.
Beta waves	14-25	These waves are produced during alertness, consciousness and active phase of mental activity. They are active during making decision and stress also.
Alpha waves	8-13	These waves are produced at a time when a person at a stage of rest, positive thought or consciousness. But person cannot act according to thoughts. It links between conscious and unconscious mind.
Theta waves	3-8	Theta waves are very active during sleep, mental stress, and meditation as well as many types of mental disorders. Senses from the external world are withdrawn and focused on signals originating from the brain.
Delta waves	1-4	They are also called 'slow waves' and are active during deep sleep and unconsciousness, mainly in babies. They trigger immunity in body.
Lambda waves	Maximum	Lambda waves are difficult to be measured accurately because of having the least frequency. They synthesize the brain function.
Mu waves	9-11	Mu waves or sensory motor rhythms are more active when body is at rest. They are the synchronized patterns of electrical activity that include large numbers of neurons of the brain controlling voluntary movement of body organs.

The consciousness come comes like the ladder of these waves. For example, the gamma waves are present abundantly in the brain of a person who becomes spiritually-enlightened. But the gamma waves are not produced in a person who is not in deep consciousness. The frequency (energy level) of gamma waves is the highest as compared to the other among brainwaves. A substantial amount of brainwaves (i.e. alpha to gamma waves) are generated uninterruptedly in the brain to flow Prāna/PCE incessantly through the energy centre (Cakras) so that the good health of Yajña performers can be maintained (Nair, 2017). The desired benefit of performing Hawan is not obtained when there is reluctance, excitement or tension in the mind.

3. Eight Energy Centres (Aṣṭa Cakras)

It is impossible for a human body to function without maintaining the energetic continuity driven by the Sun's light. Because the energy sources of all organisms are the sun's rays. There are eight Cakras (*Aṣṭacakrā navdvārā devānāṁ purayodhyā. Tasyāṁ hiraṇyayaḥ koṣah swargo jayotiṣāvṛtah.* Atharvaveda 10.2.31) are located on the Suṣumnā Nāḍi that help in maintaining this energetic avidity. There are nine gates in human body, such as one mouth, two eyes, two nasal cavities, two ears, two places of stools and urine. The Cakras are the vital energy centre of highly concentrated energy along the spinal cord of our body. There are associated with eight major hormonal glands.

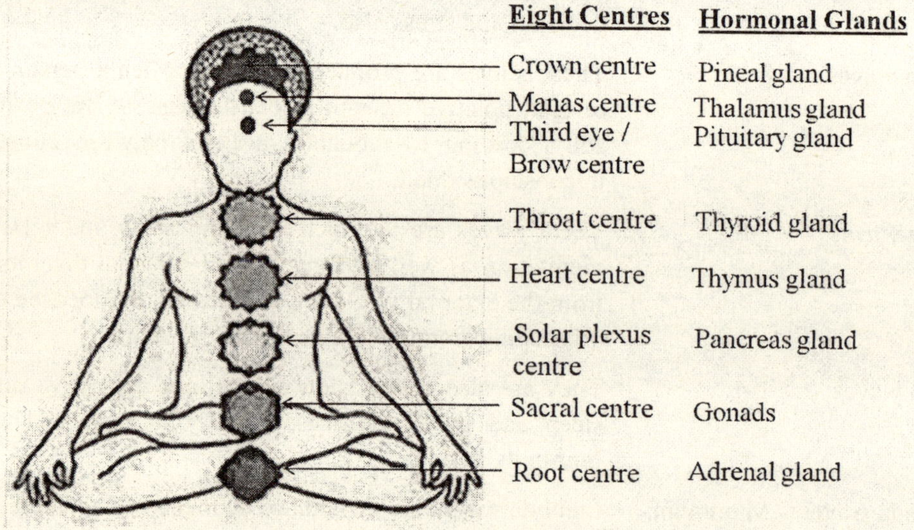

Figure 9.5. Eight energy centers (Cakras) in human body.

These eight Cakras, moving from root to crown centres of body, are Mulādhār Cakra, Swādhiṣṭhān Cakra, Maṇipūr Cakra, Anāhata Cakra, Viśuddhi Cakra, Ājñā Cakra, Manaścakra and Sahasrāra Cakra. All these eight chakras are mainly eight energy centers, which are located atop the spinal cord of our body and control the energetic avidity (Figure 9.5).

These eight energy centres (Cakras) are located at different places on spinal cord of the human body. These centres act in well coordinated ways and spread the vital energy in the body of Yogic practiceners and sacrifice performers. These centres generate energy only when excited, otherwise not. The excited and synchronized energy moves upwardly and in joins the Cosmic Energy, resulting in extremely overwhelming experience by the yogic practiceners. The yogic practices must be learnt by the expert teachers and should be practice in his/her advice only. The energy centres and their function are briefly given in Table 9.3.

Table 9.3. Eight Cakras (Energy Centers) and its Functions in Human Body.

	Cakras	Endocrine glands	Functions of energy centres
1.	Mulādhār	Adrenal gland (Root centre)	This centre is located on the spinal cord between the anus and the urethra, and provides energy to the malaise, the anus and the urethra to function.
2.	Svādhiṣṭhān	Gonads (Spleen centre)	This centre is situated on the spinal cord below the navel. It is related to the person's consciousness. It provides energy to the genitals, spinal cord and kidneys. When this centre is not active, the prostate glands, uterus and urethra do not function properly.
3.	Maṇipur	Pancreas	This centre is located on the spinal cord near the navel, which keeps the digestive power healthy by providing energy to the digestive system.
4.	Anāhat	Thymus gland (heart centre)	This centre is located in the middle of the chest, inside the spinal cord. It helps in proper functioning by providing energy to the nervous system, heart, respiratory and immune systems.
5.	Viśuddhi	Thyroid gland	This centre is situated on the vertebral column of the vertebra behind the neck and controls the physical growth by affecting the larynx, hunger, thirst, temperature, nose, ear, lungs and breathing. It affects metabolism of the body.
6.	Ājñā Cakra	Pituitary gland	This centre is an active form of energy that lies between the two eyebrows. The person's wishes and brain are controlled due to its activation. If it is not active, it causes epilepsy, fainting, paralysis, depression, memory loss, etc.
7.	Manaścakra	Hypothalamus	This centre is also called Lalanā Cakra. The energy stored in this centre is directly related to the hypothalamus and the cerebellum (cerebro-cortex). This centre controls the mind, heart, endocrine gland, intelligence and sleep.
8.	Sahasrāra	Pineal gland (Crown centre)	This is the energy center of martyrdom and intelligence. The awakening of this centre brings physical and spiritual energy. In this cycle, the power of life becomes constant and the person becomes stable of mind.

What is Kuṇḍalinī (Coiled Power) ?

All eight energy centres (Cakras) are the doors of Kuṅḍalinī. For the Kuṅḍalinī-awakening (kuṅḍalinī jāgaraṇa), all the doors located in the middle of it have to be pierced through Yogic practice. The word 'Kuṅḍalinī' has been mentioned in the Hindu texts. It is a force that, being 'coiled like a serpent', generally rests at the base of the spine. Hence, it is called Kuṅḍalinī or 'the coiled power', i.e. a type of 'cosmic energy' accumulated at the base of spine. The awakened Kuṅḍalinī rises up from the Mulādhāra Cakra to the top of the crown centre i.e. pineal gland (Sahasrāra Cakra) through the spinal cord (Suṣumnā) along the spines. A mystical experience of awakened Kuṅḍalinī at different energy centres (Cakras) differs due to achieving of differential awakening energy. Finally, the ultimate progress of awakened Kuṅḍalinī at the crown centre imparts the highest level of deeply transformed consciousness

There is a continuous flow of energy, through the meridian line, located in the body of the sacrifice performers, which is called 'Letting Incessant Flow of Energy' (LIFE). Before understanding the continuous flow of energy, knowledge of the properties of some of the basic energy centres (Cakras) of human body is necessary. Pure cosmic energy (PCE) or Prāṇa is the LIFE that flows continuously over these eight energy centres (Nair, 2017). In Yogic postures, it seems as if the downward facing lotus is blooming upward. The awakenings of these Cakras illuminate the body in the same way as the darkness disappears with the sun rise and the whole earth becomes illuminated. On awakening the Kuṅḍalini, the life energy starting from Mulādhār moves to upwardly facing Sahasrār Cakra dissolves in the body.

The complete random (wasted) energy (entropy) of the 'body-mind-spirit complex' (BMS complex) of the sacrifice performers is reduced by balancing and aligning the eight energy centers of our body (Figure 9.5). When these energy centres are aligned, the PCE/Prāṇa flows uninterruptedly through meridian or 'Nāḍis' over the vortexes formed by the perpetual rotation of eight energy centres. The concept of Cakras can be compared with 'electrical substances', Nāḍi/meridian with 'power line', and PCE/ Prān with the 'electricity'. There must be a balance in the Cakra system. PCE/Prān flows from Cakras through Nāḍis/meridians line i.e. energy channels. Any imbalance in alignment of Cakra system hinders the flow of PCE/Prāṇa and has an adverse effect on human health. The less active Cakras have the adverse effect on the endocrine glands. Therefore, these eight Cakras work collaboratively to have the perfectly health. These Cakras emanate radiations of different colours and each one absorbs a colour specific wavelength and energy (Nair, 2017).

4. Effect of Odoriferous Smoke on Body

The Agnihotra Yajña helps to maintain the balance of these eight Cakras, while reducing the wasted energy of the body. After the burning of sacrificial fire, the flammable chemical substances evaporate, spread in the atmosphere and enter the body from the nasal cavity of the sacrifice performers and affect the body and mind. Our ancient Ṛṣis and Yogis have mentioned the eight major energy centers in our body called Cakras situated over the spinal cord. These Cakras regulate the energetic continuum of body of every human. Thus, the total entropy of the

BMS complex is minimized by all the Cakras (Azeemi and Raza, 2005). In India, copper, silver, brass, etc. have been used for centuries. All of these metals kill a variety of microorganisms through oligodynamic effects. Since the time of Maharṣi Suṣruta, copper tools were used so that the infectious microorganism could be killed and the wound healed quickly. Therefore, the same effect is seemed by using inverted pyramidal copper (IPC) pot and copper vessels during sacrificial fire worship. IPC pots are designed in such a ways that the size at bottom is less that of top, that facilitates the less burning of fire and controlled production of oxides of nitrogen. But the design of IPC pot helps to supply the sufficient amount of oxygen and ensures the complete combustion of fire (Abhang and Pathade, 2017). According to the book 'Chemistry of Agnihotra' by Satya Prakāśa (2011), there is a change in the temperature gradient adjacent to the inverted pyramidal copper (IPC) pot. At the base of IPC pot, the temperature remains 300-400°C and above 1200-1300°C. When the intensity of flame of the fire decreases, the base temperature at the base remains 200–300°C and above the IPC pot it remains 600–700°C (Figure 9.6).

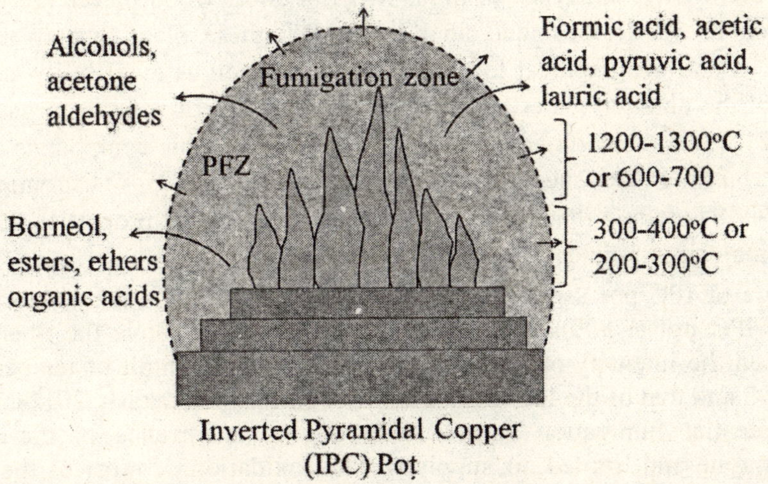

Figure 9.6. Temperature in and around the inverted pyramidal copper pot during Yajña (diagrammatic).

The IPC pot used in Agnihotra has a unique shape i.e. square-shaped flattened top and that of less-flattened bottom. This structure emanates the odoriferous medicinal smoke most efficiently spreading around the sacrificial place. It also effectively attracts the PCE/Prāṇa and spreads in the surrounding areas. While performing the Agnihotra Yajña, the solid matter is subtilized into energy, in the phase of vapour of colloid, generating the electromagnetic waves. The Prāṇa/PCE increases in the surrounding atmosphere after combustion of odoriferous medicinal herbs used as Samidha offered in the IPC pot (Kratz and Schnug, 2007). When the increased quantum of Prāṇa/PCE is taken through the breathing the alignment of energy centres (Cakras) on spinal cord is optimized. Consequently, the energy connection between the physical body and the electromagnetic body is established through the energy centres (Freshwater, 1997).

In this way, the generated electromagnetic waves potentially pose the health benefits jointly with sonic signals originated by chanting of Vedic hymns of Agnihotra (Saraswati, 2009). Moreover, it has been postulated that the bones, the solid crystalline structure of the body, absorbs the vibrations generated during Agnihotra Yajña. Later on these vibrations are amplified and transduced as biological signals. These signals are important for the functioning of the human body in proper ways (Cousens, 2005).

5. Volatile Substances Emanated from Smoke of Odoriferous Medicinal Herbs

Since ancient time, several ailments/diseases have been cured by applying the smoke liberated after combustion of different parts of odoriferous medicinal plants. The odoriferous medicinal smoke emanates at high temperatures and inhaled by the individuals. It is a simple way of administering a drug for quick pharmacological action in the individuals (Nautiyal *et al.*, 2007). During the process of Agnihotra Yajña, emanation of volatile substances depends on the oblation material used. Different types of plant twigs or short wood pieces are used in Hawan along with oblation of odoriferous medicinal herbs. But these plant twigs/wood pieces vary according to seasons and geographical locations, rituals as well as availability and costs. Since the compositions of the oblation material differ, the constituents of volatiles organic compounds also vary. Nair (2017) in an experiment analysed the volatile organic compounds emanated from the smoke after burning the medicinal plant by using the Gas Chromatography-Mass Spectrometry (GC-MS) method that have potential pharmacological properties. He has reported approximately 17 major compounds present in the smoke.

The structure of IPC pot used in Agnihotra pyramid creates a temperature-gradient i.e., the bottom of the IPC pot at 300-400°C, and the upper portion above the liberating flame at 1200-1300°C. When the intensity of flame is low, the maximum limit of temperature-gradient becomes 600-700°C and that of the lower limit 200-300°C (Satya Prakāsh, 2011). This zone may be called the 'potential fumigation zone' (PFZ) due to occurrence of the most efficient fumigation in this zone and limited air supply. Partial oxidation of most of the hydrocarbons occurs in PFZ producing several products because several hydrocarbons have its 'autogenous ignition temperatures' ranging from 500 to 600°C (Dixon and Coward, 1909; Satya Prakāsh, 2011).

Nair (2017) has given a list of volatile compounds liberated from smokes during the Hawan in different fumigation zones of IPC pot by using the modified ingredients and categorized them as below:

***(a)* Compounds in PFZ in upper region of IPC pot:** The aromatic compounds of high boiling point and other oils vaporize in the PFZ and emanated into the atmosphere. Vaporization of aromatic substances occurs at its boiling point according to the temperature of IPC pot. After the burning of odoriferous oblation materials, its cellulosic components burn away and evaporate abundantly. In the fumigation zone, the aromatic compounds with high boiling point and other types of fat or oil are freed after being vaporized and have a good effect on the environment and human health.

(b) **Compounds at the bottom of IPC pot:** The bottom of the IPC pot remains cold as compared the upper region. The main volatile compounds emanated from the colder bottom region are- borneol, esters and organic acids, etc. These are the main compounds that are mostly free from temperatures at the bottom of the IPC pot.

Different types of solids materials used in oblation in fire in IPC pot and its chemical reactions, such as distillation, evaporation, fumigation, oxidation, and pre-chemical reactions can be understood under the following points:

- **Fumigation-** Fumigation of the incense material and smoke removal depends on the oblation material used, the amount of materials, the temperature, the oxygen supply and the reaction of different products. The distillation of the material depends on the availability of oxygen.
- **Partial oxidation of hydrocarbons-** The hydrocarbons liberated in the smoke undergoes partial oxidation and produce alcohols (methyl alcohol, ethyl alcohol), aldehydes (formaldehyde, acetaldehyde) and acids (formic acid and acetic acid). After burning of glycerol, acetone-containing compounds, pyruvic acid and glycoxal are formed.
- **Vaporization-** All types of evaporative compounds spread in the surrounding environment. Subsequently, different types of compounds are produced with photochemical reaction (e.g. decomposition, oxidation and reduction). Formaldehyde is produced by the reduction of oxygen ($CO_2 + H_2O = HCHO + O_2$). Therefore Agnihotra should be done during the day. While performing, Hawan, the as much material should be offered in the IPC pot as the flame does not go above the height of the Hawan performers.
- **Photochemical reactions-** Sunlight is the main factor for photochemical reactions i.e. the chemical reaction with sun light. Therefore, Agnihotra Yajña must be performed during daytime in sunlight. After performing Hawan, the volatile compounds, transmitted in the atmosphere, react with sunlight and form several kinds of beneficial compounds (Satya Prakash, 2011).
- **Narration of Vedic hymns-** The systematically pronounced sound energy with the chanting of Vedic mantras is progressively dispersed by merging into Brahman energy (cosmic energy). The effect of the Vedic mantras narrated in Yajña can be studied with the help of spectrographic and other techniques such as multichannel tonography and retro-meter.

6. Pharmacological Properties of Volatile Compounds from Smoke

Several volatile compounds are produced from the smoke liberated after burning of odoriferous medicinal herbs and oblation materials (Samidhā) in the IPC pots (Hawan Kuṅḍa). Several compounds have been identified. Certain essential oils (concentrated hydrophobic liquid containing volatile aromatic compounds from plants) have been identified (Nair, 2017). Pharmacological properties of few identified compounds, such as essential oils, partially oxidized aromatic hydrocarbons and formaldehyde (Bone and Wheeler, 1904), and its effects on health management have been studied.

(a) **Antimicrobial Aldehydes-** A little amount of formaldehyde along with water vapour is liberated during performing the Agnihotra Yajña (Satya Prakāsh, 2011). Formaldehyde is the most simple and basic antimicrobial aldehyde as it kills the microorganisms by reacting with their peptides and proteins components of cells. Like formaldehyde, the other higher groups of aldehydes are not effective as antimicrobial agents.

(b) **Effect of Camphor-** Camphor is used in Agnihotra as firing agent of odoriferous material in oblation pot. It is derived from a plant (*Cinnamomum camphora*); it is not an effective disinfectant but it imparts foul smell. The breathing systems are cleared of Hawan-performers inhaling the fumes liberated from the IPC pot. Thus, the oblation-performers experience an enhanced feeling (Bansal *et al.*, 2015).

(c) **Germicidal Action of Volatilized Aliphatic Acids-** The combustion process of organic materials is slow due to gradual offering of oblation into fire along with chanting of hymns. Therefore, the concentration of volatilized aliphatic acids is maintained for some time in the surrounding environment enhancing the germicidal property of smoke (Huang *et al.*, 2011). For example, acne inflammation- causing *Propionibacterium acnes* is inhibited by lauric acid (Nakatsuji, 2009). Further, Nair (2017) reported the volatilization of several fatty acid esters, for example caprylic acid ethyl ester, behenic acid ethyl ester, decanoic acid ethyl ester and lauric acid ethyl ester, which may liberate organic acids into the smoke. Hence, the beneficial effects of the Agnihotra smoke are enhanced by the fatty acid esters.

(d) **Effect of Esters on Hypothalamus-** The esters are also produced from smoke of Agnihotra Yajña (Nair, 2017). Its odors have pleasing experience and affect the hypothalamus gland controlling the hormone production in a balance way. Esters also induce the neurotransmitters by stimulating certain responses through the olfactory system (Bansal *et al.*, 2015).

(e) **Anticancer Compounds-** Certain anticancer compounds have been identified in the smoke, such as lirioresinol beta-dimethyl ether, which has an inhibitory property against bone destruction mediated by breast cancer. It blocks the cycle between cancer cells, osteoblasts, and osteoclasts (Jun *et al.*, 2014). Similarly, β-elemene that has anti-lung cancer activity reduces the side effects arising from chemotherapy (Chen *et al.*, 2012).

(f) **Antioxidants Compounds-** Many antioxidant compounds are produced from smoke. For example, 2,4-bis (tert-butyl)-phenol has anti-inflammatory and antioxidant properties (Nair, 2017).

(g) **Beneficial Effects of Cow Ghee-** Cow ghee is another important traditional ingredient that is poured into the fire to facilitate the easy burning of oblation materials. Ghee helps in the rapid combustion of celluloses present in oblation materials offered to fire and releases the chemical constituent like acetone, aldehyde, etc. in the surrounding environment. The fumes liberated after combustion of ghee protect the respiratory system by facilitating the removal of blood clots. Further, bacterial infections are also removed by the fumes, present in nasal cavity,

lungs as well as and veins Hawan (Bansal *et al.*, 2015). Hence, one should perform daily Hawan so that he/she should be exposed daily to the medicinal smoke and get benefits from the favorable effects on the mind, body and health of fume-inhaling persons.

***(h)* Antibacterial Effect of Fumigation Sticks (Dhūpa)-** Prabhu *et al.* (2009) conducted an experiment on 'biofumigation' by burning the mixture of selected plant with cow dung cakes and ghee (fat). Different types of plant-product based sticks (Dhūpa) were prepared using different trees, such as *Mangifera indica, Azadirachta indica, Achyranthus aspera, Calotropis gigantic, Ficus bengalensis, Ficus religiosa* and *Pongamia pinnata*. The sticks were also used to produce fumes along with ghee and cow dung cake. Many pathogenic bacteria were screened from various sources; they were exposed to fumes (Dhūpa) liberated from different sticks. It was found that fumes of *A. aspera* inhibited the growth of *Streptococcus pyogenes*. However, the sticks of other plants were also effective in inhibiting the growth of other pathogenic bacteria.

EFFECT OF AGNIHOTRA ON PLANT HEALTH

Yajña Ash (Bhaṣma, Bhabhūta, Vibhūtī) is the plant residues left after complete burning of wood pieces or plant twigs, odoriferous medicinal materials, ghee, etc. Since ancient time, Agnihotra Yajña has been performed from environmental cleaning, maintenance of good health and organic forming (Vedic farming). But in recent years, Hawan-based farming is called 'Homa Organic Farming' (HOF) or 'Homa Farming System' (HFS). The HOF is used to solve the problems associated with the atmosphere, the water, the soil, the plants, pests and diseases by exposing the smoke and applying the ash in soil and water. Some of the major areas of effects have briefly been described in this section.

1. Effect of Ash on Soil Fertility

Kumar *et al.* (2015) studied the physico-chemical properties of 26 medicinal plants used in Hawan and analysed mineral elements in ash, i.e. phosphorus, potassium, magnesium, calcium, iron, manganese, zinc and nickel in completely burnt oblation material i.e. ash by using Atomic Absorption Spectroscopy (AAS) and Flame Photometry. The maximum amount of potassium was contributed by *Acacia catechu, Cassia fistula, Jasminum grandiflorum* and *Vitex negundo*, and that of calcium by *Olea europaea*

Some scientific studies have been carried for validation of the positive effects of Agnihotra ash on plants in organic farming. Kratz and Schnug (2007) have reported an increase the solubility of phosphorus content in the soil by applying the Agnihotra ash. Further, positive effects of Agnihotra ash on soil fertility have also been demonstrated by Devi *et al.* (2004).

2. Effect of Smoke on Plant Growth

Plant growth is affected by the temperature, brightness of sun light, presence of soil moisture, precipitation, nutrient status of soil, quality of gases present in the surrounding environment.

(a) **Effect of Agnihotra on Seed Germination-** Devi *et al.* (2004) have reported an increase in seed germination of rice with the treatment of full ritual of Agnihotra during sunrise and sunset with oblation to fire and chanting of hymns (Mantras) as compared to *(i)* seeds treatment at normal conditions, *(ii)* seed treatment plus fire lit, *(iii)* seed treatment at with chanting hymns without fir lit. Furthermore, positive effects of Agnihotra ash on germination of rice seeds have also been demonstrated by Devi *et al.* (2004). Similarly, Abhang and Palade (2017) also reported a faster increase in germination of Mung bean (*Vigna radiata*) seed treated with Agnihotra ash as compared to control set of experiment. Increased germination of grape seeds and crop productivity by the Agnihotra fumes, through breaking of seed dormancy and reducing the time of germination, have been reported by Indira *et al.* (2010). They advocated for the presence of signal molecules in Agnihotra fumes that break the seed dormancy aggravating it fast germination.

(b) **Induction in Photosynthesis and Diameter of Vascular Bundles-** It has been postulated that the fumes liberated from Hawan (Homa) into the surrounding atmosphere induce the plants to develop vascular bundles with more diameters and allow the faster movement water and nutrients resulting in better growth and reproduction in plants (Priyadarshini, 2005). Furthermore, the fumigated surrounding atmosphere also stimulates the photosynthesis and plant respiration thereby improving the entire oxygen cycle (Paranjpe, 1989). Hawan fumes significantly affect on the growth and development of plants. The methods of HOF are globally used to increase the crop yield and develop disease resistance in plants.

(c) **Induction of Plant Hormone (Brassinosteroids)-** The effects of the smoke of Hawan, performed at the time of sunrise and sunset, on plants are mostly similar to that of the brassinolide, which is a plant hormone. Brassinosteroids are 'a group of steroidal compounds' that occur naturally in plants. These change plant metabolism causing an increase in crop yields and protect plants from abiotic and biotic stresses (Krishna, 2003). Limaye (2019) has discussed the possible triggering/production of brassinosteroids or phytosteroid precursors after exposure of the plant to the fumes emanated from the oblation to fire during Hawan. The leaf surface of the plants perceives the volatile substances liberated during Agnihotra Hawan. The fumes from Agnihotra result in an increase in numbers and area of plant leaves. But in rainy season, long roots are produced from the nodes of the same plant. Furthermore, a reduction in the effect of salt stress on growth of rice plants, prevention in loss of photosynthetic pigments and increase in nitrate reductase activity have been recorded after application of brassinosteroids to rice seeds (*Oryza sativa*).

An increase in crop yields, via altering the plant metabolism and protecting the plants from environmental stresses, is facilitated by brassinosteroids. Plants exposed to Agnihotra fumes displayed flowering, triggering of new cells and senescence. These effects certainly establish the possibility of occurring crosstalk between brassinosteroids and many environmental signals, such as temperature, light and water along with and other hormones secreted by the plants (Limaye, 2019).

3. Effect of Smoke on Plant Pathogens

Smokes liberated from Hawan spreads in the surrounding environment and pose inhibitory effects on plant pathogens also. For example, smoke of Hawan has been reported to inhibit spore germination and hyphal growth of *Fusarium oxysporum*, which is an important plant pathogen (Dharni *et al.,* 2014). The other compounds liberated from the smoke also possess antimicrobial properties of varying levels (Nair, 2017).

Banana is the staple food in most of the population. A fungal disease Black Sigatoka, caused by a fungus *Mycospherella fijiensis* showing black leaf streak, occurred in banana plantations in Peru (South America) and destroyed about 90% of the crops. *M. fijiensis* developed resistance towards the fungicides, thereby developed survival mechanisms in the environment. Several farmers made up their mind to quit the cultivation of banana. Being worried with Black Sigatoka disease, for the first time agricultural engineers of Peru started systematic studies for control of the disease. Hence, they started 'Homa Organic Farming' (HOF) by applying Agnihotra Yajña using ten inverted pyramids to energize about 80 hectares area of land. The government engineers completely eradicated the Black Sigatoka infection by using the HOF technique (Ulrich, 2017). By applying the same the HOF technique certain agricultural crops, such as banana, sugarcane and tomatoes could also be protected against the infection of insect pests (Ulrich, 2018).

Kadam *et al.* (2020) studied how to manage *Alternaria solani* of potato crop, and *A. solani* and *Xanthomonas compestris* pv. *vesicatoria* of tomato by performing Agnihotra under the controlled conditions in the polyhouses? They reported a substantial reduction in the incidence of bacterial blight of tomato and early blight of potato and tomato along with a decline in about 70% microbial pathogens in the polyhouses.

4. Effect of Ash on Mushroom Cultivation

The nutritive values (in terms of carbohydrates, amino acids and protein contents), biological efficiency, size and weight, and yield of mushroom get increased along with reduced harvesting time while cultivating the mushroom on straw substrates mixed with Agnihotra ash (Indira *et al*., 2010).

5. Effect of Ash on Radioactivity in Food

An experiment was conducted, after the Fukushima catastrophe, in the Physics Institute of Academy of Science, Kiev (Ukraine) (formerly a part of Soviet Union). The Japanese seeds (50 grams) from Fukushima region, contaminated with radioactive isotopes (^{134}Cs and ^{137}Cs)

displaying the radioactivity of about 200 Bq (Becquerel)/kg, were mixed with water solution of Agnihotra ash (one spoon/litre water). Ash water of Agnihotra fully neutralized the radioactivity in rice food within two weeks of treatment (Anonymous, 2018).

References 11.

Abhang, P. 2015. Scientific study of *Somyag Yadnya*. *Indian J. Scientific Res*. 4: 2080-2083.

Abhang, P.; Patil M. and M. Pramod. 2015. Beneficial effects of *Agnihotra* on environment and agriculture. *In. J. Agri. Sci.*5: 111-120.

Adler, A.C. 2009. Tuberculosis: old world treatment for new world disease. *Clin. Imaging*. 33: 136.

Al-Qattan, M.M. *et al.* 2011. Tuberculosis of the hands. *J. Hand. Surg. Am.* 36(8): 1413-1422.

Anonymous 2018. www.agnihotra.org/2018/02/16/scientific-aspects-of-agnihotra-agnihotra-and-radioactivity-2/

Azeemi, S.T.Y. and Raza, S.M. 2005. A critical analysis of chromotherapy and its scientific evolution. *Evid Based Complement Alternat Med*. 2: 481-488.

Balkrishna, Acharya. 2017. *Yoga Vijanam*. Divya Publication, Haridwar

Bansal, P.; Kaur, R.; Gupta, V.; Kumar, S. and Kaur, R. 2015. Is there any scientific basis of hawan to be used in epilepsy-prevention/cure? *J. Epilepsy Res*. 5:33-45.

Bansal, P.; Kaur R., Gupta, V., Kumar S. and Kaur R. 2015. Is there any scientific basis of Hawan to be used in epilepsy- prevention/cure. *J. Epilepsy Research*. 5: 33-45.

Baydur, A. 1977. The expectrum of extrapulmonary tuberculosis. *West J. Med*. 126(4): 253-262.

Bhatia, A.; Bharti, S.K.; Tripathi, T.; Mishra, A.; Sidhu, O.P.; Roy, R.; and Nautiyal, C.S. 2015. Metabolic profiling of *Commiphora wightii* (guggul) reveals a potential source for pharmaceuticals and nutraceuticals. *Phytochemistry*. 110: 29–36.

Bone, W.A. and Wheeler, R.V. 1904. The slow oxidation of ethane at low temperatures. *J Chem Soc Trans*. 85:1637-1663.

Brainworks. Neurofeedback clinic. Available at: http://www.brainworksneurotherapy.com/what-are-brainwaves [Date accessed: October 12, 2016].

Chen, M.; Zhang, J.; Yu, S.; Wang, S.; Zhang, Z.; Chen, J. *et al.* 2012. Antilung-cancer activity and liposome-based delivery systems of β-elemene. *J. Evid. Based Complementary Altern. Med.* 2012; http://dx.doi.org/10.1155/2012/259523.

Chhou, Ping-Song, *et al.* 2012. Central nervous system tuberculosis. *Neurologist*. 18(4): 219-222.

Chopra, L.C., Khajuria B.N. and Chopra C.L. 1957. Antibacterial properties of volatile principles from *Alpinia galanga* and *Acorus calamus*. *Antibiotic Chemotherapy*. 7: 378-383.

Cousens, G. 2005. Spiritual Nutrition: Six foundations for spiritual life and the awakening of Kundalini. California: North Atlantic Books.

Cowley, A., Dobson, L., Kurian, J. and Saunderson, C.. 2017. Acute myocarditis secondary to cardiac tuberculosis: a case report. *Eco Research Practice*. DOI: 10.1530/ERP-17-0024

Daher, E.D.F., da Silva Junior, G.B. and Barros, E.J.G. 2013. Review: renal tuberculosis in the modern era. *Am. J. Trop. Med. Hyg*. 88: 54–64.

Devi, H.J., Swamy, N.V.C. and Nagendra, H.R. 2004. Effect of Agnihotra on the germination of rice seeds. *Indian J. Traditional Knowledge*. 3(3): 231-239.

Dharni, S.; Maurya, A.; Samad, A.; Srivastava, S.K.; Sharma, A. and Patra D.D. 2014. Purification, characterization, and in vitro activity of 2,4-di-tert-butylphenol from *Pseudomonas monteilii* PsF84: conformational and molecular docking studies. *J. Agric. Food. Chem.* 62: 6138-6146.

Dillon, M.S. *et al.* 2002. Tuberculosis of foot and ankles. *Clin. Orthop. Relate. Res.* 398: 107-113.

Dixit, R. and Dave L. 2008. Primary nasal tuberculosis. *Lung India.* 25(2): 102-103.

Dixon, H.B. and Coward, H.F. 1909. Ignition temperatures of gases. *J. Chern Soc.* 98: 514-543.

Dubey, R.C. 2018. Cecak ki devi Mātā Śītalā: Pāramparik mānyatao kī vaijñānikatā (In *Madhya Himālayi Sanskriti me Jnān, Vijān evam Parāvijnān*), Eds. P.C. Pande aur Ashok Kumar Pant. PAHAL, Uttarakhand aur Vinsar Publishing Co., pp. 190-197.

Dubey, R.C. Dubey. 2020. *Vedic Microbiology- Ek Vaijñānic Dṛṣti* (Hindi Version). Aastha Prakashan, Delhi- 110053, p. 164.

Duraipandiyan, V.; Al-Harbi, N.A.; Ignacimuthu S. and Muthukumar, C. 2012. Antimicrobial activity of sesquiterpene lactones isolated from traditional medicinal plant, *Costus speciosus* (Koenex. Retz.) Sm. *BMC Compl. Alt. Med.* 12(13): 2-6.

Dwivedi, R.S. and Dubey, R.C. 1987. Effect of soil solarization on population dynamics of *Macrophomina phaseolina* and general soil mycoflora. *Int. J. Tropical Plant Diseases*. 5: 147-152.

Freshwater D. 1997. Geopathic stress. *Complement. Ther. Nurs. Midwifery*. 3:160-162.

Furugen, M. Nakamura H. *et al.* 2009. Tuberculosis of tongue initially suspected of tongue cance: a case report Including the search for recent 16 cases in Japan. Kekkaku [Tuberculosis]. 84(8): 605-610.

Gupta, G.P. and Singh K. 1996. Studies on Vedic technology for environmental health. *National Seminar on Biotechnology: New trends and prospects*, Gurukul Kangri Vishwavidyalaya, Haridwar, p. 41-42.

Hakavi, A.M. *et al.* 2006. Tuberculosis of the bone marrow: clinic-pathological study of 22 cases from Saudi Arabia. *Int. J. Tuberc. Lung Diseases,* 10(9): 1041-1044.

Harisharan Siddhantalankar (2008) *Atharv Veda Bhashyam. Bhagavati Prakashan*, Delhi.

Hiltebeitel, Alf. 2005. *Mahabaratha.* MacMillan Encyclopedia of Religion (Ed. Jones, Lindsay), MacMillan

https://www.drugs.com/tuberculosis

Huang, C.B.; Alimova, Y.; Myers, T.M. and Ebersole, J.L. 2011. Short- and medium-chain fatty acids exhibit antimicrobial activity for oral microorganisms. *Arch. Oral. Biol.* 56: 650-654.

Husaain, H. and D.K. Hore. 2006. Collection and conservation of major medicinal plants of Darjeeling and Sikkim Himalayas. *Indian J. Traditional Knowledge.* 6(2): 252-257.

Indira, V; Dasharathan, P. and Anandadevi, M. 2010. Impact of Agnihotra in mushroom cultivation technology. Biosci. Res. 1(4): 245-250.

Ishnava, K.B., Mahida Y.N. and Mohan J.S.S. 2010. *In vitro* assessments of antibacterial potential of *Commiphora wightii* (Arn.) Bhandari. gum extract. J. *Pharmacogn. Phytother.* 2(7): 91-96.

Jeswal, P. and D. Kumar. 2015. Mycobiota and natural incidence of aflatoxins, ochratoxin A and citrinin in Indian spices confirmed by LC-MS/MS. *International J. Microbiology*. Vol. 2015: 1-8.

Jun, A.Y.; Kim, H.J.; Park, K.K.; Son, K.H.; Lee, D.H.; Woo, M.H. *et al.* 2014. Tetrahydrofurofuran-type lignans inhibit breast cancer mediated bone destruction by blocking the vicious cycle between cancer cells, osteoblasts and osteoclasts. *Invest New Drugs*. 32: 1-13.

Kadam, N.A.; Raghuwanshi, K.S.; Borkar, S.G.and Mahajan, P. J.2020. Effect of Indian traditional homa (Agnihotra) in the management of *Alternaria solani* of potato crop and *Alternaria solani* and *Xanthomonas compestris* pv. *vesicatoria* of tomato under controlled environmental conditions in polyhouse. *Int. J. Chem. Studies.* 8(1): 2332-2336.

Kak, Subhash C. 1993. Astronomy of the Vedic altars. *Vistas in Astronomy*. 36: 117-140.

Kanniga, E. and Ramprakash, S. 2015. A survey based on smart medical diagnosis for epilepsy people. *Int. J. Adv. Res. Electric. Electron. Instr. Eng.* 4:7151-7155.

Kechaou, I. *et al.* 2014. Deep vein thrombosis and tuberculosis: a causative link? BMJ Case Reports, http://dx.doi.org/10.1136/bcr-2013-200807

Kratz, S. and Schnug, E. 2007. Homa Farming - A Vedic fire for agriculture: Influence of Agnihotra ash on water solubility of soil P. *Landbauforschung Volkenrode.* 57(3):207-211

Krishna, P. 2003. Brassinosteroid-mediated stress responses. *J. Plant Growth Regul.* 22: 289–297.

Kumar, A. *et al.* 2018. Comparative metabolic profiling of *Costus speciosus* leaves and rhizome using NMR, GC-MS and UPLC/ESI-MS/MS. *Nat. Prod. Res.* 32(7): 826-833.

Lidder, S, Landy K. and EI-Guindi M. 2009. Tuberculosis of knee. *Orthop. Rev.* (Pavia). 1(2): e24.

Limaye V.G. 2019. Agnihotra (the everyday Homa) and production of brassinosteroids: A scientific validation. *Int. J. Modern Engin. Res.* 8(12): 41-51

Lmekki, S and Lecanu J.B. 2013. Tuberculosis of the middle ear and nasal passage: a case report. *Int. J. Mycol.* 2:51-53.

Merlin, M. 2008. Archaeological record for ancient old world use of psychoactive plants. *Economic Botany*, 57(3): 295–323.

Moorjani, P. *et al.* 2013. Genetic evidence for recent population mixture in India. *The American J. Human Genetics*. 93, 422–438.

Mughal, M.R. 1990. Further evidence of the early Harappan culture in the Greater Indus Valley: 1971–90. *South Asian Study*. 6, 175–199.

Naidu, P.V.L., Kumar, K.K.; Kumar, C.M. Gunesh G. and Rao, M.N. 2006. Antimicrobial activity of *Achyranthes aspera*. *Biosci. Biotech. Res. Asia.* 3(1a):171-174.

Nair, R.R. 2017. *Agnihotra Yajna*: A prototype of South Asian traditional medical knowledge. *J. Acupunture and Meridian Studies.* 10: 143-150.

Nakatsuji, T.; Kao, M.C.; Fang, J.Y.; Zouboulis, C.C.; Zhang, L.; Gallo, R. *et al.* 2009. Antimicrobial property of lauric acid against *Propionibacterium acnes*: its therapeutic potential for inflammatory acne vulgaris. *J Invest Dermatol.* 129:2480-2488.

Nautiyala, C.S., Chauhana, P.S. and Nene, Y.L. 2007. Medicinal smoke reduces airborne bacteria. *J. Ethanophormacology*. 115: 446-451.

Navneet, Chand, S. and Sharma, V.K. 1998. *Agnihotra*- the air purifier. *Aryabhatta*, Gurukul Kangri University, Haridwar.

Navneet, Nidhi Handa, P. Kumar, S. Kumar and S.S. Gautam. 2011. *Yajña therapy*. Swami Śradhānanda Publication, Haridwar.

Padhy, S. 2016. Vedic Indians were aware of the microbial biodiversity, demanding 'Kannva' as the father of microbiology. *J. Biodiversity*, 7(2): 101-103.

Paranjpe, V.V. 1989. *Homa Therapy- Our last chance*. Fivefold Path Inc., Madison, VA, USA.

Pawar, V.A. and Pawar, P.R. 2012. *Costus speciosus*: an important medicinal plant. *Int. J. Sci. Res.* 3: 28–33.

Prabhu, N.; Rengaramanujam, J. and Anna, J.P. 2009. Efficacy of plants-based holy stick fumigation against infectious bacteria, Indian Journal Of Traditional Knowledge, 8(2):. 278-280

Prasad. P.V.V. 2002. General medicine in Atharvaveda with special reference to Yaksma (consumption/tuberculosis). *Bull.Ind.Inst.Hist.Med.*32: 1-14.

Priyadarshini S (2005) Homa – fire ceremony [online] Zu finden in <http://www.ayurvedahc.com/articlelive/articles/33/1/HOMA---Fire- Ceremony/print/33> [zitiert am 11.07.2007]

Rahamoz-Haghighi, S.; Asadi, M.H.; Riahi-Madvar, A. and A. Baghizadeh. 2014. Antibacterial effect of *Acorus calamus* extractions against Gram-positive and negative bacteria. *Ethno-Pharmaceutical Products*. 1(1):1-7.

Rahman, M. M., Gibbons, S. and Gray, A.I. 2007. Isoflavanones from *Uraria picta* and their antimicrobial activity. *Phytochemistry,* 68: 1692–1697.

Sairkar, P.K.; Sharma, A. and N.P. Shukla. 2016. Antimicrobial activity of guggulsterone E and Z. *Int. J. Curr. Microbiol. App. Sci.* 5(10): 20-26.

Saleh, M., Ali A.S. and Ali P. 2014. Brain tuberculosis- a case report. *J.J. Microbiol.* Doi:10.5812/jjm.11252

Saraswati, S.N. 2009. Prana and pranayama. Bihar: Yoga Publication Trust.

Satya Prakas. 1996. *Atharv Veda Samhita* (with english translation), Vol I-V. *Veda Pratiṣṭhāna*, New Delhi 100001.

Satya Prakash. 2011. *Chemistry in Agnihotra.* Calicut: *KVRF Publication* (India).

Saxena, H.O. Soni, A., Mohammad N. and Choubey, S.K. 2014. Phytochemical screening and elemental analysis in different plant parts of *Uraria picta* Desv.: A *Dashmul* species. *J. Chemical and Pharmaceutical Research*, 6: 756-760.

Sehgal, S. 1999. Encyclopaedia of Hinduism, (Vol V). Sarup & Sons, New Delhi 110002, ISBN: 81-7625-064-03.

Sharma, S.K. and Mohan A. 2015. Extrapulmonary tuberculosis. *Indian. J. Med. Res.* 120: 316-353.

Shashtri, Roop Kishor. 2014. *Uṇadi Nirukt- Vyutpatti Koṣ. Rāṣtriy Veda Pratisthān*, Ujjain, M.P. (India).

Shinde, V. *et al.* 2019. An ancient Harappan genome lacks ancestry from Steppe Pastoralists or Iranian farmers. *Cell.* 179 (October 17): 729–735. https://doi.org/10.1016/j.cell.2019.08.048

Singh, Upinder. 2009. History of ancient and early medieval India: From the Stone Age to the 12th century, Longman Press.

Trautmann, T. 2005. The Aryan Debate. Oxford University Press.

Tripathy, B.B. 1953. *Drabyaguna Kalpadruma* (Odia). 3rd Edition. Bellaguntha (Odisha): OP Tripathy Publishers. Williams

Ulrich, Berc. 2017. https://www.agnihotra.org/ 2018/02/08/scientific-aspects-o-agnihotra-agriculture-pests-and-diseases-part-1

Ulrich, Berc. 2018. https://www.agnihotra.org/ 2018/02/08/scientific-aspects-of-agnihotra-agriculture-pests-and-diseases-part-11

Uma Debi, Ravishankar V. and Sharma A.K. 2014. Abdominal tuberculosis of gastrointestinal tract: revisited. *Wolrd J. Gastroenterology.* 20(40):14831-14840.

Witzel, Michael. 2001. Autochthonous Aryans? The evidence from old Indian and Iranian texts. *Electronic J. Vedic Studies*. 7 (3).

Glossary

Abhraja	-	Caused by cloud
Ādra	-	Wet, moist
Adriṣta krimis	-	Unseen germs
Advait	-	Only one, without a second
Agnihotra	-	Fire worship
Āhāra	-	Food
Akaṅkār	-	Cosmic egoism, ego at individual level
Akṣara	-	Indestructible
Ānaṅda	-	Eternal bliss
Anātura	-	Painless i.e. healthy persons
Animitta	-	Purposeless
Āpa	-	Water
Aparā vidyā	-	Knowing the creation
Apauruṣeya	-	Revealed truth
Aprakṣālita	-	Unwashed
Arcāya	-	To worship
Artharūpa	-	Object form
Ārya	-	Civilised persons
Āryāvarta	-	The place where Āryans resided
Asthi	-	Bones
Aṣṭhi	-	Knees
Ātmā	-	SOUL that is the ***S**ubject **O**f **U**niversal **L**ife*
Bhakṣaṇa	-	To eat
Bhāsad	-	Hips
Bheṣaja	-	Drug
Brahma tattva	-	Supreme Power
Brahmāṅḍa	-	Cosmos, entire universe
Cāndāla	-	Pperson disposing corpses
Citā dhuma	-	Smokes of burning dead body
Citta	-	Person's consciousness which vibrates upon coming in the contact of object
Dhamani	-	Blood vessels
Divākirti	-	Person disposing of corpses
Diẏya cakṣu	-	Divine eyes
Driṣta krimis	-	germs visible to eyes
Ejatka	-	Vibrating microbes
Galaganda	-	Mumps, ome bulge of swelling in side pharynx
Gaṇḍamālā	-	Many bulges of swelling
Gaṅdha	-	Fragrance
Grīvā	-	Neck
Guggul	-	Indian bdellium (*Commiphora wightii*)
Guṇa	-	Properties

Harimā	-	Yellowness, jaundice
Hata	-	To kill
Hawan kuṇḍa	-	Inverted pyramidal copper pot
Hawan sāmagri	-	Odoriferous medicinal herbs used as oblation to fire
Hiraṇyagarbha	-	luminous Cosmic Womb
Hiraṇyāṅḍa	-	Cosmic Egg
Hṛdyota	-	Heart-sickness
Indriya	-	Body organs
Jambhaya	-	To kill
Jangiṇa	-	A medicine, virile
Jarā	-	Old age
Jīva	-	Life forms
Jīvalā	-	Earth that gives birth to a life and nurtures it
Jīvanta	-	Sun that makes the life alive
Jñāneṅdriya	-	Ear, skin, eyes, tongue and nose
Jyoti	-	Light
Kāmalā	-	Jaundice
Kaṇva ṛṣi	-	Father of Microbiology
Karma	-	Action
Karmeṅdriya	-	Mouth, hands, legs, anus and genital
Kāsa	-	Cough
Kaṣkaṣāsa	-	Pain-causing microbes
Kaumārya	-	Virginity
Khaṁ	-	Space
Koti	-	Crore (>1 million)), types, kinds, forms
Kotiśaḥ	-	Crores (millions)
Krama	-	To move
Kravya	-	Nourishment from the unripe meat
Krimis	-	Germs, invisible worms, microorganisms
Kṣara	-	Destructible
Kṣīra	-	Milk
Kṣīra	-	Milk
Kṣudra	-	Small, trivial or less important)
Kukṣi	-	Fanks
Kuṇḍalinī	-	Coiled power of energy
Kuṣṭhā	-	Plant that kills water-borne microbial pathogens
Kuṣṭhā	-	*Costus speciosus,* Syn. *Cheilocostus speciosus*
Lavaṇa	-	Salt
Lehya	-	Licking materials
Loka	-	Planetary world
Lokasaṅsthā	-	Planetary system
Loma	-	Follicle
Madhu	-	Homey
Mahat (buddhi)	-	All cosmic Intelligence i.e. the knowledge-dominating form
Mahāvākya	-	The Great Sayings

Mahāviṣphot	-	Big Bang
Majjā	-	Marrow
Makh	-	Yajña, hawan, homa
Malaja Krimis	-	Waste material-born microbes
Māriammā	-	Smallpox disease occuring in South India
Mātā Śītalā, masurikā-		Smallpox disease, lentil-sized eruptions
Matasna	-	Kidneys
Mūla	-	Root
Muñca	-	To set free
Nābhi	-	Naval
Nada nimota	-	Vibrating microbes
Nāḍi	-	Meridian with 'power line'
Nadyamāra	-	Plant that eliminates vectors of all germs
Nadyāriṣa	-	Plant that eliminates the river water-borne diseases
Namaste	-	Folding palms in Añjali Mudrā as a mark of respect
Navadhānya	-	Nine types of grains
Ojmāna	-	Lustrous
Palāśa (ṭesū)	-	Pliers' plant (*Butea frondosa*)
Pañca mahābhuta	-	Five cosmic elements (earth, water, fire, air and ether)
Pāndu roga	-	Jaundice with anemia
Pāṇi	-	Hands
Pāṇi	-	Hands
Pāpa	-	Sin
Parā vidyā	-	Knowing the creator
Parabrahman	-	Supreme Being
Param Mahān	-	Supreme Great
Parampitā	-	Supreme Father
Pārṣṇi	-	Heals
Pārśva	-	Sides
Parva	-	Joints
Patita	-	Unhygienic person
Peya	-	Drinkables
Plāśa	-	Mesentery
Plīhā	-	Spleen
Prajña	-	Intellectual glory
Prakṛti	-	Nature, primordial elements
Pṛakṣālita	-	Washed
Prān	-	Pure cosmic energy (PCE), vital energy that sustains life
Prithivi	-	Earth
Pṛśniparṇi	-	*Uraria picta,* regarded 'global medicine'
Purīṣaja krimis	-	Faecal material-born microbes
Puruṣa	-	Consciousness
Pūrvadhṛta	-	Pre-worn
Rajasvalā	-	Menstruating woman
Raśmi	-	Sun rays

Ṛcas	-	Hymns, mantras
Rohita varṇa	-	Red colour
Roma	-	Hairs
Romantikā	-	Measles
Ṛṣis guru	-	Seer teachers
Ṛṣis	-	Seers
Śabdarūpa	-	Verbal form
Sakriya	-	Active phase of life
Salila	-	Water
Śamaśru	-	Beard and mustaches
Samidhā	-	Small pieces of sacred plants, small twigs with bark
Saṅkalpa	-	Resolution, determination
Sannipāta	-	A disease caused jointly by Vat, Pitta and cough
Sarpi	-	Ghee
Sāṣṭāṅga	-	A gesture of touching ground with six body parts
Śava	-	Dead body
Śayanīye	-	For sleeping
Siddha	-	Supreme knowledge-attained persons
Śipavitnuka	-	Spreading on skin
Śiṣyas	-	Disciple
Śleṣmaja Krimis	-	Phlegm-born microbes
Sōma Rasa	-	Devine Elixir
Śoṇitaja krimis	-	Blood-born microbes
Sphotaka	-	Erupted blisters
Sprśa	-	To touch
Śraddhā	-	Faith
Sraṣṭā kaṇa	-	God Particle
Śroṇi	-	Waist
Sūkṣma	-	Subtle
Surabhi	-	Soothing
Susupta	-	Dormant phase of life
Sutikā	-	Accouchee *i.e.* a woman who has recently delivered a baby
Sutra	-	Action power-dominating form
Svasā	-	Sisters
Svedaj krimis	-	Sweat-born microbes
Taila	-	Oil
Takmāna	-	Painful diseases, fever
Taṅmātrā	-	Subject of those organs (words, touch, form, taste and smell)
Tridoṣa	-	Vāt, Pitta and Kapha
Tvacā	-	Skin
Udaka	-	Water
Udakya	-	Menstruating women
Udara	-	Abdomen
Udyan āditya	-	Rising sun
Uru	-	Thigh

Vaca, vacā, baca	-	*Acorus calamus,* Syn. *Acorus odoratus*
Vaniṣṭh	-	Bowels
Vāsa	-	Wearing cloths
Vasana	-	Cloths
Vātaja	-	Caused by wind
Vidyā	-	Knowledge
Vidyā	-	Knowledge
Vihāra	-	Walking peacefully
Virāṭ	-	Luminous megabody
Vīrya	-	Vigour
Vīryamaṇi	-	Conserving virile
Viṣphotaka	-	Eruptions
Viśwauṣadhi	-	Global medicine
Viveka	-	Discriminatory intelligence
Vyañjana	-	Food
Yajñik	-	Yajña performers
Yakṣmā (kṣaya)	-	Tapedic, tuberculosis
Yaktanaka	-	Liver
Yauvana	-	Youth
Yevāṣāsa	-	Fast moving microbes
Yoni	-	Creatures

Transliteration Scheme 12

अ	a	as	ग्	g	gone	न्	n	lion
ऽ	,	So,ham	घ	gh	yoghurt	प्	p	polo
आ	ā	are	ङ्	ṅ	swing	फ्	ph	phase
इ	i	ink	च्	c	chill	ब्	b	boy
ई	ī	feet	छ्	ch	pooch	भ्	bh	abhor
उ	u	put	ज्	j	jump	म्	m	mom
ऊ	ū	fool	झ्	jh	exhaust	य्	y	yes
ए	e	whey	ञ्	ñ	canyon	र्	r	raw
ऐ	ai	sail	ट्	ṭ	toast	ल्	l	love
ऋ	ṛ	grip	ठ्	ṭh	thumb	व्	v	victory
ऌ	lṛ	rivalry	ड्	ḍ	donkey	श्	ś	shut
ओ	o	so	ढ्	ḍh	adhere	ष्	ṣ	assure
औ	au	now	ण्	ṇ	drone	स्	s	son
अं	ṁ	limb/sing	त्	t	polite	ह्	h	hub
अः	ḥ	ah	थ्	th	math	क्ष्	kṣ	rikshaw
क्	k	sink	द्	d	father	त्र्	tr	Trivendram
ख्	kh	inkhorn	ध्	dh	Dhyana	ज्ञ्	jñ	guava

Index